edexcel
INTERNATIONAL

Longman
Biology
for IGCSE

Phil Bradfield
and Steve Potter

PEARSON
Longman

Pearson Education
Edinburgh Gate
Harlow
Essex CM20 2JE
England

and Associated Companies throughout the world

www.longman.co.uk

First published 2004
Fifth impression 2006

ISBN-10: 1-4058-0206-5
ISBN-13: 978-1-4058-0206-2

Produced by Cambridge Publishing Management Ltd, Cambridge
Cover design by Neil Straker Creative

The publisher's policy is to use paper manufactured from sustainable forests.

Printed in Great Britain by Scotprint, Haddington

Acknowledgments

The publisher would like to thank many people for their help, support and encouragement in the production of this book. In particular:

Sarah Evans, Teacher of Science, County Durham; Alastair Sandiforth, Head of Science at Stanborough School, Welwyn Garden City; Norma Taylor, retired biology teacher, teaching most recently at The Albany College, Hendon; Christine Woodward, Head of Biology, Moira House Girls School, Eastbourne.

Photo credits

We are grateful to the following for permission to reproduce photographs:

l = left, r = right, c = centre, t = top, b = bottom

1tl Astrid & Hanns-Frieder Michler/Science Photo Library; 1tr Eric Grave/Science Photo Library; 1bl Laguna Design/Science Photo Library; 1br Biophoto Associates/Science Photo Library; 2 © Dr Dennis Kunkel/Phototake/Robert Harding Picture Library; 3t Dr Gopal Murti/Science Photo Library; 3b J.C. Revy/Science Photo Library; 16t & b Holt Studios/Nigel Cattlin; 16c Dr Jeremy Burgess/Science Photo Library; 17tl Steve Gorton © Dorling Kindersley; 17tr Jeff Greenberg/Alamy; 17b Andrew Syred/Science Photo Library; 18l Vaughan Fleming/Science Photo Library; 18r Peter Gardner © Dorling Kindersley; 20t Moredun Animal Health Ltd/Science Photo Library; 20b Science Photo Library; 21t O. Bradfute, Peter Arnold Inc/Science Photo Library; 21b Norm Thomas/Science Photo Library; 27t Imagingbody.com; 27b Eye of Science/Science Photo Library; 31t Imagingbody.com; 31b Conor Caffrey/Science Photo Library; 32 Science Photo Library; 33 © Victor Englebert, photographersdirect.com; 34 Dorling Kindersley; 38 © Lester V. Bergman/Corbis; 40t Andy Crump, TDR, WHO/Science Photo Library; 40b J.C. Revy/Science Photo Library; 41t & b Biophoto Associates/Science Photo Library; 50 Eye of Science/Science Photo Library; 60 Imagingbody.com; 61 © Dennis Kunkel/Phototake/

Robert Harding Picture Library; 62 Biology Media/Science Photo Library; 67tr & cr Leonard Lessin/Science Photo Library; 67l Getty Images; 75 © CNRI/Phototake/Robert Harding Picture Library; 76 The Natural History Museum, London; 81r Getty Images; 81l Jane Burton © Dorling Kindersley; 82t Cordelia Molloy/Science Photo Library; 82b Saturn Stills/Science Photo Library; 97l D. Phillips/Science Photo Library; 97r Science Pictures Ltd/Science Photo Library; 110 © Food Features; 112b Holt Studios/Nigel Cattlin; 120 Bair Seitz/Science Photo Library; 125 J.C. Revy/Science Photo Library; 126l & r WG/ Science Photo Library; 128 Michael Clayton/Dept. of Botany, University of Wisconsin, Madison; 130 J.C. Revy/Science Photo Library; 131t Michael Clayton/Dept. of Botany, University of Wisconsin, Madison; 131b Dr Jeremy Burgess/Science Photo Library; 137tl OSF/photolibrary.com; 137tr OSF/photolibrary.com/Kathie Atkinson; 137b Holt Studios/Nigel Cattlin; 138 Jerome Wexler/Science Photo Library; 145 Steve Degnan, photographersdirect.com; 148 Daniel Zupanc/NHPA; 154l & inset Heather Angel/Natural Visions; 154r Covalart Photographic/Alamy; 155 Graham Burns/Photofusion, photographersdirect.com; 156 Phil Bradfield; 162 Dr Jeremy Burgess/Science Photo Library; 168l Rosenfeld Images/Science Photo Library; 168r Hank Morgan/Science Photo Library; 170 Mark Burnett/Science Photo Library; 172 © Ariadne van Zandbergen/Images of Africa, photographersdirect.com; 173 Ottmar Bierwagen/Spectrum Stock, photographersdirect.com; 174 Ron Giling/Still Pictures; 177 Adam Hart-Davis/Science Photo Library; 185t A. Barrington Brown/Science Photo Library; 185b Science Photo Library; 189l & r Dept. of Clinical Cytogenetics, Addenbrookes Hospital, Cambridge/Science Photo Library; 191 Liba Taylor/Panos Pictures, photographersdirect.com; 195t © Science Pictures Ltd/Corbis; 195b Dr Gopal Murti/Science Photo Library; 196 Science Pictures Ltd/Science Photo Library; 201 © Bettmann/Corbis; 208 Garden Picture Library/Howard Rice; 212 Downe House, Downe, Kent/Bridgeman Art Library; 213 Natural History Museum, London/Bridgeman Art Library; 214l Nuridsany & Perennou/Science Photo Library; 214r Michael W. Tweedie/Science Photo Library; 217t John Durham/Science Photo Library; 217bl Robert Harding Picture Library; 217br Bill Longcore/Science Photo Library; 224 Holt Studios/Nigel Cattlin; 225tl Tracy Morgan © Dorling Kindersley; 225tr Dave King © Dorling Kindersley; 225c Jerry Young © Dorling Kindersley; 225bl © Phillip Dowell © Dorling Kindersley; 225br © Dorling Kindersley; 226t & c Holt Studios/Nigel Cattlin; 226b Grant Heilman Photography Inc; 227 James King-Holmes/Science Photo Library; 233 Maximilian Stock Ltd/Science Photo Library; 235 © Dorling Kindersley; 236t & b Holt Studios/Nigel Cattlin; 240 Francis Leroy/Biocosmos/Science Photo Library; 244 Matt Meadows, Peter Arnold Inc/Science Photo Library; 245 Syngenta.

All other photos by Trevor Clifford

Picture Research by Anne Lyons, with additional material for new edition by Sandie Huskinson-Rolfe of PHOTOSEEKERS.

COVER: LWA-Dann Tardit/Corbis

Contents

Section A:
Organisms and Life Processes

Section B:
Animal Physiology

Section C:
Plant Physiology

Section D:
Ecology and the Environment

About this book   v

Chapter 1: Life Processes   1

Chapter 2: The Variety of Living Organisms   16

Chapter 3: Breathing and Gas Exchange   26

Chapter 4: Food and Digestion   37

Chapter 5: Blood and Circulation   54

Chapter 6: Coordination   66

Chapter 7: Chemical Coordination   79

Chapter 8: Homeostasis and Excretion   84

Chapter 9: Reproduction in Humans   97

Chapter 10: Plants and Food   110

Chapter 11: Transport in Plants   123

Chapter 12: Chemical Coordination in Plants   137

Chapter 13: Reproduction in Plants   145

Chapter 14: Ecosystems   154

Chapter 15: Human Influences on the Environment   166

Section E:
Variation and Selection

Chapter 16: Chromosomes, Genes and DNA — 185

Chapter 17: Cell Division — 194

Chapter 18: Genes and Inheritance — 201

Chapter 19: Natural Selection and Evolution — 212

Chapter 20: Selective Breeding — 222

Section F:
Microorganisms and
Genetic Engineering

Chapter 21: Using Microorganisms — 232

Chapter 22: Genetic Modification — 239

Appendices

Appendix A: Practical Investigations — 251

Appendix B: Exam Tips — 261

Index — 262

About this book

This book has several features to help you with IGCSE Biology.

Introduction
Each chapter has a short introduction to help you start thinking about the topic and let you know what is in the chapter.

End of chapter checklists
These lists summarise the material in the chapter. They could also help you to make revision notes because they form a list of things that you need to revise. (You need to check your specification to find out exactly what you need to know.)

Margin boxes
The boxes in the margin give you extra help or information. They might explain something in a little more detail or guide you to linked topics in other parts of the book.

Questions
There are short questions at the end of each chapter. These help you to test your understanding of the material from the chapter. Some of them may also be research questions – you will need to use the Internet and other books to answer these.
There are also questions at the end of each section. The end-of-section questions are written in an exam style and cover topics from all the chapters in the section.

Section B: Animal Physiology

Chapter 4: Food and Digestion

Food is essential for life. The nutrients obtained from it are used in many different ways by the body. This chapter looks at the different kinds of food, and how the food is broken down by the digestive system and absorbed into the blood, so that it can be carried to all the tissues of the body.

We need food for three main reasons:

- to supply us with a 'fuel' for energy
- to provide materials for growth and repair of tissues
- to help fight disease and keep our bodies healthy.

A balanced diet

The food that we eat is called our **diet**. No matter what you like to eat, if your body is to work properly and stay healthy, your diet must include five groups of food substances – **carbohydrates, lipids, proteins, minerals** and **vitamins** – as well as **water** and **fibre**. Food should provide you with all of these substances, but they must also be present in the *right* amounts. A diet that provides enough of these substances and in the correct proportions to keep you healthy is called a **balanced diet** (Figure 4.1). We will deal with each type of food in turn, to find out about its chemistry and the role that it plays in the body.

Figure 4.1 *A balanced diet contains all the types of food the body needs, in just the right amounts.*

Carbohydrates

Carbohydrates only make up about 5% of the mass of the human body, but they have a very important role. They are the body's main 'fuel' for supplying cells with energy. Cells release this energy by oxidising a sugar called **glucose**, in the process called cell respiration (see Chapter 1). Glucose and other sugars are one sort of carbohydrate.

Glucose is found naturally in many sweet-tasting foods, such as fruits and vegetables. Other foods contain different sugars, such as the fruit sugar

The chemical formula for glucose is $C_6H_{12}O_6$. Like all carbohydrates, glucose contains only the elements carbon, hydrogen and oxygen. The 'carbo' part of the name refers to carbon, and the 'hydrate' part refers to the fact that hydrogen and oxygen atoms are in the ratio two to one, as in water (H_2O).

37

Chapter 4: Food and Digestion

End of Chapter Checklist

You should now be able to:

- describe the structure of carbohydrates, lipids and proteins as large molecules made up from smaller units: starch and glycogen from simple sugars, lipid from fatty acids and glycerol, protein from amino acids
- describe the tests for starch, glucose, lipid and protein
- understand the meaning of a balanced diet, recall sources and functions of carbohydrate, lipid, protein, vitamins A, C and D, and the mineral ions calcium and iron
- understand that energy requirements vary with activity levels, age and pregnancy
- recall how to carry out a simple experiment to find the energy content of a sample of food
- understand the processes of ingestion, digestion, absorption, assimilation and egestion
- explain how and why food is moved through the gut by peristalsis
- understand the roles of the digestive enzymes amylase, maltase, lipases and proteases
- recall that bile is produced by the liver and stored in the gall bladder. Understand the role of bile in digestion
- explain how the structure of a villus helps absorption of the products of digestion in the ileum.

Questions

More questions on food and digestion can be found at the end of Section B on page 108.

1   The diagram shows an experiment that was set up as a model to show why food needs to be digested.

The Visking tubing acts as a model of the small intestine because it has tiny holes in it that some molecules can pass through. The tubing was left in the boiling tube for an hour, then the water in the tube was tested for starch and glucose.

a) Describe how you would test the water for starch and for glucose. What would the results be for a 'positive' test in each case?

b) The tests showed that glucose was present in the water, but starch was not. Explain why.

c) If the tubing takes the place of the intestine, what part of the body does the water in the boiling tube represent?

d) What does 'digested' mean?

distilled water

mixture of starch and glucose

visking tubing bag

52

About this book

Chapter 1: Life Processes

The cells of all living organisms have common features, and the organisms themselves share common processes. In this chapter you will read about these features and look at some of the processes that keep cells alive.

All living organisms are composed of units called **cells**. The simplest organisms are made from single cells (Figure 1.1) but more complex plants and animals, like ourselves, are multicellular, composed of millions of cells. In a **multicellular** organism there are many different types of cells, with different structures. They are specialised so that they can carry out particular functions in the animal or plant. Despite all the differences, there are basic features that are the same in all cells.

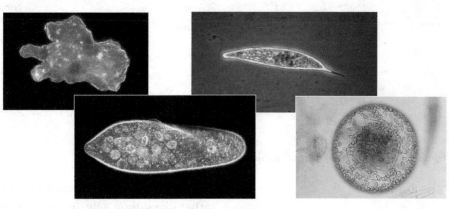

Figure 1.1 *Many simple organisms have 'bodies' made from single cells. Here are four examples.*

There are eight life processes which are common to most living things. Organisms:

- **require nutrition** – either they make their own food, as in plants, or eat other organisms, as animals do

- **excrete** – get rid of toxic waste products

- **move** – by the action of muscles in animals, and slow growth movements in plants

- **grow and develop** – increase in size and mass, using materials from their food

- **respire** – get energy from their food

- **respond to stimuli** – are sensitive to changes in their surroundings

- **reproduce** – produce offspring

- **control** – their internal conditions.

Cell structure

For over 160 years scientists have known that animals and plants are made from cells. All cells contain some common parts, such as the nucleus, cytoplasm and cell membrane. Some cells have structures missing, for instance red blood cells lack a nucleus, which is unusual. The first chapter in a biology textbook usually shows diagrams of 'typical' plant and animal cells. In fact, there is really no such thing as a 'typical' cell. Humans, for example, are composed of hundreds of different kinds of cells from nerve cells to blood cells, skin cells to liver cells. What we really mean by a 'typical' cell is a general diagram that shows all the features that you might find in most cells, without them being too specialised. Figure 1.2 shows the features you would expect to see in many animal and plant cells. However not all these are present in all cells – the parts of a plant which are not green do not have chloroplasts, for example.

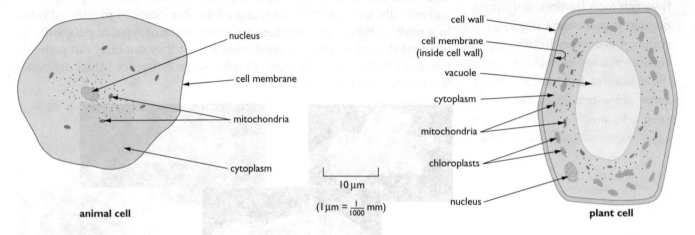

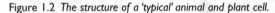

Figure 1.2 *The structure of a 'typical' animal and plant cell.*

The living material that makes up a cell is called **cytoplasm**. It has a texture rather like sloppy jelly, in other words somewhere between a solid and a liquid. Unlike a jelly, it is not made of one substance but is a complex material made of many different structures. You can't see many of these structures under an ordinary light microscope. An electron microscope has a much higher magnification, and can show the details of these structures, which are called **organelles** (Figure 1.3).

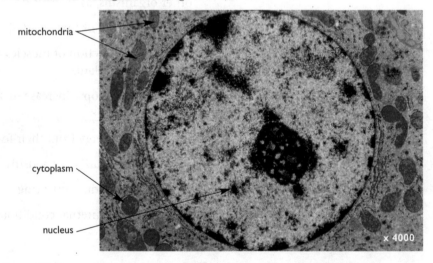

Figure 1.3 *The organelles in a cell can be seen using an electron microscope.*

The largest organelle in the cell is the **nucleus**. Nearly all cells have a nucleus. The few types that don't are usually dead (e.g. the xylem vessels in a stem, Chapter 11) or don't live for very long (e.g. mature red blood cells, Chapter 5). The nucleus controls the activities of the cell. It contains **chromosomes** (46 in human cells) which carry the genetic material, or **genes**. You will find out much more about genes and inheritance later in the book. Genes control the activities in the cell by determining which proteins the cell can make. One very important group of proteins found in cells is **enzymes** (see below). Enzymes control chemical reactions that go on in the cytoplasm.

All cells are surrounded by a **cell surface membrane** (often simply called the cell membrane). This is a thin layer like a 'skin' on the surface of the cell. It forms a boundary between the cytoplasm of the cell and the outside. However, it is not a complete barrier. Some chemicals can pass into the cell and others can pass out (the membrane is **permeable** to them). In fact, the cell membrane *controls* which substances pass in either direction. We say that it is **selectively** permeable.

One organelle that is found in the cytoplasm of all living cells is the **mitochondrion** (plural **mitochondria**). There are many mitochondria in cells that need a lot of energy, such as muscle or nerve cells. This gives us a clue to the role of mitochondria. They carry out some of the reactions of **respiration** (see page 6) to release energy that the cell can use. In fact, most of the energy from respiration is released in the mitochondria.

All of the structures we have seen so far are found in both animal and plant cells. However, some structures are only ever found in plant cells. There are three in particular – the cell wall, a permanent vacuole and chloroplasts.

The **cell wall** is a layer of non-living material that is found outside the cell membrane of plant cells. It is made mainly of a carbohydrate called **cellulose**, although other chemicals may be added to the wall in some cells. Cellulose is a tough material that helps the cell keep its shape. This is why plant cells have a fairly fixed shape. Animal cells, which lack a cell wall, tend to be more variable in shape. Plant cells absorb water, producing internal pressure which pushes against other cells of the plant, giving them support. Without a cell wall to withstand these pressures, this method of support would be impossible. The cell wall has large holes in it, so it is not a barrier to water or dissolved substances. In other words it is **freely permeable**.

Mature (fully grown) plant cells often have a large central space surrounded by a membrane, called a **vacuole**. This vacuole is a permanent feature of the cell. It is filled with a watery liquid called **cell sap**, a store of dissolved sugars, mineral ions and other solutes. Animal cells can have small vacuoles, but they are only temporary structures.

Cells of the green parts of plants, especially the leaves, have another very important organelle, the **chloroplast**. Chloroplasts absorb light energy to make food in the process of photosynthesis (see Chapter 10). The chloroplasts are green because they contain a green pigment called **chlorophyll**. Cells from the parts of a plant that are not green, such as the flowers, roots and woody stems, have no chloroplasts.

Figure 1.4 shows some animal and plant cells seen through the light microscope.

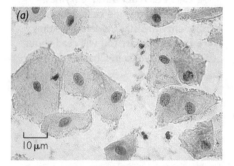

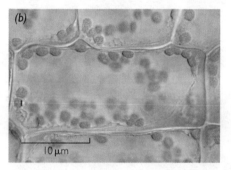

Figure 1.4 *(a) Cells from the lining of a human cheek. (b) Cells from the photosynthetic tissue of a leaf.*

Nearly all cells have cytoplasm, a nucleus, a cell membrane and mitochondria. As well as these, plant cells have a cell wall and a permanent vacuole, and plant cells which photosynthesise have chloroplasts.

Enzymes: controlling reactions in the cell

The chemical reactions that go on in a cell are controlled by a group of proteins called enzymes. Enzymes are *biological catalysts*. A catalyst is a chemical which speeds up a reaction without being used up itself. It takes part in the reaction, but afterwards is unchanged and free to catalyse more reactions. Cells contain hundreds of different enzymes, each catalysing a different reaction. This is how the activities of a cell are controlled – the nucleus contains the genes, which control the production of enzymes, which catalyse reactions in the cytoplasm:

genes → proteins (enzymes) → catalyse reactions

Everything a cell does depends on which enzymes it can make, which in turn depends on which genes in its nucleus are working.

What hasn't been mentioned is why enzymes are needed at all. This is because the temperatures inside organisms are low (e.g. the human body temperature is about 37 °C) and without catalysts, most of the reactions that happen in cells would be far too slow to allow life to go on. Only when enzymes are present to speed them up do the reactions take place quickly enough.

It is possible for there to be thousands of different sorts of enzymes because they are made of proteins, and protein molecules have an enormous range of structures and shapes (see Chapter 4). The molecule that an enzyme acts on is called its **substrate**. Each enzyme has a small area on its surface called the **active site**. The substrate attaches to the active site of the enzyme. The reaction then takes place and products are formed. When the substrate joins up with the active site, it lowers the energy needed for the reaction to happen, allowing the products to be formed more easily.

The substrate fits into the active site of the enzyme rather like a key fitting into a lock. That is why this is called the 'lock and key' model of enzyme action (Figure 1.5).

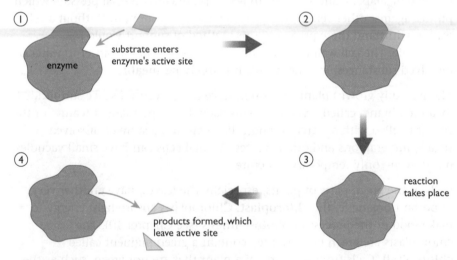

Figure 1.5 *Enzymes catalyse reactions at their active site. This acts like a 'lock' to the substrate 'key'. The substrate fits into the active site, and products are formed. This happens more easily than without the enzyme – so enzymes act as catalysts.*

Notice how, after it has catalysed the reaction once, the enzyme is free to act on more substrate molecules.

Factors affecting enzymes

Temperature affects the action of enzymes. This is easiest to see as a graph, where we plot the rate of the reaction controlled by an enzyme against the temperature (Figure 1.6).

You have probably heard of the enzymes involved in digestion of food. They are secreted by the intestine onto the food to break it down. They are called **extracellular** enzymes, which means 'outside cells'. However, most enzymes stay *inside* cells – they are **intracellular**. You will read about digestive enzymes in Chapter 4.

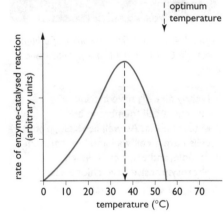

Figure 1.6 *Effect of temperature on the action of an enzyme.*

'Optimum' temperature means the 'best' temperature, in other words the temperature at which the reaction takes place most rapidly.

Enzymes in the human body have evolved to work best at about body temperature (37 °C). The graph (Figure 1.6) shows this, because the peak on the curve happens at about this temperature. In this case 37 °C is called the **optimum temperature** for the enzyme.

As the enzyme is heated up to the optimum temperature, increasing temperature speeds up the rate of reaction. This is because higher temperatures give the molecules of enzyme and substrate more energy, so they collide more often. More collisions mean that the reaction will take place more frequently. However, above the optimum temperature another factor comes into play. Enzymes are made of protein, and proteins are broken down by heat. From 40 °C upwards, the heat destroys the enzyme. We say that it is **denatured**. You can see the effect of denaturing when you boil an egg. The egg white is made of protein, and turns from a clear runny liquid into a white solid as the heat denatures the protein.

Temperature is not the only factor that affects an enzyme's activity. The rate of reaction may also be increased by raising the concentration of the enzyme or the substrate. The pH of the surroundings is also important. The pH inside cells is around neutral (pH 7) and not surprisingly, most enzymes have evolved to work best at this pH. At extremes of pH either side of neutral, the enzyme activity decreases, as shown by Figure 1.7. The pH at which the enzyme works best is called the **optimum pH** for that enzyme. Either side of the optimum, the pH affects the structure of the enzyme molecule, and changes the shape of its active site so that the substrate will not fit into it so well.

The effect of temperature on the activity of amylase

The digestive enzyme amylase breaks down starch into the sugar maltose. If you record the speed at which the starch disappears, you have a measure of the activity of the amylase.

Carry out the following:

> Not all enzymes have an optimum temperature near 37 °C, just those of animals such as mammals and birds, which all have body temperatures close to this value. Enzymes have evolved to work best at the normal body temperature of the organism. Bacteria that always live at an average temperature of 10 °C will probably have enzymes with an optimum temperature of 10 °C.

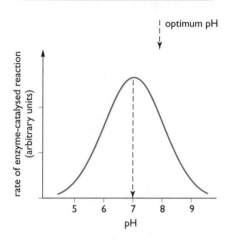

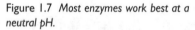

Figure 1.7 *Most enzymes work best at a neutral pH.*

> Although most enzymes work best at a neutral pH, a few have an optimum below or above pH 7. The stomach produces hydrochloric acid, which makes its contents very acidic (see Chapter 3). Most enzymes stop working at a low pH like this, but the stomach makes an enzyme called pepsin which has an optimum pH of about 2, so that it is adapted to work well in these unusually acidic surroundings.

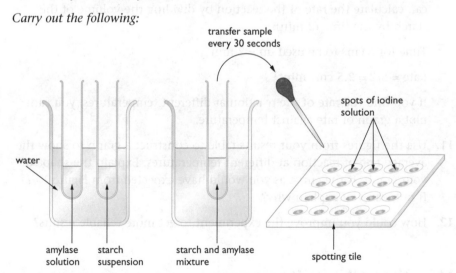

Figure 1.8 *Steps 1–6.*

1. Place 20 spots of iodine solution on to the depressions in a spotting tile.

2. Use a syringe or pipette to place 5 cm^3 of starch suspension in one boiling tube.

3. Place 5 cm^3 of amylase solution into another tube using a second syringe.

4. Half fill a beaker with water at room temperature. Stand both boiling tubes in the water for 5 minutes and record the temperature.

5. Pour the amylase into the starch suspension, leaving the tube containing the mixture in the water bath.

6. Immediately take a small sample of the mixture with the pipette and add it to the first drop of iodine on the spotting tile.

7. Record the colour of the iodine.

8. Take a sample of the mixture every 30 seconds for the remainder of the 10 minutes, testing the mixture for starch as in steps 6–7.

9. Repeat the experiment, maintaining the water bath at a different temperature. You might like to try a range of temperatures between 20 °C and 60 °C. You will find it easier if you record your results in a table like this.

	Colour of mixture at different temperatures				
Time/min	20 °C	30 °C	40 °C	50 °C	60 °C
0.5					
1.0					
1.5					
2.0					
(etc)					
10.0					

10. Suppose the mixture took 2 minutes until the starch was all broken down by the enzyme, so that the iodine stopped changing colour. You can calculate the rate of the reaction by dividing the volume of the starch by the time (2 min):

Time for 5 cm^3 to be used up = 2 min

Rate = 5/2 = 2.5 cm^3 min^{-1}

If you find the rate of the reaction at different temperatures, you can plot a graph of rate against temperature.

11. Use the figures from your results table to construct a graph to show the average rate of reaction at different temperatures. Explain the shape of your graph. Is the curve as you would have expected from Figure 1.6? If not, can you explain why?

12. How could you improve the experiment to get more reliable results?

How the cell gets its energy

To be able to carry out all the processes needed for life, a cell needs a source of energy. It gets this by breaking down food molecules to release the stored chemical energy that they contain. This process is called **cell respiration**. Many people think of respiration as meaning 'breathing', but although there are links between the two processes, the biological meaning of respiration is very different.

The process of respiration happens in all the cells of our body. Oxygen is used to oxidise food, and carbon dioxide (and water) are released as waste products. The main food oxidised is glucose (a sugar). Glucose contains stored chemical energy that can be converted into other forms of energy that the cell can use. It is rather like burning a fuel to get the energy out of it, except that burning releases all its energy as heat, whereas respiration releases some heat energy, but most is trapped as energy in other chemicals. This chemical energy can be used for a variety of purposes, such as:

- contraction of muscle cells, producing movement

- active transport of molecules and ions (see page 10)

- building large molecules, such as proteins

- cell division.

The energy released as heat is also used to maintain a steady body temperature in animals such as mammals and birds (see Chapter 8).

The overall reaction for respiration is:

$$\text{glucose} + \text{oxygen} \rightarrow \text{carbon dioxide} + \text{water} \quad (+ \text{energy})$$
$$C_6H_{12}O_6 + 6O_2 \rightarrow 6CO_2 + 6H_2O \quad (+ \text{energy})$$

This is called **aerobic** respiration, because it uses oxygen. It is not just carried out by human cells, but by all animals and plants and many other organisms. It is important to realise that the equation above is just a *summary* of the process. It actually takes place gradually, as a sequence of small steps which release the energy of the glucose in small amounts. Each step in the process is catalysed by a different enzyme. The later steps in the process are the aerobic ones, and these release the most energy. They happen in the cell's mitochondria.

There are some situations where cells can respire *without* using oxygen. This is called **anaerobic** respiration. In anaerobic respiration, glucose is not completely broken down, and less energy is released. However, the advantage of anaerobic respiration is that it can occur in situations where oxygen is in short supply. Two important examples of this are in yeast cells and muscle cells.

Yeasts are single-celled fungi. They are used in commercial processes such as making wine and beer, and baking bread. When yeast cells are prevented from getting enough oxygen, they stop respiring aerobically, and start to respire anaerobically instead. The glucose is partly broken down into ethanol (alcohol) and carbon dioxide:

$$\text{glucose} \rightarrow \text{ethanol} + \text{carbon dioxide} \quad (+ \text{some energy})$$
$$C_6H_{12}O_6 \rightarrow 2C_2H_5OH + 2CO_2$$

This process is looked at in more detail in Chapter 21. The ethanol from this respiration is the alcohol in wine and beer. The carbon dioxide is the gas that makes bread rise when it is baked. Think about the properties of ethanol – it makes a good fuel and will burn to produce a lot of heat, so it still has a lot of 'stored' chemical energy in it.

Muscle cells can also respire anaerobically when they are short of oxygen. If muscles are overworked, the blood cannot reach them fast enough to deliver enough oxygen for aerobic respiration. This happens when a person does a

In respiration, carbon passes from glucose out into the atmosphere as carbon dioxide. The carbon can be traced through this pathway using radioactive C^{14}.

'burst' activity, such as a sprint, or quickly lifting a heavy weight. This time the glucose is broken down into a substance called **lactic acid**:

$$glucose \quad \rightarrow \quad lactic \ acid \quad \quad (+ \ some \ energy)$$
$$C_6H_{12}O_6 \quad \rightarrow \quad 2C_3H_6O_3$$

Anaerobic respiration provides enough energy to keep the overworked muscles going for a short period, but continuing the 'burst' activity makes lactic acid build up in the bloodstream, producing muscle cramps. The person then has to rest, to oxidise the lactic acid fully. This uses oxygen. The volume of oxygen needed to completely oxidise the lactic acid that builds up in the body during anaerobic respiration is called the **oxygen debt**.

Anaerobic respiration has two main disadvantages over aerobic respiration. It converts much less of the energy stored in food into a form of chemical energy that cells can use. It also produces toxic waste products, such as lactic acid or ethanol.

Demonstration of the production of carbon dioxide by small living organisms

Hydrogencarbonate indicator solution is normally orange, but turns yellow if carbon dioxide is added to it. Collect three samples of small living organisms, such as germinating seeds, maggots and woodlice. You will be placing one sample at a time in the apparatus shown in Figure 1.9. The gauze platform supports the organisms above the hydrogencarbonate indicator solution.

From your observations of your three sample organisms, you could predict which of them will respire the quickest, and show the highest rate of production of carbon dioxide. When you have developed your prediction (called a **hypothesis**) you can plan how to test it. You will need to ensure that your plan means that the comparison between the three organisms is 'fair'. Don't forget to include a description of a control that you would set up.

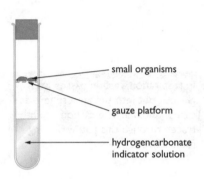
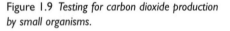

small organisms

gauze platform

hydrogencarbonate indicator solution

Figure 1.9 *Testing for carbon dioxide production by small organisms.*

Demonstration that heat is produced by respiration

Carry out the following:

1. Soak some peas in water for 24 hours, so that they start to germinate.

2. Boil a second batch of peas, to kill them.

3. Wash each set of peas in a disinfectant, such as 1% bleach solution, to surface-sterilise them and so kill any bacteria that may be present.

4. Place each batch of peas in a vacuum flask as shown in Figure 1.10. Leave some air in each flask.

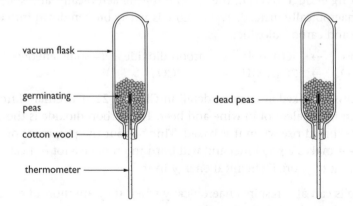

vacuum flask

germinating peas

cotton wool

thermometer

dead peas

Figure 1.10 *Experiment to show that heat is produced during respiration in germinating peas.*

5. Support each flask upside down, as shown. The seeds will produce carbon dioxide gas, which is denser than air. The inverted flasks and porous cotton wool allows this to escape. It might otherwise kill the peas.

6. Record the temperature inside each flask at the start.

7. Leave the apparatus set up for a couple of days and record the temperature inside the flask at the end of the experiment.

8. Write up the experiment and explain your results.

9. The purpose of using vacuum flasks is to insulate the contents, so that any temperature change can be measured. Which flask showed a higher temperature at the end of the experiment? Why?

10. Why is it necessary to kill any microorganisms on the surface of the peas?

11. Explain the importance of the flask containing dead peas.

Movements of materials in and out of cells

Cell respiration shows the need for cells to be able to take in certain substances from their surroundings, such as glucose and oxygen, and get rid of others, such as carbon dioxide and water. As you have seen, the cell surface membrane is selective about which chemicals can pass in and out. There are three main ways that molecules and ions can move through the membrane. They are diffusion, active transport and osmosis.

Many substances can pass through the membrane by **diffusion**. Diffusion happens when a substance is more concentrated in one place than another. For example, if the cell is making carbon dioxide by respiration, the concentration of carbon dioxide inside the cell will be higher than outside. This difference in concentration is called a **concentration gradient**. The molecules of carbon dioxide are constantly moving about because of their kinetic energy. The cell membrane is permeable to carbon dioxide, so they can move in either direction through it. Because there is a higher concentration of carbon dioxide molecules inside the cell than outside, over time more molecules will move from inside the cell to outside than move in the other direction. We say that there is a *net* movement of the molecules from inside to outside (Figure 1.11).

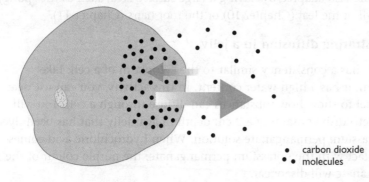

• carbon dioxide
•• molecules

Figure 1.11 *Carbon dioxide is produced by respiration, so its concentration builds up inside the cell. Although the carbon dioxide molecules diffuse in both directions across the cell membrane, the overall (net) movement is out of the cell, down the concentration gradient.*

Diffusion is the net movement of particles (molecules or ions) from a region of high concentration to a region of low concentration, i.e. down a concentration gradient.

The rate of diffusion of a substance is greater at higher temperatures. The reason for this is that a higher temperature will give the diffusing particles more kinetic energy.

The opposite happens with oxygen. Respiration uses up oxygen, so there is a concentration gradient of oxygen from outside to inside the cell. There is therefore a net movement of oxygen *into* the cell by diffusion.

Diffusion happens because of the kinetic energy of the particles. It does not need an 'extra' source of energy from respiration. However, sometimes a cell needs to take in a substance when there is very little of that substance outside the cell, in other words *against* a concentration gradient. It can do this by another process, called **active transport**. The cell uses energy from respiration to take up the particles, rather like a pump uses energy to move a liquid from one place to another. In fact, biologists usually speak of the cell 'pumping' ions or molecules in or out. The pumps are large protein molecules located in the cell membrane. An example of a place where this happens is in the human small intestine, where some glucose in the gut is absorbed into the cells lining the intestine by active transport. The roots of plants also take up certain mineral ions in this way (Chapter 11).

> Active transport is the movement of particles against a concentration gradient, using energy from respiration.

Water moves across cell membranes by a special sort of diffusion, called **osmosis**. Osmosis happens when the total concentrations of all dissolved substances inside and outside the cell are different. Water will move across the membrane from the more dilute solution to the more concentrated one. Notice that this is still obeying the rules of diffusion – the water moves from where there is a higher concentration of *water* molecules to a lower concentration of *water* molecules. Osmosis can only happen if the membrane is permeable to water but not to some other solutes. We say that it is **partially** permeable.

> Earlier in this chapter we called the cell membrane 'selectively' permeable. This term is sometimes used when describing osmosis. It means that the membrane has control over which molecules it lets through (e.g. by active transport). 'Partially' permeable just means that small molecules such as water and gases can pass through, while larger molecules cannot. Strictly, the two words are not interchangeable, but they are often used this way in biology books.

Osmosis is important for moving water from cell to cell, for example in plant roots. You can read about osmosis in much more detail in Chapter 11.

All cells exchange substances with their surroundings, but some parts of animals or plants are specially adapted for the exchange of materials because they have a very large surface area in proportion to their volume. In animals, two examples are the alveoli of the lungs (Chapter 3) and the villi of the small intestine (Chapter 4). Diffusion is a slow process, and organs that rely on diffusion need a large surface over which it can take place. The alveoli (air sacs) allow exchange of oxygen and carbon dioxide to take place between the air and the blood, during breathing. The villi of the small intestine provide a large surface area for the absorption of digested food. In plants, exchange surfaces are also adapted by having a large surface area, such as the spongy mesophyll of the leaf (Chapter 10) or the root hairs (Chapter 11).

> Osmosis in cells is the net movement of water from a dilute solution to a more concentrated solution across the partially permeable cell membrane.

Demonstrating diffusion in a jelly

Agar jelly has a consistency similar to the cytoplasm of a cell. Like cytoplasm, it has a high water content. In this activity, you can use agar as a model to show how substances can diffuse through a cell. You will need a Petri dish containing a 2 cm depth of agar jelly that has been dyed with potassium permanganate solution. When hydrochloric acid comes into contact with the potassium permanganate, the purple colour of the permanganate will disappear.

Carry out the following:

1. Cut out some cubes of the agar jelly with the following side lengths: 2 cm, 1 cm, and 0.5 cm.

2. Place about 100 cm^3 of dilute hydrochloric acid in a 250 cm^3 beaker.

3. Carefully drop, at the same time, each of the cubes of agar into the acid (Figure 1.12) and note the time.

4. Record the time taken for each cube to turn colourless.

5. Write up this investigation. In your conclusion, explain the differences in the times taken for the cubes to turn colourless.

6. If the three cubes represent cells of different sizes, which cell would have the most difficulty in obtaining substances by diffusion?

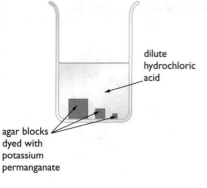

dilute hydrochloric acid

agar blocks dyed with potassium permanganate

Figure 1.12 *Investigating diffusion in a jelly.*

Cell division and differentiation

Multicellular organisms like animals and plants begin life as a single fertilised egg cell, called a **zygote**. This divides into two cells, then four, then eight and so on, until the adult body contains countless millions of cells (Figure 1.13).

This type of cell division is called **mitosis** and is under the control of the genes. You can read a full account of mitosis in Chapter 17, but it is worthwhile considering an outline of the process now. First of all the chromosomes in the nucleus are copied, then the nucleus splits into two, so that the genetic information is shared equally between the two 'daughter' cells. The cytoplasm then divides (or in plant cells a new cell wall develops) forming two smaller cells. These then take in food substances to supply energy and building materials so that they can grow to full size. The process is repeated, but as the developing **embryo** grows, cells become specialised to carry out particular roles. This specialisation is also under the control of the genes, and is called **differentiation**. Different kinds of cells develop depending on where they are located in the embryo, for example a nerve cell in the spinal cord, or an epidermal cell in the outer layer of the skin (Figure 1.14). Throughout this book you will read about cells that have a structure adapted for a particular function.

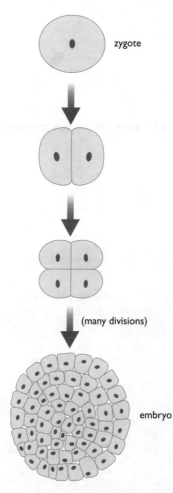

zygote

(many divisions)

embryo

Figure 1.13 *Animals and plants grow by cell division.*

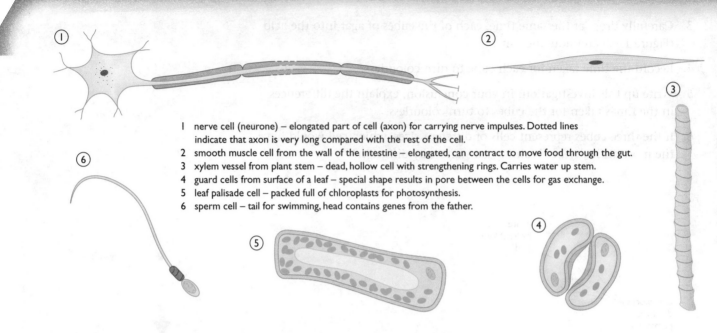

1 nerve cell (neurone) – elongated part of cell (axon) for carrying nerve impulses. Dotted lines indicate that axon is very long compared with the rest of the cell.
2 smooth muscle cell from the wall of the intestine – elongated, can contract to move food through the gut.
3 xylem vessel from plant stem – dead, hollow cell with strengthening rings. Carries water up stem.
4 guard cells from surface of a leaf – special shape results in pore between the cells for gas exchange.
5 leaf palisade cell – packed full of chloroplasts for photosynthesis.
6 sperm cell – tail for swimming, head contains genes from the father.

Figure 1.14 *Some cells with very specialised functions. They are not drawn to the same scale.*

What is hard to understand about this process is that through mitosis all the cells of the body have the *same* genes. How is it that some genes are 'switched on' and others are 'switched off' to produce different cells? The answer to this question is very complicated, and scientists are only just beginning to work it out.

Cells, tissues and organs

Cells with a similar function are grouped together as **tissues**. For example the muscle of your arm contains millions of similar muscle cells, all specialised for one function – contraction to move the arm bones. This is muscle tissue. However, a muscle also contains other tissues, such as blood, nervous tissue and epithelium (lining tissue). A collection of several tissues carrying out a particular function is called an **organ**. The main organs of the human body are shown in Figure 1.15. Plants also have tissues and organs. Leaves, roots, stems and flowers are all plant organs.

In animals, jobs are usually carried out by several different organs working together. This is called an **organ system**. For example, the digestive system consists of the gut, along with glands such as the pancreas and gall bladder. The function of the whole system is to digest food and absorb the digested products into the blood. There are seven main systems in the human body, these are the:

- **digestive** system

- **respiratory** system – including the lungs, which exchange oxygen and carbon dioxide

- **circulatory** system – including the heart and blood vessels, which transport materials around the body

- **excretory** system – including the kidneys, which filter toxic waste materials from the blood

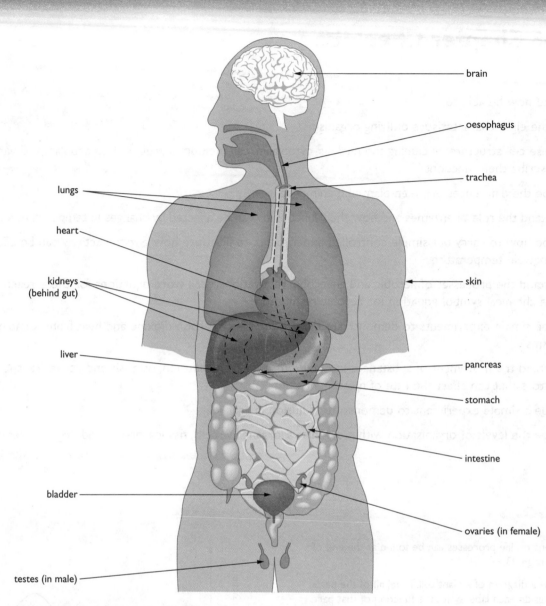

Figure 1.15 *Some of the main organs of the human body.*

- **nervous** system – consisting of the brain, spinal cord and nerves, which coordinate the body's actions

- **endocrine** system – glands secreting hormones, which act as chemical messengers

- **reproductive** system – producing sperm in males and eggs in females, and allowing the development of the embryo.

End of Chapter Checklist

You should now be able to:

● recall the eight characteristics of living organisms

● recognise cell structures, including the nucleus, cytoplasm, cell membrane, cell wall, chloroplast and vacuole, and describe their functions

● describe the differences between plant and animal cells

● understand the role of enzymes and how their functioning can be affected by changes in temperature and pH

● describe how to carry out simple controlled experiments to illustrate how enzyme activity can be affected by changes in temperature

● understand the processes of aerobic and anaerobic respiration; recall word equations for these reactions, and the chemical symbol equation for aerobic respiration

● describe simple experiments to demonstrate the production of carbon dioxide and heat from suitable living organisms

● understand the movement of substances into and out of cells by diffusion, osmosis and active transport, and the factors that can affect the rate of movement

● describe a simple experiment to demonstrate diffusion in agar jelly

● describe the levels of organisation within organisms: organelles, cells, tissues, organs and organ systems.

Questions

More questions on life processes can be found at the end of Section A on page 23.

1 a) Draw a diagram of a plant cell. Label all of the parts. Alongside each label write the function of that part.

   b) Write down *three* differences between the cell you have drawn and a 'typical' animal cell.

2 Write a short description of the nature and function of enzymes. It would be easier if you worked on a computer. Include in your description:

   • a definition of an enzyme

   • a description of the 'lock and key' model of enzyme action

   • an explanation of the difference between intracellular and extracellular enzymes.

   Your description should be about a page in length, including a labelled diagram.

3 The graph shows the effect of temperature on an enzyme. The enzyme was extracted from a microorganism that lives in hot mineral springs near a volcano.

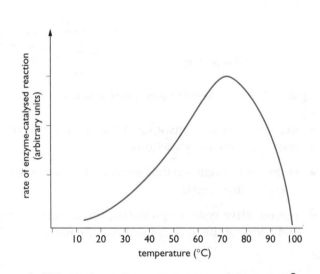

a) What is the optimum temperature of this enzyme?

b) Explain why the activity of the enzyme is greater at 60 °C than at 30 °C.

c) The optimum temperature of enzymes in the human body is about 37 °C. Explain why this enzyme is different.

d) What happens to the enzyme at 90 °C?

4 Explain the differences between diffusion and active transport.

5 The nerve cell called a **motor neurone** (page 68) and a **palisade** cell of a leaf (page 114) are both very specialised cells. Read about each of these and explain very briefly (three or four lines) how each is adapted to its function.

6 The diagram shows a cell from the lining of a human kidney tubule. A major role of the cell is to absorb glucose from the fluid passing along the tubule and pass it into the blood, as shown by the arrow on the diagram.

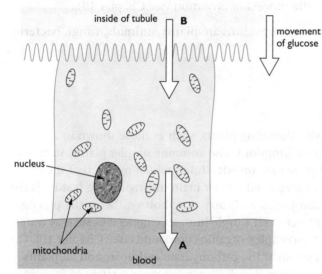

a) What is the function of the mitochondria?

b) The tubule cell contains a large number of mitochondria. They are needed for the cell to transport glucose across the cell membrane into the blood at 'A'. Suggest the method that the cell uses to do this and explain your answer.

c) The mitochondria are *not* needed to transport the glucose into the cell from the tubule at 'B'. Name the process by which the ions move across the membrane at 'B' and explain your answer.

d) The surface membrane of the tubule cell at 'B' is greatly folded. Explain how this adaptation helps the cell to carry out its function.

Chapter 2: The Variety of Living Organisms

There is an enormous variety of living organisms. Biologists put them into groups, or classify them, according to their structure and function. Each group of organisms shares common features.

There are more than ten million species of organisms alive on the Earth today, and many more that once lived and are now extinct. In order to make sense of this enormous variety, biologists **classify** organisms, putting them into groups. Each group reflects similarities of structure and function that have come about because the organisms in the group are related through their common ancestry. In other words, they are descended from the same ancestors by the process of evolution (see Chapter 19).

Five of the major groups of organisms are **plants**, **animals**, **fungi**, **bacteria** and **viruses**.

Plants

You will be familiar with flowering plants, such as those shown in Figure 2.1. This group, or **kingdom**, also contains simpler plants, such as mosses and ferns. All plants are **multicellular**, which means that their 'bodies' are made up of many cells. Their main distinguishing feature is that their cells contain chloroplasts, and carry out photosynthesis: the process that uses light energy to convert simple inorganic molecules such as water and carbon dioxide into complex organic compounds (see Chapter 10). One of these organic compounds is the carbohydrate **cellulose**, and all plants have cell walls made of this material. Plants can make a range of organic compounds as a result of photosynthesis. One of the first compounds that they make is the storage carbohydrate **starch**, which is often found inside plant cells. Another is the sugar **sucrose**, which is transported around the plant and is sometimes stored in fruits and other plant organs. The structure of plant cells is described in Chapter 1, and the structure and function of flowering plants is dealt with in Section C of this book.

Figure 2.1 *(a) A pea plant. Its leaves and stem cells contain chloroplasts, giving them their green colour. The white flowers are pollinated by insects. (b) Maize plants are pollinated by wind. These are the male flowers, which make the pollen. (c) The female maize flowers produce seeds after pollination.*

Animals

You will be even more familiar with this kingdom, since it contains the species *Homo sapiens*, i.e. humans! The variety of the animal kingdom is also enormous, including organisms such as sponges, molluscs, worms, starfish, insects and crustaceans, through to larger animals such as fish, amphibians, reptiles, birds and mammals (Figure 2.2). The last five groups are all **vertebrates**, which means that they have a vertebral column, or backbone. All other animals lack this feature, and are called **invertebrates**.

Animals are also multicellular organisms. Their cells never contain chloroplasts, so they are unable to carry out photosynthesis. Instead, they gain their nutrition by feeding on other animals or plants. Animal cells also lack cell walls, which allows their cells to change shape, an important feature for organisms that need to move from place to place. Movement in animals is achieved in various ways, but often involves coordination by a nervous system (see Chapter 6). Another feature common to most animals is that they store carbohydrate in their cells as the compound **glycogen** (see Chapter 3). The structure of animal cells is described in detail in Chapter 1.

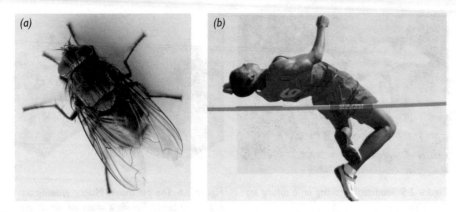

(a)

(b)

Figure 2.2 (a) The housefly is an insect, which is the largest sub-group of all the animals. About 60% of all animal species are insects. (b) This high jumper's movement is coordinated by a complex nervous system.

Fungi

Fungi include mushrooms and toadstools, as well as moulds. These groups of fungi are multicellular. Another group of fungi are the yeasts, which are **unicellular** (made of single cells). Different species of yeasts live everywhere – on the surface of fruits, in soil, water, and even on dust in the air. The yeast powder used for baking contains millions of yeast cells (Figure 2.3). The cells of fungi never contain chloroplasts, so they cannot photosynthesise. Their cells have cell walls, but they are not composed of cellulose (Figure 2.4).

Because fungi have cell walls, they were once thought to be plants that had lost their chlorophyll. We now know that their cell wall is not made of cellulose as in plants, but of a different chemical called **chitin** (the same material that makes up the outside skeleton of insects). Fungi are quite different from plants in many ways (the most obvious is that they do not photosynthesise) and they are not closely related to plants at all.

Figure 2.3 Yeast cells, highly magnified.

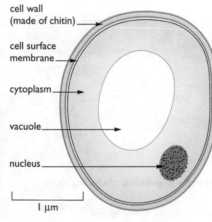

cell wall (made of chitin)

cell surface membrane

cytoplasm

vacuole

nucleus

1 µm

Figure 2.4 Structure of a yeast cell.

A mushroom or toadstool is the reproductive structure of the organism, called a fruiting body (Figure 2.5). Under the soil, the mushroom has many fine thread-like filaments called **hyphae** (pronounced *high-fee*). A mould is rather like a mushroom without the fruiting body. It just consists of the network of hyphae (Figure 2.6). The whole network is called a **mycelium** (pronounced *my-sea-lee-um*). Moulds feed by absorbing nutrients from dead (or sometimes living) material, so they are found wherever this is present, for example, in soil, rotting leaves or decaying fruit.

Figure 2.5 *Toadstools growing on a rotting log.*

Figure 2.6 *The 'pin mould'* Mucor *growing on a piece of bread. The dark spots are structures that produce spores for reproduction.*

If you leave a piece of bread or fruit exposed to the air for a few days, it will soon become mouldy. Mould spores carried in the air have landed on the food and grown into a mycelium of hyphae (Figure 2.7).

The thread-like hyphae of *Mucor* have cell walls surrounding their cytoplasm. The cytoplasm contains many nuclei, in other words the hyphae are not divided up into separate cells.

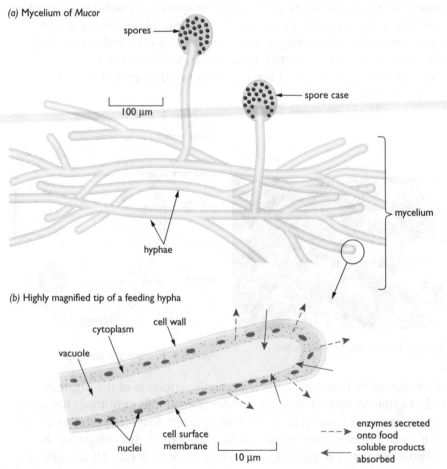

(a) Mycelium of *Mucor*

spores

spore case

100 μm

mycelium

hyphae

(b) Highly magnified tip of a feeding hypha

cell wall

cytoplasm

vacuole

nuclei

cell surface membrane

10 μm

enzymes secreted onto food

soluble products absorbed

Figure 2.7 *The structure of a typical mould fungus, the 'pin mould'* Mucor.

When a spore from *Mucor* lands on the food, a hypha grows out from it. The hypha grows and branches again and again, until the mycelium covers the surface of the food. The hyphae secrete digestive enzymes on to the food, breaking it down into soluble substances such as sugars, which are then absorbed by the mould. Eventually, the food is used up and the mould must infect another source of food, by producing more spores.

When an organism feeds on dead organic material in this way, and digestion takes place outside of the organism, this is called **saprotrophic** nutrition. Enzymes that are secreted out of cells for this purpose are called **extracellular** enzymes (see Chapter 1).

Bacteria

Bacteria are very small, single-celled organisms. To give you some idea of their size, a typical animal cell might be 10 to 50 μm in diameter (1 μm, or one micrometre, is a millionth of a metre, or a thousandth of a millimetre). Compared with this, a typical bacterium is only 1 to 5 μm in length (Figure 2.8) and its volume can be thousands of times less than the larger cell.

There are three basic shapes of bacteria: spheres, rods and spirals, but they all have a similar internal structure (Figure 2.9).

(a) Some different bacterial shapes

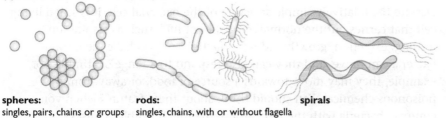

spheres:
singles, pairs, chains or groups

rods:
singles, chains, with or without flagella

spirals

(b) Internal structure of a bacterium

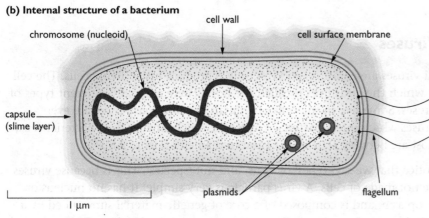

Figure 2.9 *Structure of bacteria.*

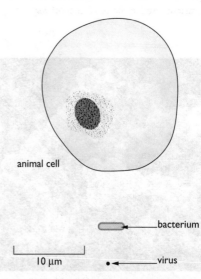

Figure 2.8 *A bacterium is much smaller than an animal cell. The relative size of a virus is also shown.*

All bacteria are surrounded by a cell wall, which protects the bacterium and keeps the shape of the cell. Whereas the cell wall of a plant cell is made of cellulose, and cell walls of fungi are made of chitin, bacterial cell walls contain neither of these two substances. Instead, they are composed of complex chemicals made of polysaccharides and proteins. Some species have

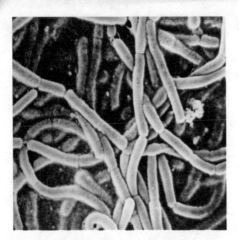

Figure 2.10 *The bacterium* Lactobacillus bulgaricus, *used in the production of yoghurt.*

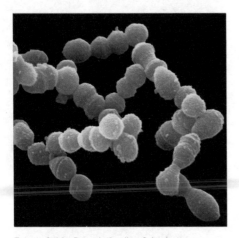

Figure 2.11 *Rounded cells of the bacterium* Pneumococcus, *the cause of pneumonia.*

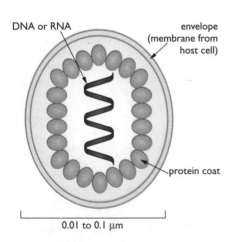

Figure 2.12 *The structure of a typical virus, such as the type causing influenza (flu).*

another layer outside this wall, called a **capsule** or **slime layer**. Both give the bacterium extra protection. Underneath the cell wall is the cell membrane, as in other cells. The middle of the cell is made of cytoplasm. One major difference between a bacterial cell and the more complex cells of animals and plants is that the bacterium has no nucleus. Instead, its genetic material (DNA) is in a **single chromosome**, loose in the cytoplasm, forming a circular loop.

Some bacteria can swim, and are propelled through water by corkscrew-like movements of structures called **flagella** (a single one of these is called a flagell*um*). However, many bacteria do not have flagella and cannot move by themselves. Other structures present in the cytoplasm include the **plasmids**. These are small circular rings of DNA, carrying some of the bacterium's genes. Not all bacteria contain plasmids, although about three-quarters of all known species do. Plasmids have very important uses in **genetic engineering** (see Chapter 22).

Some bacteria contain a form of chlorophyll in their cytoplasm, and can carry out photosynthesis. However, most bacteria feed off other living or dead organisms. Along with the fungi, many bacteria and fungi are important **decomposers** (see Chapter 14), recycling dead organisms and waste products in the soil and elsewhere. Some bacteria are used by humans to make food, such as *Lactobacillus bulgaricus*, a rod-shaped species used in the production of yoghurt from milk (Figure 2.10). Other species are **pathogens**, which means that they cause disease (Figure 2.11).

Despite the relatively simple structure of the bacterial cell, it is still a living cell that carries out the normal 'processes of life', such as respiration, feeding, excretion, growth and reproduction. As you have seen, some bacteria can move, and they can also respond to a range of stimuli. For example, they may move towards a source of food, or away from a poisonous chemical. You should think about these features when you compare bacteria with the next group, the much simpler viruses.

Viruses

All viruses are parasites, and can only reproduce inside living cells. The cell in which the virus lives is called the host. There are many different types of viruses. Some live in the cells of animals or plants, and there are even viruses which infect bacteria. Viruses are much smaller than bacterial cells: most are between 0.01 and 0.1 μm in diameter (Figure 2.8).

Notice that we say 'types' of virus, and not 'species'. This is because viruses are not made of cells. A virus particle is very simple. It has no nucleus or cytoplasm, and is composed of a core of genetic material surrounded by a protein coat (Figure 2.12). The genetic material can be either DNA, or a similar chemical called RNA (see Chapter 16). In either case, the genetic material makes up just a few genes – all that is needed for the virus to reproduce inside its host cell.

Sometimes a membrane called an **envelope** may surround a virus particle, but the virus does not make this. Instead it is 'stolen' from the surface membrane of the host cell.

Viruses do not feed, respire, excrete, move, grow or respond to their surroundings. They do not carry out any of the normal 'characteristics' of living things except reproduction, and they can only do this parasitically. This is why some scientists think of viruses as being on the border between a living organism and a non-living chemical.

A virus reproduces by entering the host cell and taking over the host's genetic machinery to make more virus particles. After many virus particles have been made, the host cell dies and the particles are released to infect more cells. Many human diseases are caused in this way, including colds, influenza, measles, mumps, polio and rubella (German measles). Of course, the reproduction process does not go on forever. Usually, the body's **immune system** destroys the virus and the person recovers. Sometimes, however, a virus cannot be destroyed by the immune system quickly enough, and it may cause permanent damage or death. With other infections, the virus may attack cells of the immune system itself. This is the case with **HIV** (the Human Immunodeficiency Virus), which eventually causes the disease **AIDS** (Acquired Immune Deficiency Syndrome).

Viruses don't just parasitise animal cells. Some infect plant cells, such as the tobacco mosaic virus (Figure 2.13), which interferes with the ability of the tobacco plant to make chloroplasts, causing mottled patches to develop on the leaves (Figure 2.14).

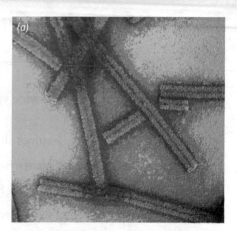

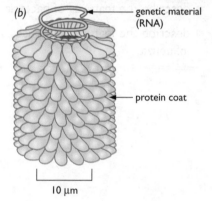

Figure 2.13 (a) Tobacco mosaic virus (TMV), seen through an electron microscope.
(b) Structure of part of a TMV particle, magnified 1.25 million times.

Figure 2.14 Discolouration of the leaves of a tobacco plant, caused by infection with tobacco mosaic virus.

End of Chapter Checklist

You should now be able to:

- understand that there is a wide variety of living organisms and that they are classified on the basis of their structure and function
- describe the common features shown by organisms
- describe the features of plants. Recognise examples of flowering plants such as maize, peas and beans
- describe the features of animals. Recognise examples such as mammals (humans) and insects (houseflies)
- describe the features of fungi. Recognise examples such as *Mucor* and yeast
- describe the features of bacteria. Recognise examples such as *Lactobacillus bulgaricus* and *Pneumococcus*
- describe the features of viruses. Recognise examples such as tobacco mosaic virus and the virus that causes influenza.

End of Section Questions

1 These three organelles are found in cells: nucleus, chloroplast and mitochondrion.

a) Which of the above organelles would be found in:

   i) a cell from a human muscle?   *(1 mark)*

   ii) a palisade cell from a leaf?   *(1 mark)*

   iii) a cell from the root of a plant?   *(1 mark)*

b) Explain fully why the answers to *ii)* and *iii)* above are different.   *(1 mark)*

c) What is the function of each organelle? *(3 marks)*

                            Total 7 marks

2 In multicellular organisms, cells are organised into tissues, organs and organ systems.

a) The diagram shows a section through an artery and a capillary.

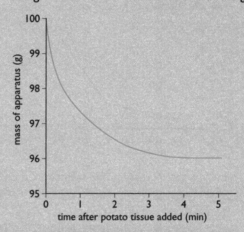

note: artery and capillary are drawn to different scales

artery

— outer layer made of tough fibrous cells

— middle layer containing smooth muscle fibres and elastic fibres

— inner layer of lining (endothelial) cells

capillary

— endothelial cells

Explain why an artery can be considered to be an organ whereas a capillary cannot.   *(2 marks)*

b) Organ systems contain two or more organs whose functions are linked. The digestive system is one human organ system. (See Chapter 3.)

   i) What does the digestive system do? *(2 marks)*

   ii) Name three organs in the human digestive system. Explain what each organ does as part of the digestive system.   *(6 marks)*

   iii) Name two other human organ systems and, for each system, name two organs that are part of the system.   *(6 marks)*

                            Total 16 marks

3 Catalase is an enzyme found in many plant and animal cells. It catalyses the breakdown of hydrogen peroxide into water and oxygen.

$$\text{hydrogen peroxide} \quad \xrightarrow{\text{catalase}} \quad \text{water} + \text{oxygen}$$

a) In an investigation into the action of catalase in potato, 20 g potato tissue was put into a small beaker containing hydrogen peroxide weighing 80 g in total. The temperature was maintained at 20 °C throughout the investigation. As soon as the potato was added, the mass of the beaker and its contents was recorded until there was no further change in mass. The results are shown in the graph.

   i) How much oxygen was formed in this investigation? Explain your answer.   *(2 marks)*

   ii) Estimate the time by which half this mass of oxygen had been formed.   *(2 marks)*

   iii) Explain, in terms of collisions between enzyme and substrate molecules, why the rate of reaction changes during the course of the investigation.   *(2 marks)*

b) The students repeated the investigation at 30 °C. What difference, if any, would you expect in:

   i) the mass of oxygen formed?

   ii) the time taken to form this mass of oxygen?

   Explain your answers.   *(4 marks)*

                            Total 10 marks

4 Different particles move across cell membranes using different processes.

a) The table (on the next page) shows some ways in which active transport, osmosis and diffusion are similar and some ways in which they are different. Copy and complete the table with ticks and crosses.   *(12 marks)*

Feature	Active transport	Osmosis	Diffusion
particles must have kinetic energy			
requires energy from respiration			
particles move down a concentration gradient			
process needs special carriers in the membrane			

b) The graph shows the results of an investigation into the rate of diffusion of sodium ions across the membranes of potato cells.

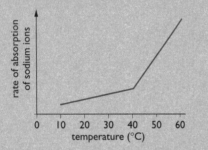

i) Explain the increase in the rate of diffusion up to 40 °C. *(2 marks)*

ii) Suggest why the rate of increase is much steeper at temperatures above 40 °C. *(2 marks)*

Total 16 marks

5 Cells in the wall of the small intestine divide by mitosis to replace cells lost as food passes through.

a) Chromosomes contain DNA. The graph shows the changes in the DNA content of a cell in the wall of the small intestine as it divides by mitosis.

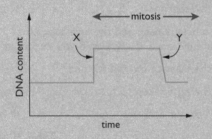

i) Why is it essential that the DNA content is doubled (X) before mitosis commences? *(2 marks)*

ii) What do you think happens to the cell at point Y? *(1 mark)*

b) The diagram shows a cell in the wall of a villus in the small intestine. Some of the processes involved in the absorption of glucose are also shown.

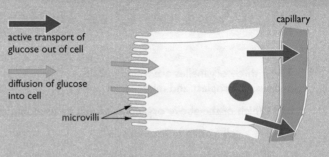

i) What is the importance of the small intestine having villi? *(1 mark)*

ii) Suggest how the microvilli adapt this cell to its function of absorbing glucose. *(1 mark)*

iii) Suggest how the active transport of glucose out of the cell and into the blood stream helps with the absorption of glucose from the small intestine. *(2 marks)*

Total 7 marks

6 A respirometer is used to measure the rate of respiration. The diagram shows a simple respirometer. The sodium hydroxide solution in the apparatus absorbs carbon dioxide. Some results from the investigation are also shown.

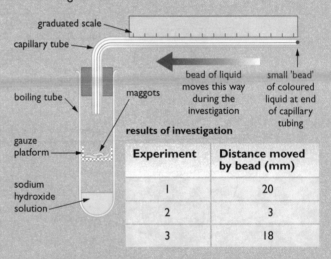

results of investigation

Experiment	Distance moved by bead (mm)
1	20
2	3
3	18

a) Assume that the maggots in the apparatus respire aerobically.

i) Write the symbol equation for aerobic respiration. *(4 marks)*

ii) From the equation, what can you assume about the amount of oxygen taken in and carbon dioxide given off by the maggots? Explain your answer. *(3 marks)*

iii) Result 2 is significantly different from the other two results. Suggest a reason for this. *(2 marks)*

iv) How would the results be different if the organisms under investigation respired anaerobically? *(2 marks)*

Total 11 marks

7 The table below shows some features of different groups of organisms. Copy and complete the table by putting a tick in the box if the organism has that feature, or a cross if it lacks the feature.

Feature	Type of organism		
	plant	fungus	virus
They are all parasites.			
They are made up of a mycelium of hyphae.			
They can only reproduce inside living cells.			
They feed by extracellular digestion by enzymes.			
They store carbohydrate as starch.			

Total 5 marks

8 Copy and complete the following account.

Plants have cell walls made of _____ .
They store carbohydrate as the insoluble compound
called _____ or sometimes as the
sugar _____ . Plants make these
substances as a result of the process called
_____ . Animals, on the other
hand, store carbohydrate as the compound
_____ . Both animals' and plants' cells
have nuclei, but the cells of bacteria lack a true nucleus,
having their DNA in a circular chromosome. They
sometimes also contain small rings of DNA called
_____ , which are used in genetic
engineering. Bacteria and fungi break down organic
matter in the soil. They are known as
_____ . Some bacteria are pathogens,
which means that they _____ .

Total 8 marks

Chapter 3: Breathing and Gas Exchange

When we breathe, air is drawn into and out of the lungs so that gas exchange can take place between the air and the blood. This chapter looks at these processes, and also deals with some ways that smoking can damage the lungs and stop these vital organs from working properly.

Cells get their energy by oxidising foods such as glucose. This process is called cell respiration (see Chapter 1). If the cells are to respire aerobically, they need a continuous supply of oxygen from the blood. In addition, the waste product of respiration, carbon dioxide, needs to be removed from the body. In humans, these gases are exchanged between the blood and the air in the lungs.

Respiration and breathing

We need to understand the difference between respiration and breathing. Respiration is the oxidation reaction (described in Chapter 1) that releases energy from foods, such as glucose. We can use the term **ventilation** to describe the mechanism that moves air into and out of the lungs, which then allows gas exchange to take place. We also use the term **breathing** in a more general way for this process. The lungs and associated structures are often called the 'respiratory system' but this can be confusing. It is better to call them the **gas exchange system** and this is the term we adopt in this book.

The structure of the gas exchange system

The lungs are enclosed in the chest or **thorax** by the ribcage and a muscular sheet of tissue called the **diaphragm** (Figure 3.1). As you will see, the actions of these two structures bring about the movements of air into and out of the lungs. Joining each rib to the next are two sets of muscles called **intercostal muscles** ('costals' are rib bones). If you eat meat, you will have seen intercostal muscle attached to the long bones of 'spare ribs'. The diaphragm separates the contents of the thorax from the abdomen. It is not flat, but a shallow dome shape, with a fibrous middle part forming the 'roof' of the dome, and muscular edges forming the walls.

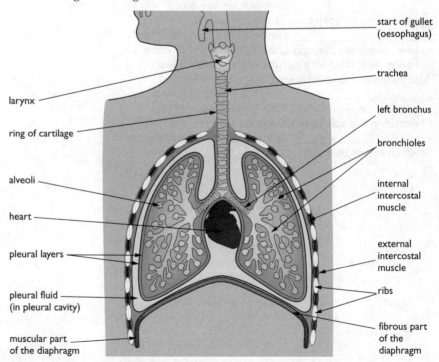

Figure 3.1 *The human gas exchange system.*

The air passages of the lungs form a highly branching network (Figure 3.2). This is why it is sometimes called the **bronchial tree**.

When we breathe in, air enters our nose or mouth and passes down the windpipe or **trachea**. The trachea splits into two tubes called the **bronchi**, one leading to each lung. Each **bronchus** divides into smaller and smaller tubes called **bronchioles**, eventually ending at microscopic air sacs, called **alveoli**. It is here that gas exchange with the blood takes place.

The walls of trachea and bronchi contain rings of gristle or **cartilage**. These support the airways and keep them open when we breathe in. They are rather like the rings in a vacuum cleaner hose – without them the hose would squash flat when the cleaner sucks air in.

The inside of the thorax is separated from the lungs by two thin, moist membranes called the **pleural layers**. They make up a continuous envelope around the lungs, forming an airtight seal. Between the two layers is a space called the **pleural cavity**, filled with a thin layer of liquid called **pleural fluid**. This acts as lubrication, so that the surfaces of the lungs don't stick to the inside of the chest wall when we breathe.

Keeping the airways clean

The trachea and larger airways are lined with a layer of cells that have an important role in keeping the airways clean. Some cells in this lining secrete a sticky liquid called **mucus**, which traps particles of dirt or bacteria that are breathed in. Other cells are covered with tiny hair-like structures called **cilia** (Figure 3.4). The cilia beat backwards and forwards, sweeping the mucus and trapped particles out towards the mouth. In this way, dirt and bacteria are prevented from entering the lungs, where they might cause an infection. As you will see, one of the effects of smoking is that it destroys the cilia and stops this protection mechanism from working properly.

Ventilation of the lungs

Ventilation means moving air in and out of the lungs. This requires a difference in air pressure – the air moves from a place where the pressure is high to one where it is low. Ventilation depends on the fact that the thorax is an airtight cavity. When we breathe, we change the volume of our thorax, which alters the pressure inside it. This causes air to move in or out of the lungs.

There are two movements that bring about ventilation, those of the ribs and the diaphragm. If you put your hands on your chest and breathe in deeply, you can feel your ribs move upwards and outwards. They are moved by the intercostal muscles (Figure 3.5). The outer (external) intercostals contract, pulling the ribs up. At the same time, the muscles of the diaphragm contract, pulling the diaphragm down into a more flattened shape (Figure 3.6a). Both these movements increase the volume of the chest and cause a slight drop in pressure inside the thorax compared with the air outside. Air then enters the lungs.

The opposite happens when you breathe out deeply. The external intercostals relax, and the internal intercostals contract, pulling the ribs down and in. At the same time, the diaphragm muscles relax and the diaphragm goes back to its normal dome shape. The volume of the thorax decreases, and the pressure

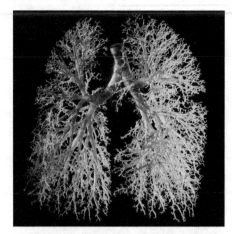

Figure 3.2 *This cast of the human lungs was made by injecting a pair of lungs with a liquid plastic. The plastic was allowed to set, then the lung tissue was dissolved away with acid.*

In the bronchi, the cartilage forms complete, circular rings. In the trachea, the rings are incomplete, and shaped like a letter 'C'. The open part of the ring is at the back of the trachea, next to where the oesophagus (gullet) lies as it passes through the thorax. When food passes along the oesophagus by peristalsis (see Chapter 4) the gaps in the rings allow the lumps of food to pass through more easily, without the peristaltic wave 'catching' on the rings (Figure 3.3).

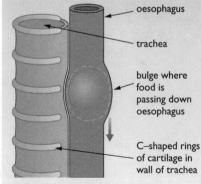

oesophagus

trachea

bulge where food is passing down oesophagus

C–shaped rings of cartilage in wall of trachea

Figure 3.3 *C-shaped cartilage rings in the trachea.*

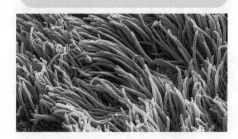

Figure 3.4 *This electron microscope picture shows cilia from the lining of the trachea.*

During normal (shallow) breathing, the elasticity of the lungs and the weight of the ribs acting downwards is enough to cause exhalation. The internal intercostals are only really used for deep (forced) breathing out, for instance when we are exercising.

It is important that you remember the changes in volume and pressure during ventilation. If you have trouble understanding these, think of what happens when you use a bicycle pump. If you push the pump handle, the air in the pump is squashed, its pressure rises and it is forced out of the pump. If you pull on the handle, the air pressure inside the pump falls a little, and air is drawn in from outside. This is similar to what happens in the lungs. In exams, students sometimes talk about the lungs *forcing* the air in and out – they don't!

in the thorax is raised slightly above atmospheric pressure. This time the difference in pressure forces air out of the lungs (Figure 3.6b). Exhalation is helped by the fact that the lungs are elastic, so that they tend to empty like a balloon.

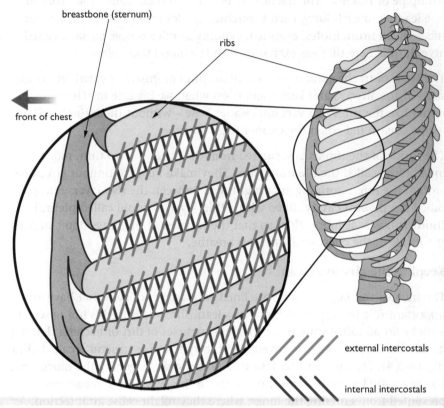

Figure 3.5 *X-ray of side view of the chest wall, showing the ribs. The diagram shows how the two sets of intercostal muscles run between the ribs. When the external intercostals contract, they move the ribs upwards. When the internal intercostals contract, the ribs are moved downwards.*

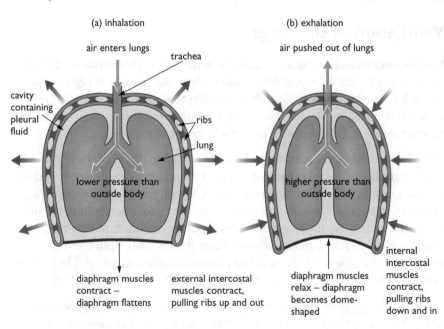

Figure 3.6 *Changes in the position of the ribs and diaphragm during breathing.*
(a) Breathing in (inhalation). (b) Breathing out (exhalation).

Gas exchange in the alveoli

You can tell what is happening during gas exchange if you compare the amounts of different gases in atmospheric air with the air breathed out (Table 3.1).

Gas	Atmospheric air	Exhaled air
nitrogen	78	79
oxygen	21	16
carbon dioxide	0.04	4
other gases (mainly argon)	1	1

Table 3.1: *Approximate percentage volume of gases in atmospheric (inhaled) and exhaled air.*

Exhaled air is also warmer than atmospheric air, and is saturated with water vapour. The amount of water vapour in the atmosphere varies, depending on weather conditions.

Clearly, the lungs are absorbing oxygen into the blood and removing carbon dioxide from it. This happens in the alveoli. To do this efficiently, the alveoli must have a structure which brings the air and blood very close together, over a very large surface area. There are enormous numbers of alveoli. It has been calculated that the two lungs contain about 700 000 000 of these tiny air sacs, giving a total surface area of 60 m². That's bigger than the floor area of an average classroom! Viewed through a high-powered microscope, the alveoli look rather like bunches of grapes, and are covered with tiny blood capillaries (Figure 3.7).

Be careful when interpreting percentages! The *percentage* of a gas in a mixture can vary, even if the actual *amount* of the gas stays the same. This is easiest to understand from an example. Imagine you have a bottle containing a mixture of 20% oxygen and 80% nitrogen. If you used a chemical to absorb all the oxygen in the bottle, the nitrogen left would now be 100% of the gas in the bottle, despite the fact that the *amount* of nitrogen would still be the same. That is why the percentage of nitrogen in inhaled and exhaled air is slightly different.

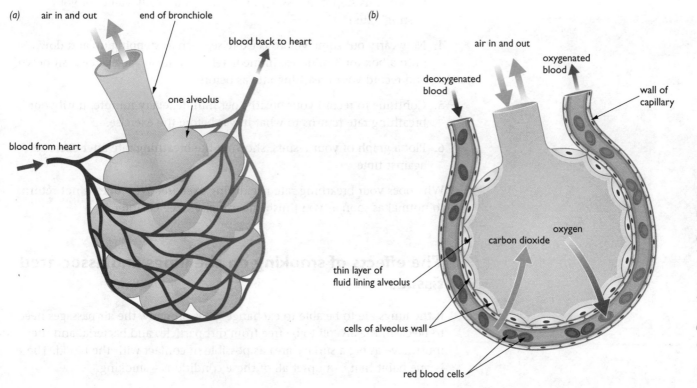

Figure 3.7 *(a) Alveoli and the surrounding capillary network. (b) Diffusion of oxygen and carbon dioxide takes place between the air in the alveolus and the blood in the capillaries.*

Blood is pumped from the heart to the lungs and passes through the capillaries surrounding the alveoli. The blood has come from the respiring tissues of the body, where it has given up some of its oxygen to the cells, and gained carbon dioxide. Around the lungs, the blood is separated from the air inside each alveolus by only two cell layers; the cells making up the wall of the alveolus, and the capillary wall itself. This is a distance of less than a thousandth of a millimetre.

Because the air in the alveolus has a higher concentration of oxygen than the blood entering the capillary network, oxygen diffuses from the air, across the wall of the alveolus and into the blood. At the same time there is more carbon dioxide in the blood than there is in the air in the lungs. This means that there is a diffusion gradient for carbon dioxide in the other direction, so carbon dioxide diffuses the other way, out of the blood and into the alveolus. The result is that the blood which leaves the capillaries and flows back to the heart has gained oxygen and lost carbon dioxide. The heart then pumps the blood around the body again, to supply the respiring cells (see Chapter 5).

> The thin layer of fluid lining the inside of the alveoli comes from the blood. The capillaries and cells of the alveolar wall are 'leaky' and the blood pressure pushes fluid out from the blood plasma into the alveolus. Oxygen dissolves in this moist surface before it passes through the alveolar wall into the blood.

Investigating the effect of exercise on breathing rate

You can easily show the effect of exercise on your breathing rate.

Carry out the following:

1. Sit quietly for five minutes, making sure that you are completely relaxed.

2. Count the number of breaths that you take in 1 minute. Record your results in a table.

3. Wait a minute, then count your breaths again, recording your result. (Repeat this step if necessary, until you get a steady value for your 'resting' rate.)

4. Now carry out some vigorous exercise, such as stepping up and down onto a box for 3 minutes. Immediately you finish the exercise, sit down and record your breathing rate as before.

5. Continue to record your breaths per minute, every minute, until your breathing rate returns to what it was before the exercise.

6. Plot a graph of your results, showing the breathing rate after exercise against time.

Why does your breathing rate rise during exercise? Why does it not return to normal as soon as you finish the exercise? (See Chapter 1.)

The effects of smoking on the lungs and associated tissues

If the lungs are to be able to exchange gases properly, the air passages need to be clear, the alveoli to be free from dirt particles and bacteria, and they must have as big a surface area as possible in contact with the blood. There is one habit that can upset all of these conditions – smoking.

Links between smoking and diseases of the lungs are now a proven fact. Smoking is associated with lung cancer, bronchitis and emphysema. It is also a major contributing factor to other problems, such as coronary heart disease and ulcers of the stomach and duodenum (part of the intestine). Pregnant women who smoke are more likely to give birth to underweight babies. We need to deal with some of these effects in more detail.

Effects of smoke on the lining of the air passages

You saw above how the lungs are kept free of particles of dirt and bacteria by the action of mucus and cilia. In the trachea and bronchi of a smoker, the cilia are destroyed by the chemicals in cigarette smoke. Compare Figure 3.4 with the same photo taken of the lining of a smoker's airways (Figure 3.8).

The reduced numbers of cilia mean that the mucus is not swept away from the lungs, but remains to clog the air passages. This is made worse by the fact that the smoke irritates the lining of the airways, stimulating the cells to secrete more mucus. The clogging mucus is the source of 'smoker's cough'. Irritation of the bronchial tree, along with infections from bacteria in the mucus can cause the lung disease **bronchitis**. Bronchitis blocks normal air flow, so the sufferer has difficulty breathing properly.

Emphysema

Emphysema is another lung disease that kills about 20 000 people in Britain every year. Smoke damages the walls of the alveoli, which break down and fuse together again, forming enlarged, irregular air spaces (Figure 3.9).

This greatly reduces the surface area for gas exchange, which becomes very inefficient. The blood of a person with emphysema carries less oxygen. In serious cases, this leads to the sufferer being unable to carry out even mild exercise, such as walking. Emphysema patients often have to have a supply of oxygen nearby at all times (Figure 3.10). There is no cure for emphysema, and usually the sufferer dies after a long and distressing illness.

Figure 3.8 *This electron micrograph shows cilia from the trachea of a smoker. Notice the reduced numbers of cilia compared with a normal trachea.*

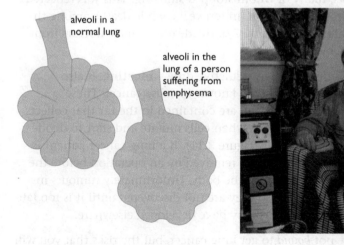

alveoli in a normal lung

alveoli in the lung of a person suffering from emphysema

Figure 3.9 *The alveoli of a person suffering from emphysema have a greatly reduced surface area and inefficient gas exchange.*

Figure 3.10 *This man suffers from emphysema and has to breathe from an oxygen cylinder to stay alive.*

Lung cancer

Evidence of the link between smoking and lung cancer first appeared in the 1950s. In one study, a number of patients in hospital were given a series of questions about their lifestyles. They were asked about their work, hobbies, housing and so on, including a question about how many cigarettes they smoked. The same questionnaire was given to two groups of patients. The first group were all suffering from lung cancer. The second, **control** group were in hospital with various other illnesses, but not lung cancer. To make it a fair comparison, the control patients were matched with the lung cancer patients for sex, age and so on.

When the results were compared, one difference stood out (Table 3.2). A greater proportion of the lung cancer patients were smokers than in the control patients. There seemed to be a connection between smoking and getting lung cancer.

	Percentage of patients who were non-smokers	Percentage of patients who smoked more than 15 cigarettes a day
lung cancer patients	0.5	25
control patients (with illnesses other than lung cancer)	4.5	13

Table 3.2: *Comparison of the smoking habits of lung cancer patients and other patients.*

Although the results didn't prove that smoking caused lung cancer, there was a statistically significant link between smoking and the disease: this is called a 'correlation'.

Over 20 similar investigations in nine countries have revealed the same findings. In 1962 a report called 'Smoking and health' was published by the Royal College of Physicians of London, which warned the public about the dangers of smoking. Not surprisingly, the first people to take the findings seriously were doctors, many of whom stopped smoking. This was reflected in their death rates from lung cancer. In ten years, while deaths among the general male population had risen by 7%, the deaths of male doctors from the disease had *fallen* by 38%.

Cigarette smoke contains a strongly addictive drug – **nicotine**. It also contains at least 17 chemicals that are known to cause cancer. These chemicals are called **carcinogens**, and are contained in the **tar** that collects in a smoker's lungs. Cancer happens when cells mutate and start to divide uncontrollably, forming a **tumour** (Figure 3.11). If a lung cancer patient is lucky, he or she may have the tumour removed by an operation before the cancer cells spread to other tissues of the body. Unfortunately tumours in the lungs usually cause no pain, so they are not discovered until it is too late – it may be inoperable, or tumours may have developed elsewhere.

If you smoke you are not *bound* to get lung cancer, but the risks that you will get it are much greater. In fact, the more cigarettes you smoke, the more the risk that you will get the disease increases (Figure 3.12).

The obvious thing to do is not to start smoking. However, if you are a smoker, giving up the habit soon improves your chance of survival (Figure 3.13). After a few years, the likelihood of your dying from a smoking-related disease is almost back to the level of a non-smoker.

People often talk about 'yellow nicotine stains'. In fact it is the *tar* that stains a smoker's fingers and teeth. Nicotine is a colourless, odourless chemical.

Figure 3.11 *This lung is from a patient with lung cancer.*

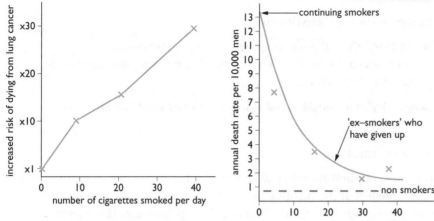

Figure 3.12 *The more cigarettes a person smokes, the more likely it is they will die of lung cancer. For example, smoking 20 cigarettes a day increases the risk by about 15 times.*

Figure 3.13 *Death rates from lung cancer for smokers, non-smokers and ex-smokers.*

Studies have shown that the type of cigarette smoked makes very little difference to the smoker's risk of getting lung cancer. Filtered and 'low tar' cigarettes only reduce the risk slightly.

Carbon monoxide in smoke

One of the harmful chemicals in cigarette smoke is the poisonous gas **carbon monoxide**. When this gas is breathed in with the smoke, it enters the bloodstream and interferes with the ability of the blood to carry oxygen. Oxygen is carried around in the blood in the red blood cells, attached to a chemical called **haemoglobin** (see Chapter 5). Carbon monoxide can combine with the haemoglobin much more tightly than oxygen can, forming a compound called **carboxyhaemoglobin**. The haemoglobin will combine with carbon monoxide in preference to oxygen. When this happens, the blood carries much less oxygen around the body. Carbon monoxide from smoking is also a major cause of heart disease (Chapter 5).

If a pregnant woman smokes, she will be depriving her unborn fetus of oxygen (Figure 3.14). This has an effect on its growth and development, and leads to the mass of the baby at birth being lower, on average, than the mass of babies born to non-smokers.

Some recent smoking statistics

- 13 million people in the UK smoke cigarettes, 28% of men and 26% of women.

- Smoking is highest among the 20–24 age group: 42% of men and 39% of women.

- More than 80% of smokers take up the habit as teenagers. In the UK about 450 children start smoking every day.

- Among 15 year-olds, 21% of boys and 25% of girls are regular smokers.

- In the UK, smoking kills around 120 000 people every year, about 37 times more people than are killed in road traffic accidents.

- Every year several hundred lung cancer deaths are due to passive smoking (breathing other people's smoke).

Figure 3.14 *Smoking during pregnancy affects the growth and development of the baby.*

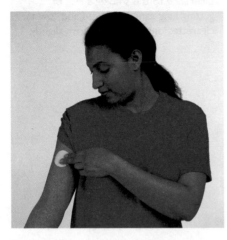

Figure 3.15 *Increasing numbers of young women are smokers. Many turn to nicotine patches to help them give up.*

You could carry out an Internet search to find out about the different methods people use to help them give up smoking. Which methods have the highest success rate?

Some smoking statistics *cont.*

- In 1998, the UK government received £10 090 million from tax on tobacco (in 1997 the cost of treating smoking-related diseases was £1 700 million).

Source: Action on Smoking and Health (ASH) fact sheet (January 2001)

Giving up smoking

Most smokers admit that they would like to find a way to give up the habit. The trouble is that the nicotine in tobacco is a very addictive drug, and causes withdrawal symptoms when people stop smoking. These include cravings for a cigarette, restlessness and a tendency to put on weight (nicotine depresses the appetite).

There are various ways that smokers can be helped to 'kick the habit'. One of the most successful methods is the use of nicotine patches (Figure 3.15) or nicotine chewing gum. These provide the smoker who is trying to give up with a source of nicotine, without the harmful tar of cigarettes. The nicotine is absorbed through the skin (with patches) or through the mouth (from gum) and reduces the craving for a cigarette. Gradually the 'ex-smoker' reduces the nicotine dose until they are weaned off the habit.

There are several other ways that people use to help them give up smoking, including the use of drugs that reduce withdrawal symptoms, acupuncture and even hypnotism.

End of Chapter Checklist

You should now be able to:

- recall the structure of the thorax, including the ribs, intercostal muscles, diaphragm, trachea, bronchi, bronchioles, alveoli and pleural membranes
- understand the role of the intercostal muscles and the diaphragm in ventilation
- explain how alveoli are adapted for gas exchange
- describe a simple experiment to investigate the effect of exercise on breathing in humans
- understand the biological consequences of smoking on the lungs.

Questions

More questions on breathing can be found at the end of Section B on page 108.

1 Copy and complete the table, which shows what happens in the thorax during ventilation of the lungs. Two boxes have been completed for you.

	Action during inhalation	Action during exhalation
external intercostal muscles	contract	
internal intercostal muscles		
ribs		move down and in
diaphragm		
volume of thorax		
pressure in thorax		
volume of air in lungs		

2 A student wrote the following about the lungs.

> When we breathe in, our lungs inflate, sucking air in and pushing the ribs up and out, and forcing the diaphragm down. This is called respiration. In the air sacs of the lungs the air enters the blood. The blood then takes the air around the body, where it is used by the cells. The blood returns to the lungs to be cleaned. When we breathe out, our lungs deflate, pulling the diaphragm up and the ribs down. The stale air is pushed out of the lungs.

The student did not have a good understanding of the workings of the lungs. Re-write her description, using correct biological words and ideas.

3 Sometimes, people injured in an accident such as a car crash suffer from a *pneumothorax*. This is an injury where the chest wall is punctured, allowing air to enter the pleural cavity (see Figure 3.1). A patient was brought to the casualty department of a hospital, suffering from a pneumothorax on the left side of his chest. His left lung had collapsed, but he was able to breathe normally with his right lung.

a) Explain why a pneumothorax caused the left lung to collapse.

b) Explain why the right lung was not affected.

c) If a patient's lung is injured or infected, a surgeon can sometimes 'rest' it by performing an operation called an *artificial pneumothorax*. What do you think might be involved in this operation?

4 Briefly explain the importance of the following.

    a) The trachea wall contains C-shaped rings of cartilage.

    b) The distance between the air in an alveolus and the blood in an alveolar capillary is less than 1/1000th of a millimetre.

    c) The lining of the trachea contains mucus-secreting cells and cells with cilia.

    d) Smokers have a lower concentration of oxygen in their blood than non-smokers.

    e) Nicotine patches and nicotine chewing gum can help someone give up smoking.

    f) The lungs have a surface area of about 60 m² and a good blood supply.

5 Explain the differences between the lung diseases bronchitis and emphysema.

6 A long-term investigation was carried out into the link between smoking and lung cancer. The smoking habits of male doctors aged 35 or over were determined while they were still alive, then the number and causes of deaths among them were monitored over a number of years. (Note that this survey was carried out in the 1950s – very few doctors smoke these days!) The results are shown in the graph.

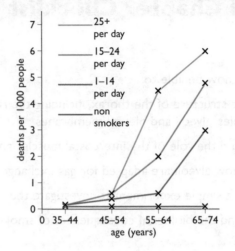

    a) Write a paragraph to explain what the researchers found out from the investigation.

    b) How many deaths from lung cancer would be expected for men aged 55 who smoked 25 cigarettes a day up until their death? How many deaths from lung cancer would be expected for men in the same age group smoking 10 a day?

    c) Table 3.2 (page 32) shows the findings of another study linking lung cancer with smoking. Which do you think is the more convincing evidence of the link, this investigation or the findings illustrated in Table 3.2?

7 Design and make a hard-hitting leaflet explaining the link between smoking and lung cancer. It should be aimed at encouraging an adult smoker to give up the habit. You could use a suitable computer software package to produce your design. Include some smoking statistics, perhaps from an Internet search. However don't use too many, or they may put the person off reading the leaflet!

Chapter 4: Food and Digestion

Food is essential for life. The nutrients obtained from it are used in many different ways by the body. This chapter looks at the different kinds of food, and how the food is broken down by the digestive system and absorbed into the blood, so that it can be carried to all the tissues of the body.

We need food for three main reasons:

- to supply us with a 'fuel' for energy
- to provide materials for growth and repair of tissues
- to help fight disease and keep our bodies healthy.

A balanced diet

The food that we eat is called our **diet**. No matter what you like to eat, if your body is to work properly and stay healthy, your diet must include five groups of food substances – **carbohydrates**, **lipids**, **proteins**, **minerals** and **vitamins** – as well as **water** and **fibre**. Food should provide you with all of these substances, but they must also be present in the *right* amounts. A diet that provides enough of these substances and in the correct proportions to keep you healthy is called a **balanced diet** (Figure 4.1). We will deal with each type of food in turn, to find out about its chemistry and the role that it plays in the body.

Figure 4.1 *A balanced diet contains all the types of food the body needs, in just the right amounts.*

Carbohydrates

Carbohydrates only make up about 5% of the mass of the human body, but they have a very important role. They are the body's main 'fuel' for supplying cells with energy. Cells release this energy by oxidising a sugar called **glucose**, in the process called cell respiration (see Chapter 1). Glucose and other sugars are one sort of carbohydrate.

Glucose is found naturally in many sweet-tasting foods, such as fruits and vegetables. Other foods contain different sugars, such as the fruit sugar

The chemical formula for glucose is $C_6H_{12}O_6$. Like all carbohydrates, glucose contains only the elements carbon, hydrogen and oxygen. The 'carbo' part of the name refers to carbon, and the 'hydrate' part refers to the fact that the hydrogen and oxygen atoms are in the ratio two to one, as in water (H_2O).

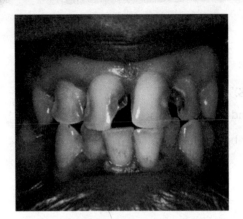

Figure 4.2 *A bad case of tooth decay. One of the causes was too much sugar in the person's diet.*

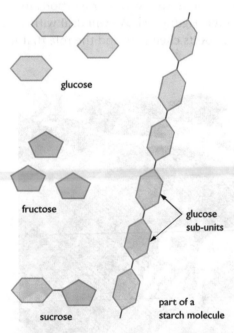

glucose

fructose

glucose sub-units

sucrose

part of a starch molecule

Figure 4.3 *Glucose and fructose are 'single sugar' molecules. A molecule of glucose joined to a molecule of fructose forms the 'double sugar' called sucrose. Starch is a polymer of many glucose sub-units.*

'Single' sugars such as glucose and fructose are called **monosaccharides**. Sucrose molecules are made of two monosaccharides (glucose and fructose) joined together, so sucrose is called a **disaccharide**. Lactose is also a disaccharide of glucose joined to a monosaccharide called galactose. Polymers of sugars, such as starch and glycogen, are called **polysaccharides**.

called **fructose**, and the milk sugar, **lactose**. Ordinary table sugar, the sort some people put in their tea or coffee, is called **sucrose**. Sucrose is the main sugar that is transported through plant stems. This is why we can extract it from sugar cane, which is the stem of a large grass-like plant. Sugars have two physical properties that you will probably know: they all taste sweet, and they are all soluble in water.

We can get all the sugar we need from natural foods such as fruits and vegetables, and from the digestion of starch. Many 'processed' foods contain large amounts of *added* sugar. For example, a typical can of cola can contain up to 27 g, or seven teaspoonfuls! There is hidden sugar in many other foods. A tin of baked beans contains about 10 g of added sugar. This is on top of all the food that we eat with a more obvious sugar content, such as cakes, biscuits and sweets. One of the health problems resulting from all this sugar in our diet is **tooth decay**. Bacteria in the mouth feed on sugar, breaking it down and making acids that dissolve the tooth enamel. Once the enamel is penetrated, the acid breaks down the softer dentine underneath, and eventually a cavity is formed in the tooth (Figure 4.2). Bacteria can then enter this cavity and enlarge it until the decay reaches the nerves at the centre of the tooth. Then you feel the pain!

In fact, we get most of the carbohydrate in our diet not from sugars, but from **starch**. Starch is a large, *insoluble* molecule. Because it does not dissolve, it is found as a storage carbohydrate in many plants, such as potato, rice, wheat and millet. The 'staple diets' of people from around the world are starchy foods like rice, potatoes, bread and pasta. Starch is made up of long chains of hundreds of glucose molecules joined together. It is called a **polymer** of glucose (Figure 4.3).

Starch is only found in plant tissues, but animal cells sometimes contain a very similar carbohydrate called **glycogen**. This is also a polymer of glucose, and is found in tissues such as liver and muscle, where it acts as a store of energy for these organs.

As you will see, large carbohydrates such as starch and glycogen have to be broken down into simple sugars during digestion, so that they can be absorbed into the blood.

Another carbohydrate that is a polymer of glucose is **cellulose**, the material that makes up plant cell walls. Humans are *not* able to digest cellulose, because our gut doesn't make the enzyme needed to break down the cellulose molecule. This means that we are not able to use cellulose as a source of energy. However, it still has a vitally important function in our diet. It forms **dietary fibre** or **roughage**, which gives the muscles of the gut something to push against as the food is moved through the intestine. This keeps the gut contents moving, avoiding constipation and helping to prevent serious diseases of the intestine, such as colitis and bowel cancer.

Lipids (fats and oils)

Lipids contain the same three elements as carbohydrates – carbon, hydrogen and oxygen – but the proportion of oxygen in a lipid is much lower than in a carbohydrate. For example, beef and lamb both contain a fat called tristearin, which has the formula $C_{51}H_{98}O_6$. This fat, like other animal fats, is a solid at room temperature, but melts if you warm it up. On the other hand, plant lipids are usually liquid at room temperature, and are called **oils**. Meat, butter, cheese, milk, eggs and oily fish are all rich in animal fats, as well as foods fried in fat or oil, such as chips. Plant oils include many types used for cooking, such as olive oil, corn oil and rapeseed oil, as well as products made from oils, such as margarine (Figure 4.4).

Lipids make up about 10% of our body's mass. They form an essential part of the structure of all cells, and fat is deposited in certain parts of the body as a long-term store of energy, for example under the skin and around the heart and kidneys. The fat layer under the skin acts as insulation, reducing heat loss through the surface of the body. Fat around organs such as the kidneys also helps to protect them from mechanical damage.

Fats and oils are both known as **lipids**.

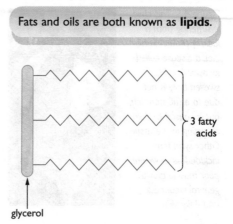

Figure 4.5 *Lipids are made up of a molecule of glycerol joined to three fatty acids. The many different fatty acids form the variable part of the molecule.*

Figure 4.4 *These foods are all rich in lipids.*

The chemical 'building blocks' of lipids are two types of molecule called **glycerol** and **fatty acids**. Glycerol is an oily liquid. It is also known as glycerine, and is used in many types of cosmetics. In lipids, a molecule of glycerol is joined to three fatty acid molecules. There are a large number of different fatty acid molecules, which gives us the many different kinds of lipid found in food (Figure 4.5).

Although lipids are an essential part of our diet, too much lipid is unhealthy, especially a type called **saturated** fat, and a lipid compound called **cholesterol**. These substances have been linked to heart disease (see Chapter 5).

Proteins

Proteins make up about 18% of the mass of the body. This is the second largest fraction after water. All cells contain protein, so we need it for growth and repair of tissues. Many compounds in the body are made from protein, including enzymes.

Most foods contain some protein, but certain foods such as meat, fish, cheese and eggs are particularly rich in it. You will notice that these foods are animal products. Plant material generally contains less protein, but some foods, especially beans, peas and nuts, are richer in protein than others.

Saturated lipids (fats) are more common in food from animal sources, such as meat and dairy products. 'Saturated' is a word used in chemistry, which means that the fatty acids of the lipids contain no double bonds. Other lipids are **unsaturated**, which means that their fatty acids contain double bonds. These are more common in plant oils. There is evidence that unsaturated lipids are healthier for us than saturated ones.

Cholesterol is a substance that the body gets from food such as eggs and meat, but we also make cholesterol in our liver. It is an essential part of all cells, but too much cholesterol causes heart disease.

Figure 4.6 *This child is suffering from a lack of protein in his diet, a disease called kwashiorkor. His swollen belly is not due to a full stomach, but is caused by fluid collecting in the tissues. Other symptoms include loss of weight, poor muscle growth, general weakness and flaky skin.*

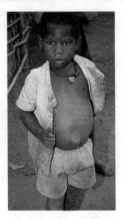

Humans can make about half of the 20 amino acids that they need, but the other 10 have to be taken in as part of the diet. These 10 are called **essential amino acids**. There are higher amounts of essential amino acids in meat, fish, eggs and dairy products. If you are a vegetarian, you can still get all the essential amino acids you need, as long as you eat a varied diet that includes a range of different plant materials.

(a)

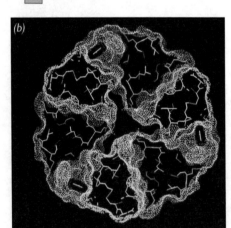

(b)

Figure 4.7 *(a) A chain of amino acids forming part of a protein molecule. Each shape represents a different amino acid. (b) A computer model of the protein insulin. This substance, like all proteins, is made of a long chain of amino acids arranged in a specific order.*

However, we don't need much protein in our diet to stay healthy. Doctors recommend a maximum daily intake of about 70 g. In more economically developed countries, people often eat far more protein than they need, whereas in many poorer countries a protein-deficiency disease called **kwashiorkor** is common (Figure 4.6).

Like starch, proteins are also polymers, but whereas starch is made from a single molecular building block (glucose), proteins are made from 20 different sub-units called **amino acids**. All amino acids contain four chemical elements: carbon, hydrogen and oxygen (as in carbohydrates and fats) along with nitrogen. Two amino acids also contain sulphur. The amino acids are linked together in long chains, which are usually folded up or twisted into spirals, with cross-links holding the chains together (Figure 4.7).

The *shape* of a protein is very important in allowing it to carry out its function, and the *order* of amino acids in the protein decides its shape. Because there are 20 different amino acids, and they can be arranged in any order, the number of different protein structures that can be made is enormous. As a result, there are thousands of different kinds of proteins in organisms, from structural proteins such as collagen and keratin in skin and nails, to proteins with more specific functions, such as enzymes and haemoglobin.

Minerals

All the foods you have read about so far are made from just five chemical elements: carbon, hydrogen, oxygen, nitrogen and sulphur. Our bodies contain many other elements which we get from our food. Some are present in large amounts in the body, for example calcium, which is used for making teeth and bones. Others are present in much smaller amounts, but still have essential jobs to do. For instance our bodies contain about 3 g of iron, but without it our blood would not be able to carry oxygen. Table 4.1 shows just a few of these elements and the reasons they are needed. They are called **minerals** or **mineral elements**.

Mineral	Approximate mass in an adult body (g)	Location or role in body	Examples of foods rich in minerals
calcium	1 000	making teeth and bones	dairy products, fish, bread, vegetables
phosphorus	650	making teeth and bones; part of many chemicals, e.g. DNA	most foods
sodium	100	in body fluids, e.g. blood	common salt, most foods
chlorine	100	in body fluids, e.g. blood	common salt, most foods
magnesium	30	making bones; found inside cells	green vegetables
iron	3	part of haemoglobin in red blood cells, helps carry oxygen	red meat, liver, eggs, some vegetables, e.g. spinach

Table 4.1: *Some examples of minerals needed by the body.*

If a person doesn't get enough of a mineral from their diet, they will show the symptoms of a **mineral deficiency disease**. For example, a one-year-old child needs to consume about 0.6 g (600 mg) of calcium every day, to make the bones grow properly and harden. Anything less than this over a prolonged period could result in poor bone development. The bones will become deformed, resulting in a disease called **rickets** (Figure 4.8). Rickets can also be caused by lack of vitamin D in the diet (see below).

Similarly, 16-year-olds need about 12 mg of iron in their daily food intake. If they don't get this amount, they can't make enough haemoglobin for their red blood cells (see Chapter 5). This causes a condition called **anaemia**. People who are anaemic become tired and lack energy, because their blood doesn't carry enough oxygen.

Vitamins

During the early part of the twentieth century, experiments were carried out that identified another class of food substances. When young laboratory rats were fed a diet of pure carbohydrate, lipid and protein, they all became ill and died. If they were fed on the same pure foods with a little added milk, they grew normally. The milk contained chemicals that the rats needed in small amounts to stay healthy. These chemicals are called **vitamins**. The results of one of these experiments are shown in Figure 4.9.

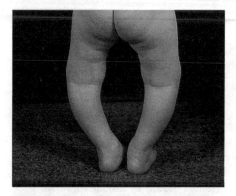

Figure 4.8 *The legs of this child show the symptoms of rickets. This is due to lack of calcium or a lack of vitamin D in the diet, leading to poor bone growth. The bones stay soft and can't support the weight of the body, so they become deformed.*

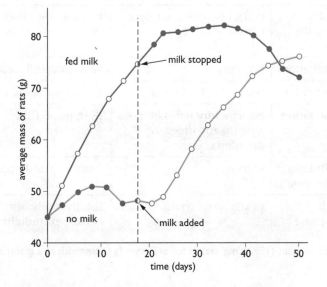

Figure 4.9 *Rats were fed on a diet of pure carbohydrate, lipid and protein, with and without added milk. Vitamins in the milk had a dramatic effect on their growth.*

At first, the chemical nature of vitamins was not known, and they were given letters to distinguish between them, such as vitamin A, vitamin B and so on. Each was identified by the effect a lack of the vitamin, or **vitamin deficiency**, had on the body. For example, **vitamin D** is needed for growing bones to take up calcium salts. A deficiency of this vitamin can result in rickets (Figure 4.8), just as a lack of calcium can.

We now know the chemical structure of the vitamins and the exact ways in which they work in the body. As with vitamin D, each has a particular function. **Vitamin A** is needed to make a light-sensitive chemical in the retina of the eye (see Chapter 6). A lack of this vitamin causes **night blindness**,

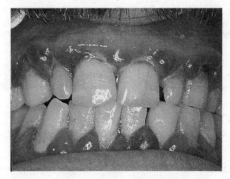

Figure 4.10 *Vitamin C helps lining cells such as those in the mouth and gums stick to each other. Lack of vitamin C causes scurvy, where the mouth and gums become damaged and bleed.*

The cure for scurvy was discovered as long ago as 1753. Sailors on long voyages often got scurvy because they ate very little fresh fruit and vegetables (the main source of vitamin C). A ship's doctor called James Lind wrote an account of how the disease could quickly be cured by eating fresh oranges and lemons. The famous explorer Captain Cook, on his world voyages in 1772 and 1775, kept his sailors healthy by making sure that they ate fresh fruit. By 1804, all British sailors were made to drink lime juice to prevent scurvy. This is how they came to be called 'limeys', a word that was later used by Americans for all British people.

where the person finds it difficult to see in dim light. **Vitamin C** is needed to make fibres of a material called connective tissue. This acts as a 'glue', bonding cells together in a tissue. It is found in the walls of blood vessels and in the skin and lining surfaces of the body. Vitamin C deficiency leads to a disease called **scurvy**, where wounds fail to heal, and bleeding occurs in various places in the body. This is especially noticeable in the gums (Figure 4.10).

Vitamin B is not a single substance, but a collection of many different substances called the vitamin B group. It includes **vitamins B1 (thiamine), B2 (riboflavin)** and **B3 (niacin)**. These compounds have roles in helping with the process of cell respiration. A different deficiency disease is produced if any of them is lacking from the diet. For example, lack of vitamin B1 results in weakening of the muscles and paralysis, a disease called **beri-beri**.

The main vitamins, their role in the body and some foods which are good sources of each, are summarised in Table 4.2.

Notice that the amounts of vitamins that we need are very small, but we cannot stay healthy without them.

Vitamin	Recommended daily amount in diet[1]	Use in the body	Effect of deficiency	Some foods that are a good source of the vitamin
A	0.8 mg	making a chemical in the retina; also protects the surface of the eye	night blindness, damaged cornea of eye	fish liver oils, liver, butter, margarine, carrots
B1	1.4 mg	helps with cell respiration	beri-beri	yeast extract, cereals
B2	1.6 mg	helps with cell respiration	poor growth, dry skin	green vegetables, eggs, fish
B3	18 mg	helps with cell respiration	pellagra (dry red skin, poor growth, and digestive disorders)	liver, meat, fish.
C	60 mg	sticks together cells lining surfaces such as the mouth	scurvy	fresh fruit and vegetables
D	5 µg	helps bones absorb calcium and phosphate	rickets, poor teeth	fish liver oils; also made in skin in sunlight

[1]Figures are the European Union's recommended daily intake for an adult (1993). 'mg' stands for milligram (a thousandth of a gram) and 'µg' for microgram (a millionth of a gram).

Table 4.2: *Summary of the main vitamins.*

Food tests

You can carry out some simple chemical tests to find out if a food contains starch, glucose, protein or fat. In the following descriptions we will use pure food samples to try out the tests, but you can do them on normal foods too. Unless the food is already a liquid, like milk, you may need to cut it up into small pieces and grind these with a pestle and mortar, then shake it up with some water in a test tube. This is done to extract the components of the food and dissolve any soluble substances, such as sugars.

Test for starch

Place a little starch powder in a spotting tile. Add a couple of drops of dilute **iodine** solution. The iodine reacts with the starch, forming a very dark blue, or **'blue-black'** colour (Figure 4.11a). Starch is insoluble, but this test will work on a solid sample of food, such as a potato, or a suspension of starch in water.

Test for glucose

Glucose is called a **reducing sugar**. This is because the test for glucose involves chemically reducing an alkaline solution of copper sulphate to copper(I) oxide.

HARMFUL

HEAT

USE EYE PROTECTION

Place a small spatula measure of glucose in a test tube and add a little water (about 2 cm deep). Now add several drops of **Benedict's solution**, which contains alkaline copper sulphate. You must add enough to colour the mixture blue (Figure 4.11b1). Half fill a beaker with water and heat it on a tripod and gauze. Place the test tube in the beaker and allow the water to boil (using a beaker as a water bath is safer than heating the tube directly in the Bunsen burner). Continue boiling the water for a few seconds. The clear blue solution will gradually change colour, forming a cloudy orange or 'brick red' precipitate of copper(I) oxide (Figure 4.11b2).

All other 'single' sugars, such as fructose, are reducing sugars, as well as some 'double' sugars, such as the milk sugar, lactose. However, ordinary table sugar (sucrose) is not. Try boiling some sucrose with Benedict's solution – it will stay a clear blue colour.

Test for protein

The test for protein is sometimes called the 'biuret' test, after the coloured compound that is formed.

CORROSIVE

USE EYE PROTECTION

Add a little powdered egg white (albumen) to 2 cm depth of water in a test tube (Figure 4.11c1). Shake to mix the powder with the water. Now add an equal volume of dilute (5%) **potassium hydroxide** solution and mix. Finally, add two drops of 1% **copper sulphate** solution. A mauve colour develops (Figure 4.11c2).

Test for lipid

Fats and oils are insoluble in water, but will dissolve in ethanol (alcohol). The test for lipid uses this fact.

FLAMMABLE

Use a pipette to place one drop of olive oil in the bottom of a test tube. Add about 2 cm (depth) of **ethanol** and shake to dissolve the oil. Pour the mixture slowly into a test tube that is about three-quarters full with cold water. A white cloudy layer forms on the top of the water (Figure 4.11d). The white layer is caused by the ethanol dissolving in the water and leaving the lipid behind as a suspension of tiny droplets, called an **emulsion**.

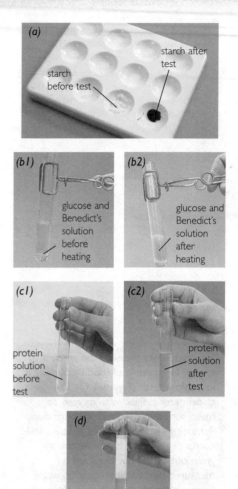

Figure 4.11 *Results of tests for (a) starch, (b) glucose, (c) protein and (d) fat.*

HARMFUL

HEAT

USE EYE PROTECTION

If sucrose is first broken down into its component monosaccharides (glucose and fructose), it will then give a positive Benedict's test. You can do this by boiling a sucrose solution with a few drops of dilute hydrochloric acid. The acid breaks the bond between the two monosaccharides. You must then let the solution cool and add a few drops of an alkali, such as sodium hydrogencarbonate, to neutralise the acid. The solution will now reduce the copper sulphate in the Benedict's test.

Energy from food

Some foods contain more energy than others. It depends on the proportions of carbohydrate, lipid and protein that they contain. Their energy content is measured in **kilojoules** (**kJ**). If a gram of carbohydrate is fully oxidised, it produces about 17 kJ, whereas a gram of lipid yields over twice as much as this (39 kJ). Protein can produce about 18 kJ. If you look on a food label, it usually shows the energy content of the food, along with the amounts of different nutrients that it contains (Figure 4.12).

Figure 4.12 *Food packaging is labelled with the proportions of different food types that it contains, along with its energy content. The energy in units called kilocalories (kcal) is also shown, but scientists no longer use this old-fashioned unit.*

Foods with a high percentage of lipid, such as butter or nuts, contain a large amount of energy. Others, like fruits and vegetables, which are mainly composed of water, have a much lower energy content (Table 4.3).

Food	kJ per 100 g	Food	kJ per 100 g
margarine	3200	fried beefburger	1100
butter	3120	white bread	1060
peanuts	2400	chips	990
samosa	2400	grilled beef steak	930
chocolate	2300	fried cod	850
Cheddar cheese	1700	roast chicken	770
grilled bacon	1670	boiled potatoes	340
table sugar	1650	milk	270
grilled pork sausages	1550	baked beans	270
cornflakes	1530	yoghurt	200
rice	1500	boiled cabbage	60
spaghetti	1450	lettuce	40

Table 4.3: *Energy content of some common foods.*

Even while you are asleep you need a supply of energy, for keeping warm, for your heartbeat, to allow messages to be sent through your nerves, and for other body functions. However, the energy you need at other times depends on the physical work that you do. The total amount of energy that a person needs to keep healthy depends on their age and body size, and also on the amount of activity they do. Table 4.4 shows some examples of how much energy is needed each day by people of different age, sex and occupation.

Food scientists measure the amount of energy in a sample of food by burning it in a calorimeter (Figure 4.13). The calorimeter is filled with oxygen, to make sure that the food will burn easily. A heating filament carrying an electrical current ignites the food. The energy given out by the burning food is measured by using it to heat up water flowing through a coil in the calorimeter.

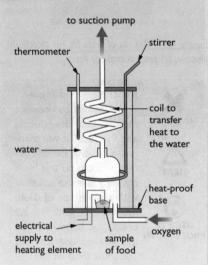

Figure 4.13 *A food calorimeter.*

If you have samples of food that will easily burn in air, you can measure the energy in them by a similar method, using the heat from the burning food to warm up water in a test tube (see question 6 at the end of this chapter).

Age/sex/occupation of person	Energy needed per day (kJ)
newborn baby	2000
child aged 2	5000
child aged 6	7500
girl aged 12–14	9000
boy aged 12–14	11000
girl aged 15–17	9000
boy aged 15–17	12000
female office worker	9500
male office worker	10500
heavy manual worker	15000
pregnant woman	10000
breast-feeding woman	11300

Table 4.4: *The daily energy needs of different types of people.*

Remember that these are approximate figures, and they are averages. Generally, the greater a person's weight, the more energy that person needs. This is why men, with a greater average body mass, need more energy than women. The energy needs of a pregnant woman are increased, mainly because of the extra weight that she has to carry. A heavy manual worker, such as a labourer, needs extra energy for increased muscle activity.

It is not only the recommended energy requirements that vary with age, sex and pregnancy, but also the *content* of the diet. For instance, during pregnancy a woman may need extra iron or calcium in her diet, for the growth of the fetus. In younger women, the blood loss during menstruation (periods) can result in anaemia, producing a need for extra iron in the diet.

Measuring the energy content of a food

If a sample of food will burn well in air, you can measure its energy content using a simplified version of the food calorimeter (Figure 4.14). Suitable foods are dry pasta, crispbread, corn curls or biscuits. It is advisable not to use nuts, since some people are allergic to them.

Carry out the following:
1. Find the mass of the piece of food.
2. Place 20 cm³ of water into a boiling tube.
3. Support the boiling tube in a clamp on a stand as shown in Figure 4.14.
4. Measure the temperature of the water.
5. Spear the food on the end of a mounted needle.
6. Light the Bunsen and hold the food in the flame until it catches fire (this may take 30 seconds or so).

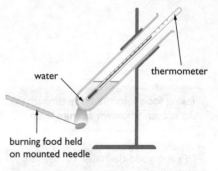

water · thermometer

burning food held on mounted needle

Figure 4.14 *Measuring the energy content of a food sample.*

7. When the food is alight, hold it underneath the boiling tube of water so that the flame heats up the water.

8. If the food stops burning, relight it in the Bunsen flame.

9. Continue until the food will no longer burn.

10. Measure the final temperature of the water (use the thermometer to stir the water gently to make sure the heat is evenly distributed).

Two facts are needed to allow you to calculate the energy content of the food.

- 4.2 joules of energy raises the temperature of one gram of water by 1 °C.

- 1 cm^3 of water has a mass of 1 g.

So, if you multiply the rise in temperature of the water by the mass of the water and then by 4.2, you have the number of joules of heat that were transferred to the water. Dividing this by the mass of the food gives the energy/gram:

energy (joules per gram) =

$$\frac{(\text{final temperature} - \text{temperature at start}) \times 20 \times 4.2 \text{ joules}}{\text{mass of food (g)}}$$

11. Calculate the energy content of the food in this way.

Comparison of the energy content of different foods

You could use the method given in the above experiment to compare the energy in different foods. Any solid foods that will burn easily in air are suitable, such as corn curls, pasta or biscuits. Suggest a hypothesis that you could test about the energy content of the foods and design an experiment to test your hypothesis. Make sure that your experiment is properly controlled, and state how you will ensure that the results are reliable.

Digestion

Food, such as a piece of bread, contains carbohydrates, lipids and proteins, but they are not the same carbohydrates, lipids and proteins as in our tissues. The components of the bread must first be broken down into their 'building blocks' before they can be absorbed through the wall of the gut. This process is called **digestion**. The digested molecules – sugars, fatty acids, glycerol and amino acids – along with minerals, vitamins and water, can then be carried around the body in the blood. When they reach the tissues they are reassembled into the molecules that make up our cells.

Digestion is speeded up by **enzymes**, which are biological catalysts (see Chapter 1). Although most enzymes stay inside cells, the digestive enzymes are made by the tissues and glands in the gut, and pass out of cells onto the gut contents, where they act on the food. This **chemical** digestion is helped by **mechanical** digestion. This is the physical breakdown of food. The most obvious place where this happens is in the mouth, where the teeth bite and chew the food, cutting it into smaller pieces that have a larger surface area. This

Taking food into the body through the mouth is known as **ingestion**.

This is a good definition of digestion, useful for exam answers:
'Digestion is the chemical and mechanical breakdown of food. It converts large insoluble molecules into small soluble molecules, which can be absorbed into the blood.'

means that enzymes can act on the food more quickly. Other parts of the gut also help with mechanical digestion. For example, muscles in the wall of the stomach contract to churn up the food while it is being chemically digested.

Muscles are also responsible for moving the food along the gut. The walls of the intestine contain two layers of muscles. One layer has fibres running in rings around the gut. This is the **circular** muscle layer. The other has fibres running down the length of the gut, and is called the **longitudinal** muscle layer. Together these two layers act to push the food along. When the circular muscles contract and the longitudinal muscles relax, the gut is made narrower. When the opposite happens, i.e. the longitudinal muscles contract and the circular muscles relax, the gut becomes wider. Waves of muscle contraction like this pass along the gut, pushing the food along, rather like squeezing toothpaste from a tube (Figure 4.15). This is called **peristalsis**. It means that movement of food in the gut doesn't depend on gravity – we can still eat standing on our heads!

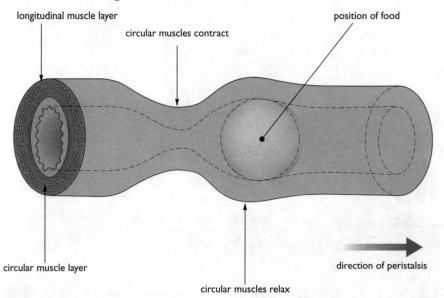

Figure 4.15 *Peristalsis: contraction of circular muscles behind the food narrows the gut, pushing the food along. When the circular muscles are contracted, the longitudinal ones are relaxed, and vice versa.*

Figure 4.16 shows a simplified diagram of the human digestive system. It is simplified so that you can see the order of the organs along the gut. The real gut is much longer than this, and coiled up so that it fills the whole space of the abdomen. Overall, its length in an adult is about 8 m. This gives plenty of time for the food to be broken down and absorbed as it passes through.

The mouth, stomach and the first part of the small intestine (called the **duodenum**) all break down the food using enzymes, either made in the gut wall itself, or by glands such as the **pancreas**. Digestion continues in the last part of the small intestine (the **ileum**) and it is here that the digested food is absorbed. The last part of the gut, the large intestine, is mainly concerned with absorbing water out of the remains, and storing the waste products (**faeces**) before they are removed from the body.

The three main classes of food are broken down by three classes of enzymes. Carbohydrates are digested by enzymes called **carbohydrases**. Proteins are

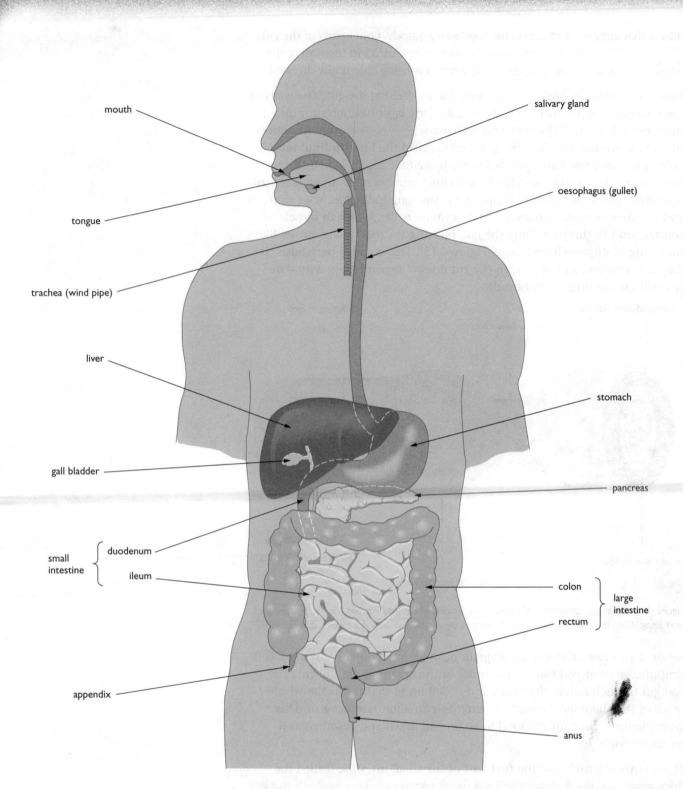

mouth

salivary gland

oesophagus (gullet)

tongue

trachea (wind pipe)

liver

stomach

gall bladder

pancreas

small intestine
duodenum

ileum

colon

large intestine

rectum

appendix

anus

Figure 4.16 *The human digestive system.*

acted upon by **proteases**, and enzymes called **lipases** break down lipids. Some of the places in the gut where these enzymes are made are shown in Table 4.5.

Digestion begins in the mouth. **Saliva** helps moisten the food and contains the enzyme **amylase**, which starts the breakdown of starch. The chewed

Class of enzyme	Examples	Digestive action	Source of enzyme	Where it acts in the gut
carbohydrases	amylase	starch → maltose[1]	salivary glands	mouth
		starch → maltose	pancreas	small intestine
		maltose → **glucose**	wall of small intestine	small intestine
proteases	pepsin	proteins → peptides[2]	stomach wall	stomach
	trypsin	proteins → peptides	pancreas	small intestine
	peptidases	peptides → **amino acids**	wall of small intestine	small intestine
lipases	lipase	lipids → **glycerol** and **fatty acids**	pancreas	small intestine

[1] Maltose is a disaccharide made of two glucose molecules joined together.
[2] Peptides are short chains of amino acids.

Table 4.5: *Some of the enzymes that digest food in the human gut. The substances shown in bold are the end products of digestion that can be absorbed from the gut into the blood.*

lump of food, mixed with saliva, then passes along the **oesophagus** (gullet) to the stomach.

The food is held in the stomach for several hours, while initial digestion of protein takes place. The stomach wall secretes **hydrochloric acid**, so the stomach contents are strongly acidic. This has a very important function. It kills bacteria that are taken into the gut along with the food, helping to protect us from food poisoning. The protease enzyme that is made in the stomach, called **pepsin**, has to be able to work in these acidic conditions, and has an optimum pH value of about 2. This is unusually low – most enzymes work best at near neutral conditions (see Chapter 1).

The semi-digested food is held back in the stomach by a ring of muscle at the outlet of the stomach, called a **sphincter** muscle. When this relaxes, it releases the food into the first part of the small intestine, called the **duodenum** (Figure 4.17).

> Amylase digests starch into maltose. In this reaction, we say that starch is the **substrate** and maltose is the **product**.

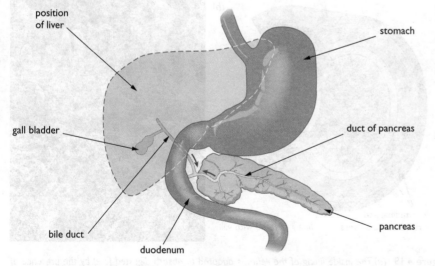

Figure 4.17 *The first part of the small intestine, the duodenum, receives digestive juices from the liver and pancreas through tubes called ducts.*

Several digestive enzymes are added to the food in the duodenum. These are made by the **pancreas**, and digest starch, proteins and lipids (Table 4.5). As

Figure 4.18 *Bile turns fats into an emulsion of tiny droplets for easier digestion.*

well as this, the **liver** makes a digestive juice called **bile**. Bile is a green liquid that is stored in the **gall bladder** and passes down the **bile duct** onto the food. Bile does not contain enzymes, but has another important function. It turns any large lipid globules in the food into an emulsion of tiny droplets (Figure 4.18). This increases the surface area of the lipid, so that **lipase** enzymes can break it down more easily.

Bile and pancreatic juice have another function. They are both alkaline. The mixture of semi-digested food and enzymes coming from the stomach is acidic, and needs to be neutralised by the addition of alkali before it continues on its way through the gut.

As the food continues along the intestine, more enzymes are added, until the parts of the food that can be digested have been fully broken down into soluble end products, which can be absorbed. This is the role of the last part of the small intestine, the **ileum**.

Absorption in the ileum

The ileum is highly adapted to absorb the digested food. The lining of the ileum has a very large surface area, which means that it can quickly and efficiently absorb the soluble products of digestion into the blood. The length of the intestine helps to provide a large surface area, and this is aided by folds in its lining, but the greatest increase in area is due to tiny projections from the lining, called **villi** (Figure 4.19). The singular of villi is 'villus'. Each villus is only about 1–2 mm long, but there are millions of them, so that the total area of the lining is thought to be about $300\,m^2$. This provides a massive area in contact with the digested food. As well as this, high-powered microscopy has revealed that the surface cells of each villus themselves have hundreds of minute projections, called **microvilli**, which increase the surface area for absorption even more (Figure 4.20).

(a)

(b)

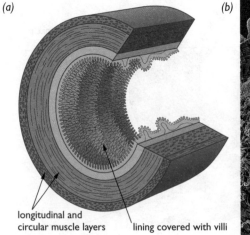
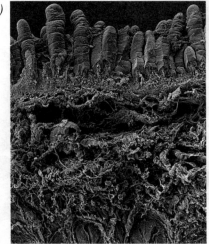

longitudinal and
circular muscle layers   lining covered with villi

Figure 4.19 *(a) The inside lining of the ileum is adapted to absorb digested food by the presence of millions of tiny villi. (b) A section through the lining, showing the villi.*

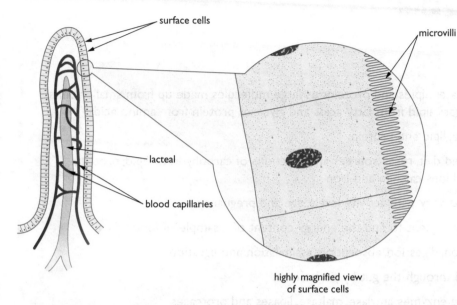

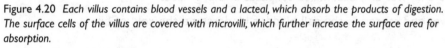

Figure 4.20 *Each villus contains blood vessels and a lacteal, which absorb the products of digestion. The surface cells of the villus are covered with microvilli, which further increase the surface area for absorption.*

Each villus contains a network of blood capillaries. Most of the digested food enters these blood vessels, but the products of fat digestion, as well as tiny fat droplets, enter a tube in the middle of the villus, called a **lacteal**. The lacteals form part of the body's **lymphatic** system, which transports a liquid called lymph. This **lymph** eventually drains into the blood system too.

The blood vessels from the ileum join up to form a large blood vessel called the **hepatic portal vein**, which leads to the liver (see Chapter 5). The liver acts rather like a food processing works, breaking some molecules down, and building up and storing others. For example, glucose from carbohydrate digestion is converted into **glycogen** and stored in the liver. Later, the glycogen can be converted back into glucose when the body needs it (see Chapter 7).

The digested food molecules are distributed around the body by the blood system (see Chapter 5). The soluble food molecules are absorbed from the blood into cells of tissues, and are used to build new parts of cells. This is called **assimilation**.

The large intestine – elimination of waste

By the time that the contents of the gut have reached the end of the small intestine, most of the digested food, as well as most of the water, has been absorbed. The waste material consists mainly of cellulose (fibre) and other indigestible remains, water, dead and living bacteria and cells lost from the lining of the gut. The function of the first part of the large intestine, called the **colon**, is to absorb most of the remaining water from the contents, leaving a semi-solid waste material called **faeces**. This is stored in the **rectum**, until expelled out of the body through the **anus**.

Removal of faeces by the body is sometimes incorrectly called excretion. Excretion is a word that should only apply to materials that are the waste products of cells of the body. Faeces are not – they consist of waste which has passed through the gut without entering the cells. The correct name for this process is **egestion**.

End of Chapter Checklist

You should now be able to:

- describe the structure of carbohydrates, lipids and proteins as large molecules made up from smaller units: starch and glycogen from simple sugars, lipid from fatty acids and glycerol, protein from amino acids

- describe the tests for starch, glucose, lipid and protein

- understand the meaning of a balanced diet, recall sources and functions of carbohydrate, lipid, protein, vitamins A, C and D, and the mineral ions calcium and iron

- understand that energy requirements vary with activity levels, age and pregnancy

- recall how to carry out a simple experiment to find the energy content of a sample of food

- understand the processes of ingestion, digestion, absorption, assimilation and egestion

- explain how and why food is moved through the gut by peristalsis

- understand the roles of the digestive enzymes amylase, maltase, lipases and proteases

- recall that bile is produced by the liver and stored in the gall bladder. Understand the role of bile in digestion

- explain how the structure of a villus helps absorption of the products of digestion in the ileum.

Questions

More questions on food and digestion can be found at the end of Section B on page 108.

I   The diagram shows an experiment that was set up as a model to show why food needs to be digested.

The Visking tubing acts as a model of the small intestine because it has tiny holes in it that some molecules can pass through. The tubing was left in the boiling tube for an hour, then the water in the tube was tested for starch and glucose.

a) Describe how you would test the water for starch, and for glucose. What would the results be for a 'positive' test in each case?

b) The tests showed that glucose was present in the water, but starch was not. Explain why.

c) If the tubing takes the place of the intestine, what part of the body does the water in the boiling tube represent?

d) What does 'digested' mean?

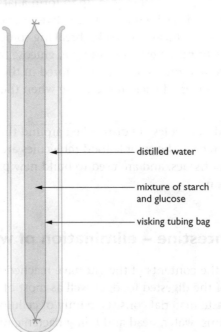

distilled water

mixture of starch and glucose

visking tubing bag

2 (Hint: page 4, Chapter 1 will help with this question.)
A student carried out an experiment to find out the best conditions for the enzyme pepsin to digest protein. For the protein, she used egg white powder, which forms a cloudy white suspension in water. The table below shows how the four tubes were set up.

Tube	Contents
A	5 cm³ egg white suspension, 2 cm³ pepsin, 3 drops of dilute acid. Tube kept at 37 °C
B	5 cm³ egg white suspension, 2 cm³ distilled water, 3 drops of dilute acid. Tube kept at 37 °C
C	5 cm³ egg white suspension, 2 cm³ pepsin, 3 drops of dilute acid. Tube kept at 20 °C
D	5 cm³ egg white suspension, 2 cm³ pepsin, 3 drops of dilute alkali. Tube kept at 37 °C

The tubes were left for 2 hours and the results were then observed. Tubes B, C and D were still cloudy. Tube A had gone clear.

a) Three tubes were kept at 37 °C. Why was this temperature chosen?

b) Explain what had happened to the protein in tube A.

c) Why did tube D stay cloudy?

d) Tube B is called a **control**. Explain what this means.

e) Tube C was left for another 3 hours. Gradually it started to clear. Explain why digestion of the protein happened more slowly in this tube.

f) The lining of the stomach secretes hydrochloric acid. Explain the function of this.

g) When the stomach contents pass into the duodenum, they are still acidic. How are they neutralised?

3 Copy and complete the following table of digestive enzymes.

Enzyme	Food on which it acts	Products
amylase		
trypsin		
		fatty acids and glycerol

4 Describe four adaptations of the small intestine (ileum) that allow it to absorb digested food efficiently.

5 Bread is made mainly of starch, protein and lipid. Imagine a piece of bread about to start its journey through the human gut. Describe what happens to the bread as it passes through the mouth, stomach, duodenum, ileum and colon. Explain how the bread is moved along the gut. Your description should be illustrated by two or three simplified diagrams. It would be easier to write up your account using a computer, leaving room for illustrations, or you might obtain these from websites or a CD-ROM.

6 The diagram shows a method that can be used to measure the energy content of some types of food. A student placed 20 cm³ of water in a boiling tube and measured its temperature. He weighed a small piece of pasta, and then held it in a Bunsen burner flame until it caught alight. He then used the burning pasta to heat the boiling tube of water, until the pasta had finished burning. Finally, he measured the temperature of the water at the end of the experiment.

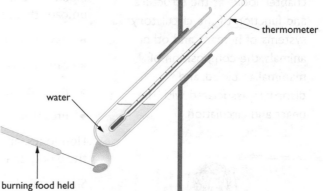

To answer the questions that follow, use the following information.

- The density of water is 1 g/cm³.
- The pasta weighed 0.22 g.
- The water temperature at the start was 21 °C and at the end was 39 °C.
- The heat energy supplied to the water can be found from the formula:

energy (in joules) = mass of water × temperature change × 4.2

a) Calculate the energy supplied to the water in the boiling tube in joules (J). Convert this to kilojoules (kJ) by dividing by 1000.

b) Calculate the energy released from the pasta as kilojoules per gram of pasta (kJ/g).

c) The correct figure for the energy content of pasta is 14.5 kJ/g. The student's result is an underestimate. Write down three reasons why he may have got a lower than expected result. (Hint: think about how the design of the apparatus might introduce errors.)

d) Suggest one way the apparatus could be modified to reduce these errors.

e) The energy in a peanut was measured using the method described above. The peanut was found to contain about twice as much energy per gram as the pasta. Explain why this is the case.

Chapter 5: Blood and Circulation

Large, multicellular animals need a circulatory system to transport substances to and from the cells of the body. This chapter looks at the structure and function of the circulatory systems of humans and other animals, the composition of mammalian blood, and disorders associated with the heart and circulation.

The need for circulatory systems

Figure 5.1 shows the circulatory system of a mammal.

Blood is pumped round and round a closed circuit made up of the heart and blood vessels. As it travels around, it collects materials from some places and unloads them in others. In mammals, blood transports:

- oxygen from the lungs to all other parts of the body
- carbon dioxide from all parts of the body to the lungs
- nutrients from the gut to all parts of the body
- urea from the liver to the kidneys.

Hormones, antibodies and many other substances are also transported by the blood. It also distributes heat around the body.

Single-celled organisms, like the ones shown in Figure 5.2, do not have circulatory systems.

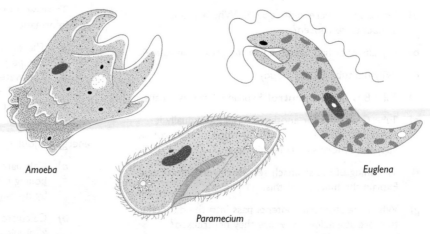

Amoeba

Paramecium

Euglena

Figure 5.2 *Unicellular organisms do not have circulatory systems.*

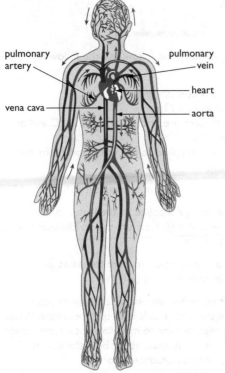

pulmonary artery

pulmonary vein

heart

vena cava

aorta

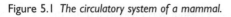

← oxygenated blood
→ deoxygenated blood

Figure 5.1 *The circulatory system of a mammal.*

There is no circulatory system to carry materials around the very small 'bodies' of these one-celled organisms. Materials can easily move around the cell without a special system. There is no need for lungs or gills to obtain oxygen from the environment either. One-celled organisms obtain oxygen through the surface membrane of the cell. The rest of the cell then uses the oxygen. The area of the cell's surface determines how much oxygen the organism can get (the supply rate), and the volume of the cell determines how much oxygen the organism uses (the demand rate).

The ratio of supply to demand can be written as: $\dfrac{\text{surface area}}{\text{volume}}$

This is called the **surface area to volume ratio** (s.a. : vol.) and it is affected by the size of an organism. Single-celled organisms have a high surface area to volume ratio. Their cell surface membrane has a large enough area to supply all the oxygen that their volume demands. In larger animals, the surface area to volume ratio is lower.

Large animals cannot get all the oxygen they need through their surface (even if the body surface would allow it to pass through) – there just isn't enough surface to supply all that volume. To overcome this problem, large organisms have evolved special gas exchange organs and circulatory systems. The gills of fish and the lungs of mammals are linked to a circulatory system that carries oxygen to all parts of the body. The same idea applies to obtaining nutrients – the gut obtains nutrients from food and the circulatory system distributes the nutrients around the body.

The circulatory systems of different animals

One of the main functions of a circulatory system in animals is to transport oxygen. Blood is pumped to a gas exchange organ to load oxygen. It is then pumped to other parts of the body where it unloads the oxygen. There are two main types of circulatory systems in animals.

- In **single circulatory systems** the blood is pumped from the heart to the gas exchange organ and then directly to the rest of the body.

- In **double circulatory systems** the blood is pumped from the heart to the gas exchange organ, back to the heart and then to the rest of the body.

Figure 5.4 shows the difference between these systems.

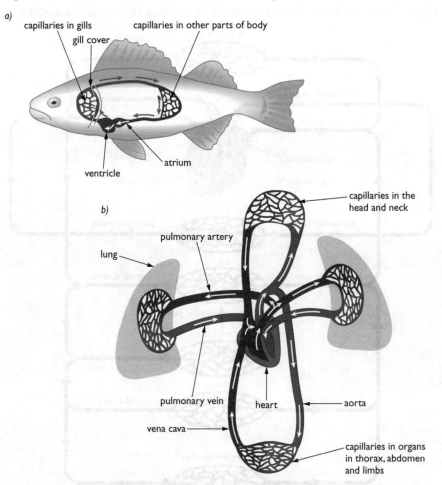

a)

capillaries in gills
gill cover
capillaries in other parts of body

ventricle
atrium

b)

capillaries in the head and neck

pulmonary artery

lung

pulmonary vein
heart
aorta

vena cava

capillaries in organs in thorax, abdomen and limbs

Figure 5.4 *(a) The single circulatory system of a fish. The blood passes through the heart once only in a complete circuit of the body. (b) The double circulatory system of a human (and other mammals). The blood passes through the heart twice in one complete circuit of the body.*

Let's pretend that the organism is the shape of a cube!

1 mm
1 mm
1 mm

surface area of one side $1 \times 1 = 1$ mm^2
total surface area $6 \times 1 = 6$ mm^2
volume $1 \times 1 \times 1 = 1$ mm^3
surface area/volume $6/1 = 6{:}1$

A larger organism has a lower surface area to volume ratio.

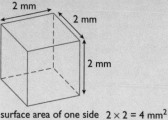

2 mm
2 mm
2 mm

surface area of one side $2 \times 2 = 4$ mm^2
total surface area $6 \times 4 = 24$ mm^2
volume $2 \times 2 \times 2 = 8$ mm^3
surface area/volume $24/8 = 3{:}1$

Figure 5.3 *An illustration of surface area to volume ratio.*

The bigger cube has a smaller surface area to volume ratio. It would be less able to obtain all the oxygen it needs through its surface.

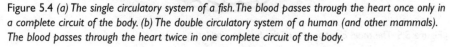

There are two distinct parts to a double circulation:

- the **pulmonary** circulation, in which blood is circulated through the lungs where it is oxygenated
- the **systemic** circulation, in which blood is circulated through all other parts of the body where it unloads its oxygen.

A double circulatory system is more efficient than a single circulatory system. The heart pumps the blood twice, so higher pressures can be maintained. The blood travels more quickly to organs. In the single circulatory system of a fish, blood loses pressure as it passes through the gills. It then travels relatively slowly to the other organs.

The human circulatory system comprises:

- the **heart** – this is a pump

- **blood vessels** – these carry the blood around the body; **arteries** carry blood away from the heart and towards other organs, **veins** carry blood towards the heart and away from other organs, **capillaries** carry blood through organs

- **blood** – the transport medium.

Figure 5.5 shows the main blood vessels in the human circulatory system.

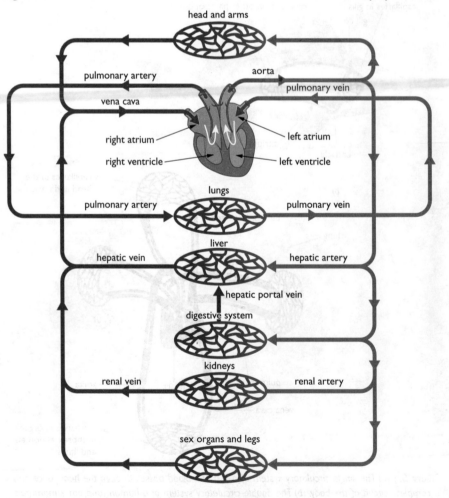

Figure 5.5 *The main components of the human circulatory system.*

The structure and function of the human heart

The human heart is a pump. It pumps blood around the body at different speeds and at different pressures according to the body's needs. It can do this because the wall of the heart is made from **cardiac muscle** (Figure 5.6).

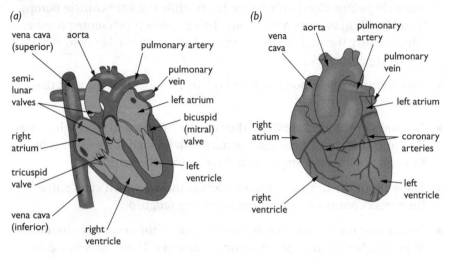

Figure 5.6 *The human heart: (a) vertical section; (b) external view.*

Blood is moved through the heart by a series of contractions and relaxations of cardiac muscle in the walls of the four chambers. These events form the **cardiac cycle**. The main stages are illustrated in Figure 5.7.

> **Cardiac** means 'to do with the heart'.

> Cardiac muscle is unlike any other muscle in our bodies. It never gets fatigued ('tired') like skeletal muscle. On average, cardiac muscle fibres contract and then relax again about 70 times a minute. In a lifetime of 70 years, this special muscle will contract over two billion times – and never take a rest!

> The bicuspid (mitral) and tricuspid valves are both sometimes called **atrio-ventricular** valves, as each controls the passage of blood from an atrium to a ventricle.

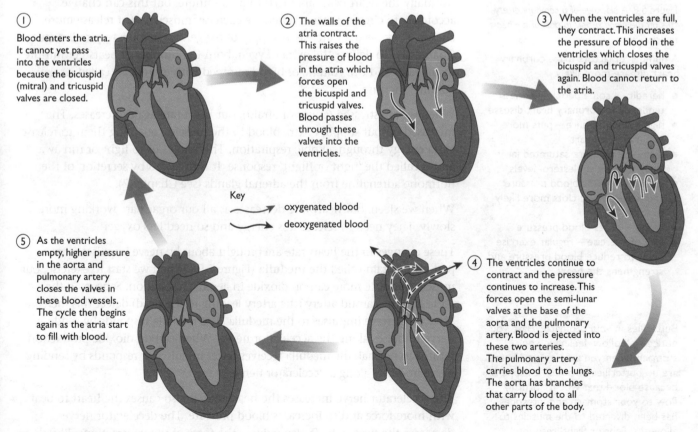

① Blood enters the atria. It cannot yet pass into the ventricles because the bicuspid (mitral) and tricuspid valves are closed.

② The walls of the atria contract. This raises the pressure of blood in the atria which forces open the bicuspid and tricuspid valves. Blood passes through these valves into the ventricles.

③ When the ventricles are full, they contract. This increases the pressure of blood in the ventricles which closes the bicuspid and tricuspid valves again. Blood cannot return to the atria.

④ The ventricles continue to contract and the pressure continues to increase. This forces open the semi-lunar valves at the base of the aorta and the pulmonary artery. Blood is ejected into these two arteries. The pulmonary artery carries blood to the lungs. The aorta has branches that carry blood to all other parts of the body.

⑤ As the ventricles empty, higher pressure in the aorta and pulmonary artery closes the valves in these blood vessels. The cycle then begins again as the atria start to fill with blood.

Key
→ oxygenated blood
→ deoxygenated blood

Figure 5.7 *The cardiac cycle.*

Coronary heart disease
The coronary arteries are among the narrowest in the body. They are easily blocked by a build-up of fatty substances (including **cholesterol**) in their walls. This can cut off the blood supply to an area of cardiac muscle. The affected muscle is unable to contract and a heart attack results.

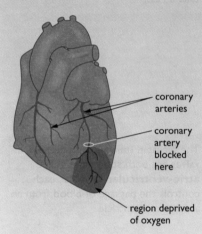

coronary arteries

coronary artery blocked here

region deprived of oxygen

Figure 5.8 *A blockage of a coronary artery cuts off the blood supply to part of the heart muscle.*

A number of factors make coronary heart disease more likely:

- heredity – some people inherit a tendency to coronary heart disease
- high blood pressure – puts more strain on the heart
- diet – eating more saturated fat is likely to raise cholesterol levels
- smoking – raises blood pressure and makes blood clots more likely to form
- stress – raises blood pressure
- lack of exercise – regular exercise helps to reduce blood pressure and strengthens the heart.

Butterflies in your stomach? Have you noticed a 'hollow' feeling in your stomach when you are anxious? There are no butterflies involved! It happens because blood that would normally flow to your stomach and intestines has been diverted to the muscles to allow the 'fight or flight' response.

When a chamber of the heart is contracting, we say it is in **systole**. When it is relaxing, we say it is in **diastole**.

The structure of the heart is adapted to its function in several ways.

- It is divided into a left side and a right side by the **septum**. The right ventricle pumps blood only to the lungs while the left ventricle pumps blood to all other parts of the body. This requires much more pressure, which is why the wall of the left ventricle is much thicker than that of the right ventricle.

- Valves ensure that blood can flow only in one direction through the heart.

- The walls of the atria are thin. They can be stretched to receive blood as it returns to the heart but can contract with enough force to push blood through the bicuspid and tricuspid valves into the ventricles.

- The walls of the heart are made of cardiac muscle which can contract and then relax continuously, without becoming fatigued.

- The cardiac muscle has its own blood supply – the **coronary circulation**. Blood reaches the muscle via **coronary arteries**. These carry blood to capillaries that supply the heart muscle with oxygen and nutrients. Blood is returned to the right atrium via **coronary veins**.

Heart rate

Normally the heart beats about 70 times a minute, but this can change according to circumstances. When we exercise, muscles must release more energy. They need an increased supply of oxygen for aerobic respiration (see Chapter 1). To deliver the extra oxygen, both the number of beats per minute (heart rate) and the volume of blood pumped with each beat (called stroke volume) increase.

When we are stressed (angry or afraid), our heart rate again increases. The increased output supplies extra blood to the muscles, enabling them to release extra energy through aerobic respiration. This allows us to fight or run away and is called the 'fight or flight' response. It is triggered by secretion of the hormone adrenaline from the adrenal glands (see Chapter 7).

When we sleep, our heart rate decreases as all our organs are working more slowly. They need to release less energy and so need less oxygen.

These changes in the heart rate are brought about by nerve impulses from a part of the brain called the **medulla** (Figure 5.9). When we start to exercise, our muscles produce more carbon dioxide in aerobic respiration. Sensors in the aorta and the carotid artery (the artery leading to the head) detect this increase. They send nerve impulses to the medulla. The medulla responds by sending nerve impulses along the accelerator nerve. When carbon dioxide production returns to normal, the medulla receives fewer impulses. It responds by sending nerve impulses along a decelerator nerve.

The accelerator nerve increases the heart rate. It also causes the heart to beat with more force and so increases blood pressure. The decelerator nerve decreases the heart rate. It also reduces the force of the contractions. Blood pressure then returns to normal.

(not to scale)

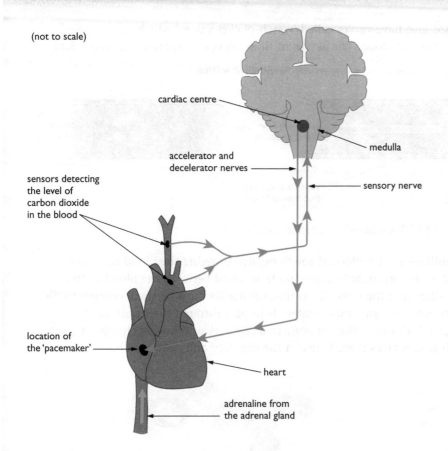

Figure 5.9 *How the heart rate is controlled.*

These controls are both examples of **reflex actions** (see Chapter 6).

Arteries, veins and capillaries

Arteries carry blood from the heart to organs of the body. This blood (**arterial blood**) has been pumped out by the ventricles and puts a lot of pressure on the walls of the arteries. They must be able to 'give' under the pressure and allow their walls to stretch. They must also have the ability to recoil (pull back into shape) and help to push the blood along.

Veins carry blood from organs back towards the heart. The pressure of this blood (**venous blood**) is much lower than that in the arteries. It puts very little pressure on the walls of the veins. Veins must be able to allow the blood to pass through easily and prevent it from flowing in the wrong direction. Figure 5.10 shows the structure of a typical artery and a typical vein with the same diameter.

Arterioles are small arteries. They carry blood into organs from arteries. Their structure is similar to the larger arteries, but they have a larger proportion of muscle fibres in their walls. They are also **innervated** (have nerve endings in their walls) and so can be made to dilate (become wider) or constrict (become narrower) to allow more or less blood into the organ.

If *all* the arterioles constrict, it is harder for blood to pass through them – there is more resistance. This increases blood pressure. Prolonged stress can cause arterioles to constrict and so increase blood pressure.

All arteries carry **oxygenated blood** (blood containing a lot of oxygen) except the pulmonary artery and the umbilical artery of an unborn baby. All veins carry **deoxygenated blood** (blood containing less oxygen) except the pulmonary vein and umbilical vein.

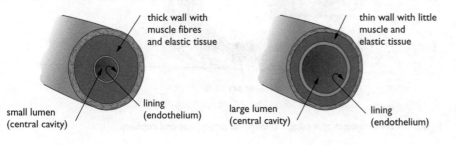

Figure 5.10 *The structure of (a) an artery and (b) a vein as seen in cross section.*

Veins also have valves called 'watch-pocket valves' which prevent the backflow of blood. The action of these valves is explained in Figure 5.11.

vein in longitudinal section

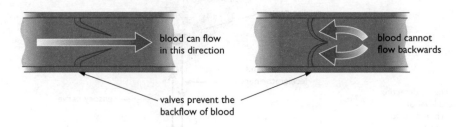

blood can flow
in this direction

blood cannot
flow backwards

valves prevent the
backflow of blood

Figure 5.11 *The action of watch-pocket valves in veins.*

Capillaries carry blood through organs, bringing the blood close to every cell in the organ. Substances are transferred between the blood in the capillary and the cells. To do this, capillaries must be small enough to 'fit' between cells, and allow materials to pass through their walls easily. Figure 5.12 shows the structure of a capillary and how exchange of substances takes place between the capillary and nearby cells.

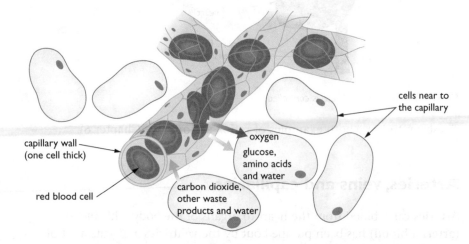

cells near to
the capillary

oxygen

glucose,
amino acids
and water

capillary wall
(one cell thick)

carbon dioxide,
other waste
products and water

red blood cell

Figure 5.12 *How capillaries exchange materials with cells.*

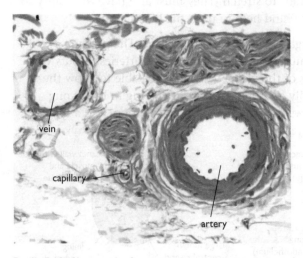

vein

capillary

artery

Figure 5.13 *Photograph of a section through an artery, vein and capillary.*

The composition of blood

Blood is a lot more than just a red liquid flowing through your arteries and veins! In fact, blood is a complex tissue. Figure 5.14 illustrates the main types of cells found in blood.

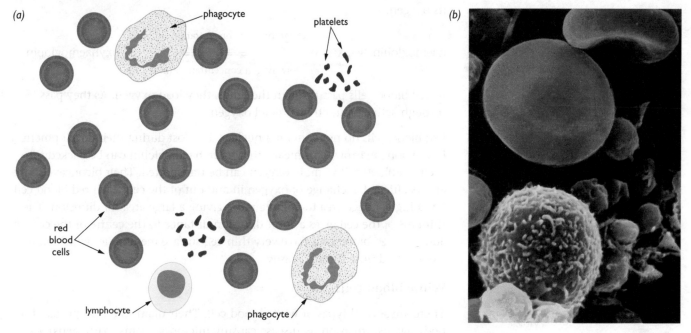

Figure 5.14 *The different types of blood cells (a) drawings of the different cells and (b) as seen in a photomicrograph.*

The different parts of blood have different functions. These are described in Table 5.1.

Component of blood	Description of component	Function of component
plasma	liquid part of blood: mainly water	carries the blood cells around the body; carries dissolved nutrients, hormones, carbon dioxide and urea; also distributes heat around the body
red blood cells	biconcave, disc-like cells with no nucleus; millions in each mm^3 of blood	transport of oxygen – contain mainly haemoglobin, which loads oxygen in the lungs and unloads it in other regions of the body
white blood cells: lymphocytes	about the same size as red cells with a large spherical nucleus	produce antibodies to destroy microorganisms – some lymphocytes persist in our blood after infection and give us immunity to specific diseases;
phagocytes	much larger cells with a large spherical or lobed nucleus	engulf bacteria and other microorganisms that have infected our bodies
platelets	the smallest cells – are really fragments of other cells	release chemicals to make blood clot when we cut ourselves

Table 5.1: *Functions of the different components of blood.*

Red blood cells

The red blood cells are highly specialised cells made in the bone marrow. They have a limited life span of about 100 days after which time they are destroyed in the spleen. They have only one function – to transport oxygen. Several features enable them to carry out this function very efficiently.

Red blood cells contain **haemoglobin**. This is an iron-containing protein that associates (combines) with oxygen to form **oxyhaemoglobin** when there is a high concentration of oxygen in the surroundings. We say that the red blood cell is *loading* oxygen. When the concentration of oxygen is low, oxyhaemoglobin turns back into haemoglobin and the red blood cell *unloads* its oxygen.

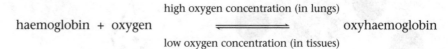

$$\text{haemoglobin} + \text{oxygen} \underset{\text{low oxygen concentration (in tissues)}}{\overset{\text{high oxygen concentration (in lungs)}}{\rightleftharpoons}} \text{oxyhaemoglobin}$$

As red blood cells pass through the lungs, they load oxygen. As they pass through active tissues they unload oxygen.

Red blood cells do not contain a nucleus. It is lost during their development in the bone marrow. This means that more haemoglobin can be packed into each red blood cell so more oxygen can be transported. Their biconcave shape allows efficient exchange of oxygen in and out of the cell. Each red blood cell has a high surface area to volume ratio, giving a large area for diffusion. The thinness of the cell gives a short diffusion distance to the centre of the cell. In addition, red blood cells have very thin cell surface membranes which allow oxygen to diffuse through easily.

White blood cells

There are several types of white blood cell. Their main role is to protect the body against invasion by disease-causing microorganisms (pathogens), such as bacteria and viruses. They do this in two main ways: **phagocytosis** and **antibody production**.

About 70% of white blood cells can ingest (take in) microorganisms such as bacteria. This is called phagocytosis, and the cells are **phagocytes**. They do this by changing their shape, producing extensions of their cytoplasm, called **pseudopodia**. The pseudopodia surround and enclose the microorganism in a vacuole. Once it is inside, the phagocyte secretes enzymes into the vacuole to break the microorganism down (Figure 5.15). Phagocytosis means 'cell eating' – you can see why it is called this.

Approximately 25% of white blood cells are **lymphocytes**. Their function is to make chemicals called **antibodies**. Antibodies are soluble proteins that pass into the plasma, where they destroy bacteria, viruses and other pathogens. They do this in a number of ways, for example by:

- causing bacteria to stick together, so that phagocytes can ingest them more easily

- acting as a 'label' on the pathogen, so that it is more easily recognised by a phagocyte

- causing bacterial cells to burst open

- neutralising poisons (toxins) produced by pathogens.

Some lymphocytes do not get involved in killing microorganisms straight away. Instead, they develop into **memory cells**. Memory cells make us **immune** to a disease. These cells remain in the blood for many years, sometimes a lifetime. If the same microorganism re-infects, the memory

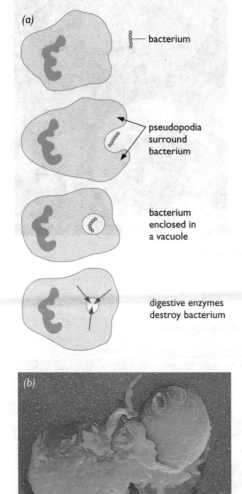

(a)

bacterium

pseudopodia surround bacterium

bacterium enclosed in a vacuole

digestive enzymes destroy bacterium

(b)

Figure 5.15 *(a) Phagocytosis by a white blood cell. (b) A phagocyte ingesting a yeast cell.*

lymphocytes start to reproduce and produce antibodies, so that the pathogen can be quickly dealt with.

Platelets

Platelets are not whole cells, but fragments of large cells made in the bone marrow. If the skin is cut, exposure to the air stimulates the platelets and damaged tissue to produce a chemical. This chemical causes the soluble plasma protein **fibrinogen** to change into insoluble fibres of another protein, **fibrin**. The fibrin forms a network across the wound, in which red blood cells become trapped. This forms a **clot**, which prevents further loss of blood and entry of pathogens. The clot develops into a scab, which protects the damaged tissue while new skin grows.

End of Chapter Checklist

You should now be able to:

- understand why simple unicellular organisms can rely on diffusion for movement of substances in and out of the cell, while multicellular organisms need a transport system
- recall the general plan of the circulatory system, including the blood vessels to and from the heart, lungs, liver and kidneys
- describe the structure and function of the heart
- understand that the heart rate changes during exercise and under the influence of adrenaline
- describe the structure of arteries, veins and capillaries and understand their roles
- recall the composition of blood: red and white blood cells, platelets and plasma
- understand the role of plasma in the transport of carbon dioxide, digested food, urea, hormones and heat energy
- describe the adaptations of red blood cells for the transport of oxygen, including shape, structure and the presence of haemoglobin
- describe the role of white blood cells in preventing disease, by phagocytosis and antibody production
- recall that platelets are involved in blood clotting, which prevents blood loss and the entry of microorganisms.

Questions

More questions on blood and circulation can be found at the end of Section B on page 108.

1   Some animals have a single circulatory system, some have a double circulatory system and some organisms have no circulatory system at all.

   a)   Name one type of animal with a single circulatory system and one type of animal with a double circulatory system.

   b)   Explain:

      i)   the difference between single and double circulatory systems

      ii)   why a double circulatory system is more efficient than a single circulatory system.

   c)   Explain why single-celled organisms do not need a circulatory system.

2   Blood transports oxygen and carbon dioxide around the body. Oxygen is transported by the red blood cells.

   a)   Give three ways in which a red blood cell is adapted to its function of transporting oxygen.

   b)   Describe how oxygen:

      i)   enters a red blood cell from the alveoli in the lungs

      ii)   passes from a red blood cell to an actively respiring muscle cell.

   c)   Describe how carbon dioxide is transported around the body.

3   Blood is carried around the body in arteries, veins and capillaries.

   a)   Describe two ways in which the structure of an artery is adapted to its function.

   b)   Describe three differences between arteries and veins.

   c)   Describe two ways in which the structure of a capillary is adapted to its function.

4 The diagram shows a section through a human heart.

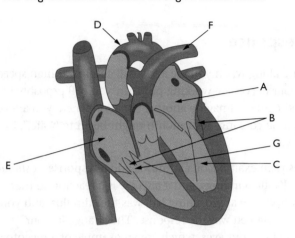

a) Name the structures labelled A, B, C, D and E.

b) What is the importance of the structures labelled B and F?

c) Which letters represent the chambers of the heart to which blood returns:

   i) from the lungs

   ii) from all the other organs of the body.

5 The diagram shows three types of cells found in human blood.

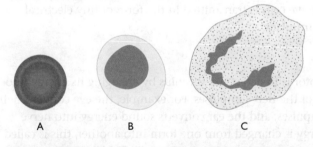

a) Giving a reason for each answer, identify the blood cell which:

   i) transports oxygen around the body

   ii) produces antibodies to destroy bacteria

   iii) engulfs and digests bacteria.

b) Name one other component of blood found in the plasma and state its function.

6 The graph shows changes in a person's heart rate over a period of time.

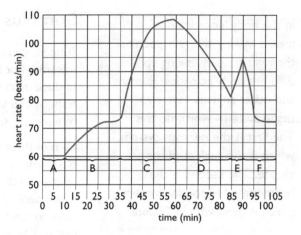

Giving reasons for your answers, give the letter of the time period when the person was:

a) running

b) frightened by a sudden loud noise

c) sleeping

d) waking.

7 The graph shows the changes that take place in heart rate before, during and after a period of exercise.

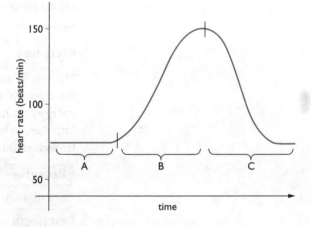

a) Describe and explain the heart rates found:

   i) at rest, before exercise (period A)

   ii) as the person commences the exercise (period B)

   iii) as the person recovers from the exercise (period C).

b) How can the recovery period (period C) be used to assess a person's fitness?

Chapter 6: Coordination

In the body 'coordination' means making things happen at the right time by linking up different body activities. Humans and other animals have two organ systems which do this. The first is the nervous system, which is the subject of this chapter. The second is the hormone or endocrine system, which is dealt with in Chapter 7.

Stimulus and response

Suppose you are walking along when you see a football coming at high speed towards your head. If your nerves are working properly, you will probably move or duck quickly to avoid contact. Imagine another situation where you are very hungry, and you smell food cooking. Your mouth might begin to 'water', in other words secrete saliva.

Each of these situations is an example of a **stimulus** and a **response**. A *stimulus* is a change in an animal's surroundings, and a *response* is a reaction to that change. In the first example, the approaching ball was the stimulus, and your movement to avoid it hitting you was the response. The change in your environment was detected by your eyes, which are an example of a **receptor** organ. The response was brought about by contraction of muscles, which are an **effector** organ (they produce an effect). Linking the two is the nervous system, an example of a coordination system. A summary of the sequence of events is:

stimulus → receptor → coordination → effector → response

In the second example, the receptor for the smell of food was the nose, and the response was the secretion of saliva from glands. Glands secrete (release) chemical substances, and they are the second type of effector organ. Again, the link between the stimulus and the response is the nervous system. The information in the nerve cells is transmitted in the form of tiny electrical signals called nerve **impulses**.

Receptors

The role of any receptor is to detect the stimulus by changing its energy into the electrical energy of the nerve impulses. For example, the eye converts light energy into nerve impulses, and the ear converts sound energy into nerve impulses. When energy is changed from one form into another, this is called **transduction**. All receptors are **transducers** of energy (Table 6.1).

Receptor	Type of energy transduced
eye (retina)	light
ear (organ of hearing)	sound
ear (organ of balance)	movement (kinetic)
tongue (taste buds)	chemical
nose (organ of smell)	chemical
skin (touch/pressure/pain receptors)	movement (kinetic)
skin (temperature receptors)	heat
muscle (stretch receptors)	movement (kinetic)

Table 6.1: *Human receptors and the energy they transduce into electrical impulses.*

Notice how a 'sense' like touch is made up of several components. When we touch a warm surface we will be stimulating several types of receptor, including touch and temperature receptors, as well as stretch receptors in the muscles (see the section on skin later in this chapter). As well as this, each sense detects different aspects of the energy it receives. For example, the ears don't just detect sounds, but different loudness and frequencies of sound, while the eye not only forms an image, but also detects intensity of light and in humans can tell the difference between different light wavelengths (colours). Senses tell us a great deal about changes in our environment.

The central nervous system

The biological name for a nerve cell is a **neurone**. The impulses that travel along a neurone are not an electric current, as in a wire. They are caused by movements of charged particles (ions) in and out of the neurone. Impulses travel at speeds between about 10 and 100 m/s, which is much slower than an electric current, but fast enough to produce a rapid response.

Impulses from receptors pass along nerves containing **sensory neurones**, until they reach the **brain** and **spinal cord**. These two organs are together known as the **central nervous system**, or CNS (Figure 6.2).

Figure 6.2 *The brain and spinal cord form the central nervous system. Cranial and spinal nerves lead to and from the CNS. The CNS sorts out information from the senses and sends messages to muscles.*

Some animals can detect changes in their environment that are not sensed by humans. Insects such as bees can see ultraviolet (UV) light. The wavelengths of UV are invisible to humans (Figure 6.1).

(a)

(b)

Figure 6.1 *This yellow flower (a) looks very different to a bee, which sees patterns on the petals reflecting UV light (b).*

Some organisms can even detect the direction of magnetic fields. Many birds, such as pigeons, have a built-in compass in their brain, which they use for navigation. A species of bacterium can also do this, but as yet no one can explain why this might be an advantage to it!

The CNS is well protected by the skeleton. The brain is encased in the skull or **cranium** (nerves connected to the brain are **cranial** nerves) and the spinal cord runs down the middle of the spinal column, passing through a hole in each vertebra. Nerves connected to the **spinal** cord are called spinal nerves.

Other nerves contain **motor neurones**, transmitting impulses to the muscles and glands. Some nerves contain only sensory or motor cells, while other nerves contain both – they are 'mixed'. A typical nerve contains thousands of individual neurones.

Both sensory and motor neurones can be very long. For instance, a motor neurone leading from the CNS to the muscles in the finger has a fibre about 1 m in length, which is 100 000 times the length of the **cell body** (Figure 6.3).

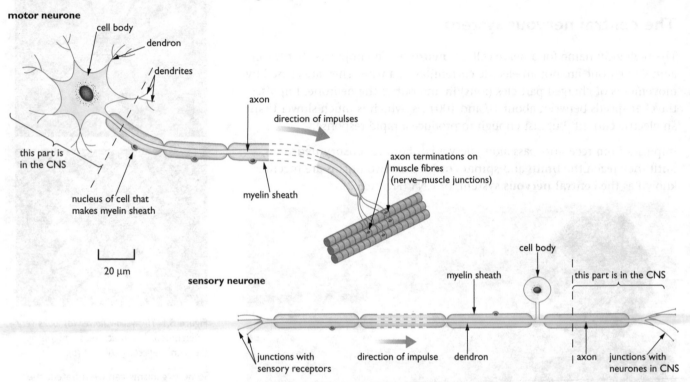

Figure 6.3 *The structure of motor and sensory neurones. The cell fibres (axon/dendron) are very long, which is indicated by the dashed sections.*

The cell body of a motor neurone is at one end of the fibre, in the CNS. The cell body has fine cytoplasmic extensions, called **dendrons**. These in turn form finer extensions, called **dendrites**. There can be junctions with other neurones on any part of the cell body, dendrons or dendrites. These junctions are called **synapses**. Later in this chapter we will deal with the importance of synapses in nerve pathways. One of the extensions from the motor neurone cell body is much longer than the other dendrons. This is the fibre that carries impulses to the effector organ, and is called the **axon**. At the end of the axon furthest from the cell body, it divides into many nerve endings. These fine branches of the axon connect with a muscle at a special sort of synapse called a **nerve-muscle junction**. In this way impulses are carried from the CNS out to the muscle. The signals from nerve impulses are transmitted across the nerve-muscle junction, causing the muscle fibres to contract. The axon is covered by a **sheath** made of a fatty material called **myelin**. The myelin sheath insulates the axon, preventing 'short circuits' with other axons, and also speeds up the conduction of the impulses. The sheath is formed by the membranes of special cells that wrap themselves around the axon as it develops.

A **sensory neurone** has a similar structure to the motor neurone, but the cell body is located on a side branch of the fibre, just outside the CNS. The fibre from the sensory receptor to the cell body is actually a dendron, while the fibre from the cell body to the CNS is a short axon. As with motor neurones, fibres of sensory neurones are often myelinated.

The eye

Many animals have eyes, but few show the complexity of the human eye. Simpler animals, such as snails, use their eyes to detect light but cannot form a proper image. Other animals, such as dogs, can form images but cannot distinguish colours. The human eye does all three. Of course it is not really the eye that 'sees' anything at all, but the brain that interprets the impulses from the eye. To find out how light from an object is converted into impulses representing an image, we need to look at the structure of this complex organ (Figure 6.4).

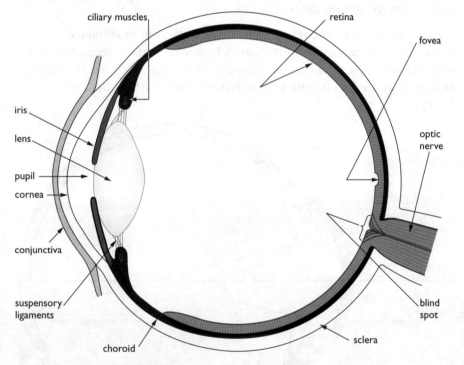

Figure 6.4 *A horizontal section through the human eye.*

The tough outer coat of the eye is called the **sclera**, which is the visible, white part of the eye. At the front of the eye the sclera becomes a transparent 'window' called the **cornea**, which lets light into the eye. Behind the cornea is the coloured ring of tissue called the **iris**. In the middle of the iris is a hole called the **pupil**, which lets the light through. It is black because there is no light escaping from the inside of the eye.

Underneath the sclera is a dark layer called the **choroid**. It is dark because it contains many pigment cells, as well as blood vessels. The pigment stops light being reflected around inside the eye. In the same way, the inside of a camera is painted matt black to stop stray light bouncing around and fogging the image on the film.

The innermost layer of the back of the eye is the **retina**. This is the light-sensitive layer, the place where light energy is transduced into the electrical energy of nerve impulses. The retina contains cells called **rods** and **cones**. These cells react to light, producing impulses in sensory neurones. The sensory neurones then pass the impulses to the brain through the **optic nerve**. Rod cells work well in dim light, but they cannot distinguish between different colours, so the brain 'sees' an image produced by the rods in black and white. This is why we can't see colours very well in dim light: only our rods are working properly. The cones, on the other hand, will only work in bright light, and there are three types which respond to different wavelengths or colours of light – red, green and blue. We can see all the colours of visible light as a result of these three types of cones being stimulated to different degrees. For example, if red, green and blue are stimulated equally, we see white. Both rods and cones are found throughout the retina, but cones are particularly concentrated at the centre of the retina, in an area called the **fovea**. Cones give a sharper image than rods, which is why we can only see objects clearly if we are looking directly at them, so that the image falls on the fovea.

To form an image on the retina, light needs to be bent or **refracted**. Refraction takes place when light passes from one medium to another of a different density. In the eye, this happens first at the air/cornea boundary, and again at the lens (Figure 6.5). In fact the cornea acts as the first lens of the eye.

The fact that the inverted image is seen the right way up by the brain makes the point that it is the brain which 'sees' things, not the eye. An interesting experiment was carried out to test this. Volunteers were made to wear special inverting goggles for long periods. These turned the view of their surroundings upside down. At first this completely disorientated them, and they found it difficult to make even simple coordinated movements. However, after a while their brains adapted, until the view through the goggles looked normal. In fact, when the volunteers removed the goggles, the world then looked upside down!

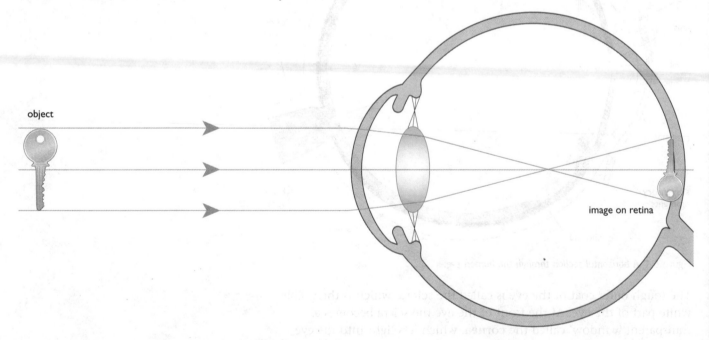

Figure 6.5 *How the eye forms an image. Refraction of light occurs at the cornea and lens, producing an inverted image on the retina.*

As a result of refraction at the cornea and lens, the image on the retina is upside down, or **inverted**. The brain interprets the image the right way up.

The role of the iris is to control the amount of light entering the eye, by changing the size of the pupil. The iris contains two types of muscles. **Circular muscles** form a ring shape in the iris, and **radial muscles** lie like the spokes of a wheel. In bright light, the pupil is made smaller, or **constricted**.

This happens because the circular muscles contract and the radial muscles relax. In dim light, the opposite happens. The radial muscles contract and the circular muscles relax, widening or **dilating** the pupil (Figure 6.6).

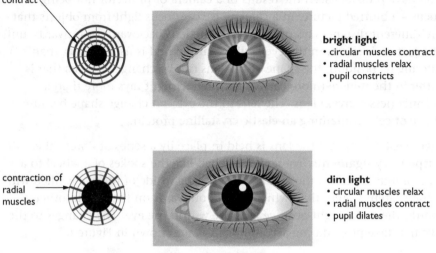

circular muscles contract

bright light
• circular muscles contract
• radial muscles relax
• pupil constricts

contraction of radial muscles

dim light
• circular muscles relax
• radial muscles contract
• pupil dilates

Figure 6.6 *The amount of light entering the eye is controlled by the iris, which alters the diameter of the pupil.*

Whenever our eyes look from a dim light to a bright one, the iris rapidly and automatically adjusts the pupil size. This is an example of a **reflex action**. You will find out more about reflexes later in this chapter. The purpose of the iris reflex is to allow the right intensity of light to fall on the retina. Light that is too bright could damage the rods and cones, and light that is too dim would not form an image. The intensity of light hitting the retina is the stimulus for this reflex. Impulses pass to the brain through the optic nerve, and straight back to the iris muscles, adjusting the diameter of the pupil. It all happens without the need for conscious thought – in fact we are not even aware of it happening.

There is one area of the retina where an image cannot be formed; this is where the optic nerve leaves the eye. At this position there are no rods or cones, so it is called the **blind spot**. The retina of each eye has a blind spot, but they are not a problem, because the brain puts the images from each eye together, cancelling out the blind spots of both eyes. As well as this, the optic nerve leaves the eye towards the edge of the retina, where vision is not very sharp anyway. To 'see' your own blind spot you can do a simple experiment. Cover or close your right eye. Hold this page about 30 cm from your eyes and look at the black dot below. Now, without moving the book or turning your head, read the numbers from left to right by moving your left eye slowly towards the right.

•   1   2   3   4   5   6   7   8   9   10   11   12   13   14   15

You should find that when the image of the dot falls on the blind spot it disappears. If you try doing this with both eyes open, the image of the dot will not disappear.

In the iris reflex, the route from stimulus to response is this:

stimulus (light intensity)
↓
retina (receptor)
↓
sensory neurones in optic nerve
↓
unconscious part of brain
↓
motor neurones in nerve to iris
↓
iris muscles (effector)
↓
response (change in size of pupil)

LOL
A way to prove to yourself that the eyes form two overlapping images is to try the '<u>sausage test</u>'. Focus your eyes on a distant object. Place your two index fingers tip to tip, and bring them up in front of your eyes, about 30 cm from your face, while still focusing at a distance. You should see a finger 'sausage' between the two fingers. Now try this with one eye closed. What is the difference?

Accommodation

The changes that take place in the eye which allow us to see objects at different distances are called **accommodation**.

You have probably seen the results of a camera or projector not being in focus – a blurred picture. In a camera, we can focus light from objects that are different distances away by moving the lens backwards or forwards, until the picture is sharp. In the eye, a different method is used. Rather than altering its position, the shape of the lens can be changed. A lens that is fatter in the middle (more convex) will refract light rays more than a thinner (less convex) lens. The lens in the eye can change shape because it is made of cells containing an elastic crystalline protein.

Figure 6.4 shows that the lens is held in place by a series of fibres called the **suspensory ligaments**. These are attached like the spokes of a wheel to a ring of muscle, called the **ciliary muscle**. The inside of the eye is filled with a transparent watery fluid which pushes outwards on the eye. In other words, there is a slight positive pressure within the eye. The changes to the eye that take place during accommodation are shown in Figure 6.7.

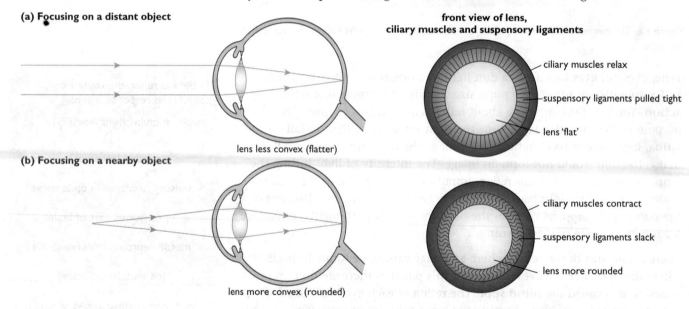

Figure 6.7 Accommodation: how the eye focuses on objects at different distances.

When the eye is focused on a distant object, the rays of light from the object are almost parallel when they reach the cornea (Figure 6.7a). The cornea refracts the rays, but the lens does not need to refract them much more to focus the light on the retina, so it does not need to be very convex. The ciliary muscles relax and the pressure in the eye pushes outwards on the lens, flattening it and stretching the suspensory ligaments. This is the condition when the eye is at rest – our eyes are focused for long distances.

When we focus on a nearby object, for example when reading a book, the light rays from the object are spreading out (diverging) when they enter the eye (Figure 6.7b). In this situation, the lens has to be more convex in order to refract the rays enough to focus them on the retina. The ciliary muscles now contract; the suspensory ligaments become slack and the elastic lens bulges outwards into a more convex shape.

Reflex actions

You saw on page 71 that the dilation and constriction of the pupil by the iris is an example of a reflex action. You now need to understand a little more about the nerves involved in a reflex. The nerve pathway of a reflex is called the **reflex arc**. The 'arc' part means that the pathway goes into the CNS and then straight back out again, in a sort of curve or arc (Figure 6.8).

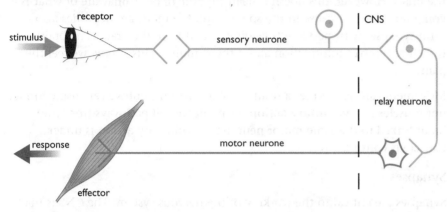

Figure 6.8 *Simplified diagram of a reflex arc.*

The iris–pupil reflex protects the eye against damage by bright light. Other reflexes are protective too, preventing serious harm to the body. Take, for example, the reflex response to a painful stimulus. This happens when part of your body, such as your hand, touches a sharp or hot object. The reflex results in your hand being quickly withdrawn. Figure 6.9 shows the nerve pathway of this reflex in more detail.

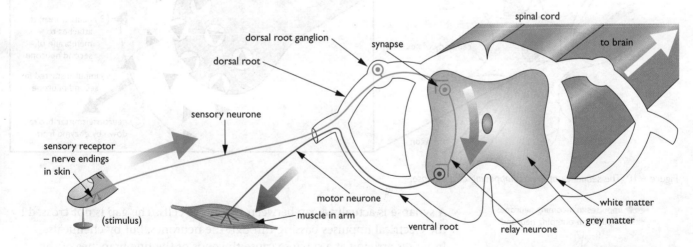

Figure 6.9 *A reflex arc in more detail.*

The stimulus is detected by temperature or pain receptors in the skin. These generate impulses in sensory neurones. The impulses enter the CNS through a part of the spinal nerve called the **dorsal root**. In the spinal cord the sensory neurones connect by synapses with short **relay neurones**, which in turn connect with motor neurones. The motor neurones emerge from the spinal cord through the **ventral root**, and send impulses back out to the muscles of the arm. These muscles then contract, pulling the arm (and thus finger) away from the harmful stimulus.

'Dorsal' and 'ventral' are words describing the back and front of the body. The dorsal roots of spinal nerves emerge from the spinal cord towards the back of the person, while the ventral roots emerge towards the front. Notice that the cell bodies of the sensory neurones are all located in a swelling in the dorsal root, called the **dorsal root ganglion**.

The middle part of the spinal cord consists mainly of nerve cell bodies, which gives it a grey colour. This is why it is known as **grey matter**. The outer part of the spinal cord is called **white matter**, and has a whiter appearance because it contains many axons with their fatty myelin sheaths.

Impulses travel through the reflex arc in a fraction of a second, so that the reflex action is very fast, and doesn't need to be started off by impulses from the brain. However, this doesn't mean that the brain is unaware of what is going on. This is because in the spinal cord, the reflex arc neurones also form synapses with nerve cells leading to and from the brain. The brain therefore receives information about the stimulus. This is how we feel the pain.

Movements are sometimes a result of reflex actions, but we can also contract our muscles as a **voluntary action**, using nerve cell pathways from the brain linked to the same motor neurones. A voluntary action is under conscious control.

Synapses

Synapses are critical to the working of the nervous system. The CNS is made of many billions of nerve cells, and these have links with many others, through synapses. In the brain, each neurone may form synapses with thousands of other neurones, so that there are an almost infinite number of possible pathways through the system.

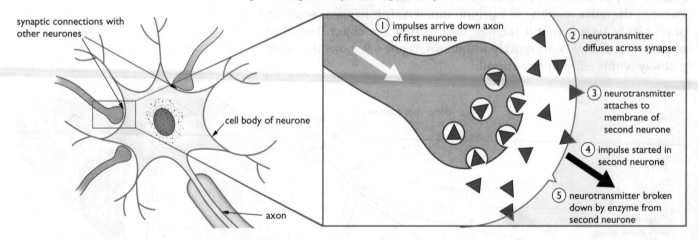

synaptic connections with other neurones

cell body of neurone

axon

① impulses arrive down axon of first neurone
② neurotransmitter diffuses across synapse
③ neurotransmitter attaches to membrane of second neurone
④ impulse started in second neurone
⑤ neurotransmitter broken down by enzyme from second neurone

Figure 6.10 *The sequence of events happening at a synapse.*

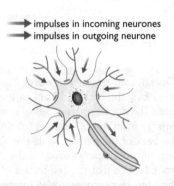

→ impulses in incoming neurones
→ impulses in outgoing neurone

Figure 6.11 *Synapses allow the output of one nerve cell to be a result of integration of information from many other cells.*

A synapse is actually a gap between two nerve cells. The gap is not crossed by the electrical impulses passing through the neurones, but by chemicals. Impulses arriving at a synapse cause the ends of the fine branches of the axon to secrete a chemical, called a **neurotransmitter**. This chemical diffuses across the gap and attaches to the membrane of the second neurone. It then starts off impulses in the second cell (Figure 6.10). After the neurotransmitter has 'passed on the message', it is broken down by an enzyme.

Remember that many nerve cells, particularly those in the brain, have thousands of synapses with other neurones. The output of one cell may depend on the inputs from many cells adding together. In this way, synapses are important for integrating information in the central nervous system (Figure 6.11).

Because synapses are crossed by chemicals, it is easy for other chemicals to interfere with the working of the synapse. They may imitate the neurotransmitter, or block its action. This is the way that many well-known drugs, both useful and harmful, work. We will return to this topic later.

The brain

The functions of different parts of the brain were first worked out through studies of people who had suffered brain damage through accident or disease. Nowadays we have very sophisticated electronic equipment that can record the activity in a normal living brain, but we are still relatively ignorant about the workings of this most complex organ of the body.

Your brain is sometimes called your 'grey matter'. This is because the positions of the grey and white matter are reversed in the brain compared with the spinal cord. The grey matter, mainly made of nerve cell bodies, is on the outside of the brain, and the axons that form the white matter are in the middle of the brain. The brain is made up of different parts, each with a particular function (Figure 6.12).

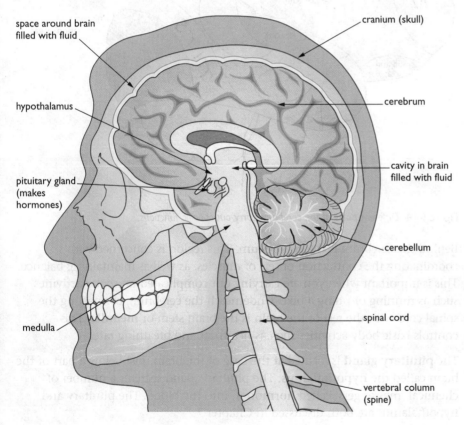

Figure 6.12 *Section through the human brain, showing its main parts.*

The largest part of the brain is the **cerebrum**, made of two **cerebral hemispheres**. The cerebrum is the source of all our conscious thoughts. It has an outer layer called the **cerebral cortex**, with many folds all over its surface (Figure 6.13).

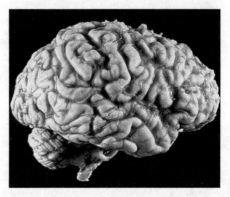

Figure 6.13 *A side view of a human brain. Notice the folded surface of the cerebral cortex.*

The cerebrum has three main functions.

- It contains **sensory areas** that receive and process information from all our sense organs.
- It has **motor areas**, which are where all our voluntary actions originate.
- It is the origin of 'higher' activities, such as memory, reasoning, emotions and personality.

Different parts of the cerebrum carry out particular functions. For example, the sensory and motor areas are always situated in the same place in the cortex (Figure 6.14). Some parts of these areas deal with more information than others. Large parts of the sensory area deal with impulses from the fingers and lips, for example. This is illustrated in Figure 6.15.

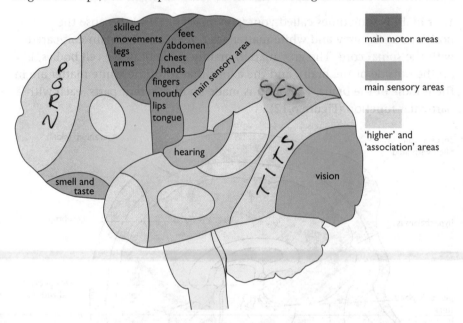

Figure 6.14 *Different parts of the cerebrum carry out specific functions.*

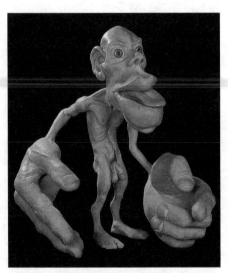

Figure 6.15 *A model of a human with its parts drawn in proportion to the amount of sensory information they send to the cortex of the brain (note that this does not apply to the eyes, which use more cortex than the rest of the body put together).*

Behind the cerebrum is the **cerebellum**. This region is concerned with coordinating the contraction of sets of muscles, as well as maintaining balance. This is important when you are carrying out complicated muscular activities, such as running or riding a bike. Underneath the cerebrum, connecting the spinal cord with the rest of the brain is the brain stem or **medulla**. This controls basic body activities such as heartbeat and breathing rate.

The **pituitary gland** is located at the base of the brain, just below a part of the brain called the **hypothalamus**. The pituitary gland secretes a number of chemical 'messengers' called **hormones**, into the blood. The pituitary and hypothalamus are both discussed in Chapter 7.

End of Chapter Checklist

You should now be able to:

● understand that organisms are able to respond to changes in their environment

● understand that a coordinated response requires a stimulus, a receptor and an effector

● describe how responses can be controlled by nervous communication

● recall that the central nervous system consists of the brain and spinal cord and is linked to sense organs by nerves

● understand that stimulation of receptors in the sense organs sends electrical impulses along nerves into and out of the central nervous system, resulting in rapid responses

● describe the structure and functioning of a simple reflex arc, illustrated by the withdrawal of a finger from a hot object

● describe the structure and function of the eye as a receptor

● understand the function of the eye in focusing near and distant objects, and in responding to changes in light intensity.

Questions

More questions on coordination can be found at the end of Section B on page 108.

I A **cataract** is an eye problem suffered by some people, especially the elderly. The lens of the eye becomes opaque (cloudy) which blocks the passage of light. It can lead to blindness. Cataracts can be treated by a simple eye operation, where a surgeon removes the lens. After the operation, the patient is able to see again, but the eye is unable to carry out accommodation, and the patient will probably need to wear glasses.

a) Explain why the eye can still form an image after the lens has been removed.

b) What is meant by 'accommodation'? Why is this not possible after a cataract operation?

c) Will the patient need glasses to see nearby or distant objects clearly? Explain your answer.

2 The diagram shows a section through a human eye.

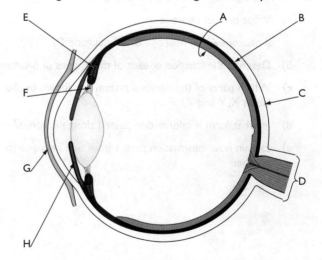

a) The table (on the next page) lists the functions of some of parts A to H. Copy the table and write the letters of the correct parts in the boxes.

Function	Letter
refracts light rays	
converts light into nerve impulses	
contains pigment to stop internal reflection	
contracts to change the shape of the lens	
takes nerve impulses to the brain	

b) **i)** Which label shows the iris?

    ii) Explain how the iris controls the amount of light entering the eye.

    iii) Why is this important?

3 The diagram shows some parts of the nervous system involved in a simple reflex action that happens when a finger touches a hot object.

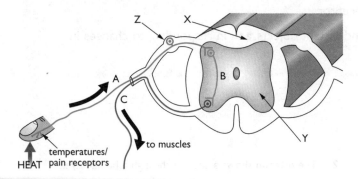

a) What type of neurone is:

    i) neurone A   ii) neurone B   iii) neurone C?

b) Describe the function of each of these types of neurone.

c) Which parts of the nervous system are shown by the labels X, Y and Z?

d) In what form is information passed along neurones?

e) Explain how information passes from one neurone to another.

4 **a)** Which part of the human brain is responsible for controlling each of the following actions:

    i) keeping your balance when you walk?

    ii) maintaining your breathing when you are asleep?

    iii) making your leg muscles contract when you kick a ball?

b) A 'stroke' is caused by a blood clot blocking the blood supply to part of the brain.

    i) One patient, after suffering a stroke, was unable to move his left arm. Which part of his brain was affected?

    ii) Another patient lost her sense of smell following a stroke. Which part of her brain was affected?

5 **a)** List five examples of stimuli that affect the body and state the response produced by each stimulus.

b) For one of your five examples, explain:

    i) the nature and role of the receptor

    ii) the nature and role of the effector organ.

c) For the same example, describe the chain of events from stimulus to response.

Chapter 7: Chemical Coordination

The nervous system (Chapter 6) is a coordination system forming a link between stimulus and response. The body has a second coordination system, which does not involve nerves. This is the **endocrine** system. It consists of organs called endocrine **glands**, which make chemical messenger substances called **hormones**. Hormones are carried in the bloodstream.

The receptors for some hormones are located in the cell membrane of the target cell. Other hormones have receptors in the cytoplasm, and some in the nucleus. Without specific receptors, a cell will not respond to a hormone at all.

Glands and hormones

A gland is an organ that releases or **secretes** a substance. This means that cells in the gland make a chemical which passes out of the cells. The chemical then travels somewhere else in the body, where it carries out its function. There are two types of glands – **exocrine** and **endocrine** glands. Exocrine glands secrete their products through a tube or **duct**. For example, salivary glands in your mouth secrete saliva down salivary ducts, and tear glands secrete tears through ducts that lead to the surface of the eye. Endocrine glands have no duct, and so are called **ductless** glands. Instead, their products, the hormones, are secreted into the blood vessels that pass through the gland (Figure 7.1).

This chapter looks at some of the main endocrine glands and the functions of the hormones they produce. Because hormones are carried in the blood, they can travel to all areas of the body. They usually only affect certain tissues or organs, called 'target organs', which can be a long distance from the gland that made the hormone. Hormones only affect particular tissues or organs if the cells of that tissue or organ have special chemical receptors for the particular hormone. For example, the hormone insulin affects the cells of the liver, which have insulin receptors.

The differences between nervous and endocrine control

Although the nervous and endocrine systems both act to coordinate body functions, there are differences in the way that they do this. These are summarised in Table 7.1.

Nervous system	Endocrine system
• works by nerve impulses transmitted through nerve cells (although chemicals are used at synapses)	• works by hormones transmitted through the bloodstream
• nerve impulses travel fast and usually have an 'instant' effect	• hormones travel more slowly and generally take longer to act
• response is usually short-lived	• response is usually longer-lasting
• impulses act on individual cells such as muscle fibres, so have a very localised effect	• hormones can have widespread effects on different organs (although they only act on particular tissues or organs if the cells have the correct receptors)

Table 7.1: *The nervous and endocrine systems compared.*

The positions of the endocrine glands

The main endocrine glands are shown in Figure 7.2, and a summary of some of the hormones that they make and their functions, is given in Table 7.2.

The **pituitary** gland is found at the base of the brain (see Figure 6.12, page 75). It produces a number of hormones, including those that regulate

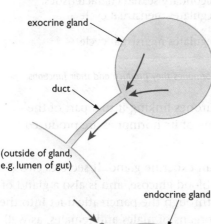

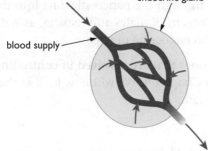

Figure 7.1 *Exocrine glands secrete their products though a duct, while endocrine glands secrete hormones into the blood.*

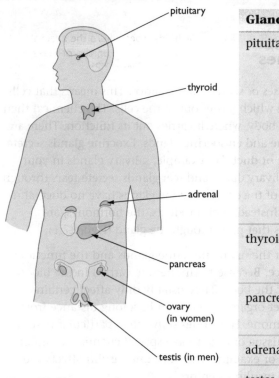

pituitary

thyroid

adrenal

pancreas

ovary
(in women)

testis (in men)

Figure 7.2 *The main endocrine glands of the body.*

Gland	Hormone	Some functions of the hormones
pituitary	follicle stimulating hormone (FSH)	stimulates egg development and oestrogen secretion in females and sperm production in males
	luteinising hormone (LH)	stimulates egg release (ovulation) in females and testosterone production in males
	anti-diuretic hormone (ADH)	controls the water content of the blood (see Chapter 8)
	growth hormone (GH)	speeds up the rate of growth and development in children
thyroid	thyroxin	controls the body's metabolic rate (how fast chemical reactions take place in cells)
pancreas	insulin	lowers blood glucose
	glucagon	raises blood glucose
adrenals	adrenaline	prepares body for physical activity
testes	testosterone	controls development of male secondary sexual characteristics
ovaries	oestrogen	controls development of female secondary sexual characteristics; regulates menstrual cycle
	progesterone	regulates menstrual cycle

Table 7.2: *Some of the main endocrine glands, the hormones they produce and their functions.*

reproduction. The pituitary contains neurones linking it to a part of the brain called the **hypothalamus**, and some of its hormones are produced under the control of the brain.

The **pancreas** is both an endocrine *and* an exocrine gland. It secretes two hormones involved in the regulation of blood glucose, and is also a gland of the digestive system, secreting enzymes through the pancreatic duct into the small intestine (see Chapter 4). The sex organs of males and females, as well as producing sex cells or gametes, are also endocrine organs.

Both the **testes** and **ovaries** make hormones that are involved in controlling reproduction. This topic is dealt with in Chapter 9. We will now look at the functions of three hormones in more detail.

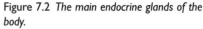

The pituitary is a link between the nervous and endocrine coordination systems.

Adrenaline – the 'fight or flight' hormone

When you are frightened, excited or angry, your **adrenal** glands secrete the hormone **adrenaline**.

Adrenaline acts at a number of target organs and tissues, preparing the body for action. In animals other than humans this action usually means dealing with an attack by an enemy, where the animal can stay and fight or run away – hence 'fight or flight'. This is not often a problem with humans, but there are plenty of other times when adrenaline is released (Figure 7.3).

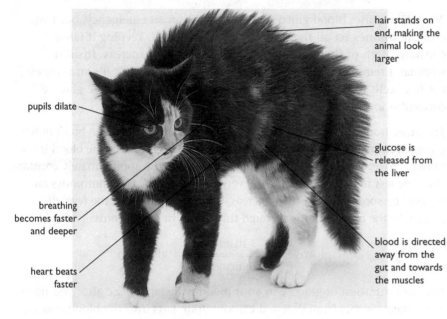

Figure 7.4 *Adrenaline affects the body of an animal in many ways.*

Figure 7.3 *Many human activities cause adrenaline to be produced, not just a 'fight or flight' situation!*

If an animal's body is going to be prepared for action, the muscles need a good supply of oxygen and glucose for respiration. Adrenaline produces several changes in the body that cause this to happen (Figure 7.4) as well as other changes to prepare for fight or flight.

- The breathing rate increases and breaths become deeper, taking more oxygen into the body.

- The heart beats faster, sending more blood to the muscles, so that they receive more glucose and oxygen for respiration.

- Blood is diverted away from the intestine and into the muscles.

- In the liver, stored carbohydrate is changed into glucose and released into the blood. The muscle cells absorb more glucose and use it for respiration.

- The pupils dilate, increasing visual sensitivity to movement.

- Body hair stands on end, making the animal look larger to an enemy.

- Mental awareness is increased, so reactions are faster.

In humans, adrenaline is not just released in a 'fight or flight' situation, but in many other stressful activities too, such as preparing for a race, going for a job interview or taking an exam.

Controlling blood glucose

You saw earlier that adrenaline can raise blood glucose from stores in the liver. The liver cells contain carbohydrate in the form of **glycogen**. Glycogen is made from long chains of glucose sub-units joined together (see Chapter 3)

Most of the cells of the pancreas are concerned with making digestive enzymes. However, in the pancreas tissue, there are small groups of cells called the **Islets of Langerhans**. These contain two types of cell. Larger α (alpha) cells secrete glucagon, and smaller β (beta) cells secrete insulin.

Insulin is a protein, and if it were to be taken by mouth in tablet form, it would be broken down in the gut. Instead it is injected into muscle tissue, where it is slowly absorbed into the bloodstream.

Figure 7.5 *Coloured test strips are used to detect glucose in urine.*

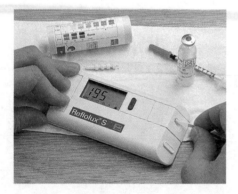

Figure 7.6 *Sensor for measuring blood glucose.*

Insulin for the treatment of diabetes has been available since 1921, and has kept millions of people alive. It was originally extracted from the pancreases of animals such as pigs and cows, and much insulin is still obtained in this way. However, since the 1970s, human insulin has been produced commercially, from genetically modified (GM) bacteria. The bacteria have their DNA 'engineered' to contain the gene for human insulin (see Chapter 22).

producing a large insoluble molecule. Being insoluble makes glycogen a good storage product. When the body is short of glucose, the glycogen can be broken down into glucose, which then passes into the bloodstream.

Adrenaline raises blood glucose concentration in an emergency, but two other hormones act all the time to control the level, keeping it fairly constant. Both of these hormones are made by the pancreas. **Insulin** stimulates removal of glucose from the bloodstream into cells and causes the liver cells to convert glucose into glycogen. This lowers the glucose concentration in the blood when it is too high.

The other hormone is **glucagon**. This stimulates the liver cells to break down glycogen into glucose, raising the concentration of glucose in the blood if it is too low. Together, they work to keep the blood glucose approximately constant, at a little less than 1 g of glucose in every dm^3 of blood. Both hormones are released by special cells in the pancreas, in direct response to the level of glucose in the blood passing through this organ. In other words:

$$glucose \xrightleftharpoons[glucagon]{insulin} glycogen$$

The concentration of glucose in your blood will start to rise after you have had a meal. Sugars from digested carbohydrate pass into the blood and are carried to the liver in the hepatic portal vein (Chapter 5). Here the glucose is converted to glycogen, so the blood leaving the liver in the hepatic vein will have a lower concentration of glucose.

Diabetes

Some people have a disease where their pancreas cannot make enough insulin to keep their blood glucose level constant – it rises to very high concentrations. The disease is called **diabetes**, or sometimes 'sugar diabetes'. One symptom of diabetes can be detected by a chemical test on urine. Normally, people have no glucose at all in their urine. Someone suffering from diabetes may have such a high concentration of glucose in the blood that it is excreted in their urine. This can be shown up by using coloured test strips (Figure 7.5).

Another symptom of this kind of diabetes is a constant thirst. This is because the high blood glucose concentration stimulates receptors in the hypothalamus of the brain. These 'thirst' centres are stimulated, so that by drinking, the person will dilute their blood.

Severe diabetes is very serious. If it is untreated, the sufferer loses weight and becomes weak and eventually lapses into a coma and dies.

Glucose in the blood is derived from carbohydrates such as starch in the diet, so mild forms of the disease can be treated by controlling the patient's diet, limiting the amount of carbohydrate that they eat. More serious cases of diabetes need daily injections of insulin to keep the glucose level in the blood at the correct level. People with diabetes can check their blood glucose using a special sensor. They prick their finger and place a drop of blood onto a test strip. The strip is then put into the sensor, which gives them an accurate reading of how much glucose is in their blood (Figure 7.6). They can then tell whether or not they need to inject insulin.

End of Chapter Checklist

You should now be able to:

● describe how responses can be controlled by hormonal communication, and understand the differences between hormonal and nervous communication

● understand the sources, roles and effects of adrenaline, insulin, anti-diuretic hormone, testosterone, progesterone and oestrogen (some of these will be dealt with in more detail in later chapters).

Questions

More questions on chemical coordination can be found at the end of Section B on page 108.

1 **a)** *Hormones* are *secreted* by *endocrine glands*. Explain the meaning of the four words in italics.

   b) Identify the hormones A to D in the table.

Hormone	One function of this hormone
A	stimulates the liver to convert glycogen to glucose
B	controls the 'fight or flight' responses
C	in boys, controls the breaking of the voice at puberty
D	completes the development of the uterus lining during the menstrual cycle

2 The number of sperm cells per cm³ of semen (the fluid containing sperm) is called the 'sperm count'. Some scientists believe that over the last 50 years, the sperm counts of adult male humans have decreased. They think that this is caused by a number of factors, including drinking water polluted with oestrogens and other chemicals. Carry out an Internet search to find out the evidence for this. Download information into a word processor and summarise your findings in no more than two sides of A4, including graphs.

3 The graph shows the changes in blood glucose in a healthy woman over a 12-hour period.

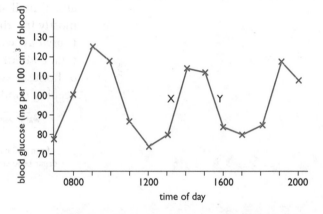

a) Explain why there was a rise in blood glucose at X.

b) How does the body bring about a decrease in blood glucose at Y? Your answer should include the words insulin, liver and pancreas.

c) Diabetes is a disease where the body cannot control the concentration of glucose in the blood.

   i) Why is this dangerous?

   ii) Describe two ways a person with diabetes can monitor their blood glucose level.

   iii) Explain two ways that a person with diabetes can help to control their blood glucose level.

Chapter 8: Homeostasis and Excretion

The kidneys play a major part in homeostasis (maintaining a balance of substances in the body) and excretion (removal of waste products from cell metabolism). This chapter is mainly concerned with the activities of the kidneys. It also deals with another important aspect of homeostasis, that of maintaining a steady body temperature.

Inside our bodies, conditions are kept relatively constant. This is called **homeostasis**. The kidneys are organs which have a major role to play in both homeostasis and in the removal of waste products, or **excretion**. They filter the blood, removing substances and controlling the concentration of water and solutes in the blood and other body fluids.

Homeostasis

If you were to drink a litre of water and wait for half an hour, your body would soon respond to this change by producing about the same volume of urine. In other words, it would automatically balance your water input and water loss. Drinking is the main way that our bodies gain water, but there are other sources (Figure 8.1). Some water is present in the food that we eat, and a small amount is formed by cell respiration. The body also loses water, mostly in urine, but also smaller volumes in sweat, faeces and exhaled air. Every day, we gain and lose about the same volume of water, so that the total content of our bodies stays more or less the same. This is an example of homeostasis. The word 'homeostasis' means 'steady state', and refers to keeping conditions inside the body relatively constant.

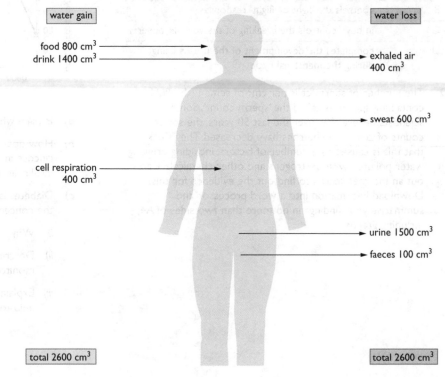

water gain	water loss

food 800 cm³
drink 1400 cm³

exhaled air 400 cm³

sweat 600 cm³

cell respiration 400 cm³

urine 1500 cm³
faeces 100 cm³

total 2600 cm³	total 2600 cm³

Figure 8.1 *The daily water balance of an adult.*

Homeostasis means 'keeping the conditions in the internal environment of the body relatively constant'.

Inside the body is known as the **internal environment**. You have probably heard of the 'environment', which means the 'surroundings' of an organism. The *internal* environment is the surroundings of the cells inside the body. It particularly means the blood, together with another liquid called **tissue fluid**.

Tissue fluid is a watery solution of salts, glucose and other solutes. It surrounds all the cells of the body, forming a pathway for the transfer of nutrients between the blood and the cells. Tissue fluid is formed by leakage from blood capillaries. It is similar in composition to blood plasma, but lacks the plasma proteins.

It is not just water and salts that are kept constant in the body. Many other components of the internal environment are maintained. For example, the level of carbon dioxide in the blood is regulated, along with the blood pH, the concentration of dissolved glucose (see Chapter 7) and the body temperature.

Homeostasis is important because cells will only function properly if they are bathed in a tissue fluid which provides them with their optimum conditions. For instance, if the tissue fluid contains too many solutes, the cells will lose water by osmosis, and become dehydrated. If the tissue fluid is too dilute, the cells will swell up with water. Both conditions will prevent them working efficiently and might cause permanent damage. If the pH of the tissue fluid is not correct, it will affect the activity of the cell's enzymes, as will a body temperature much different from 37 °C. It is also important that excretory products are removed. Substances such as urea must be prevented from building up in the blood and tissue fluid, where they would be toxic to cells.

Urine

An adult human produces about 1.5 dm³ of urine every day, although this volume depends very much on the amount of water drunk and the volume lost in other forms, such as sweat. Every litre of urine contains about 40 g of waste products and salts (Table 8.1).

Substance	Amount (g/dm³)
urea	23.3
ammonia	0.4
other nitrogenous waste	1.6
sodium chloride (salt)	10.0
potassium	1.3
phosphate	2.3

Table 8.1: *Some of the main dissolved substances in urine.*

'Salts' in urine or in the blood are present as ions. For example, the sodium chloride in Table 8.1 will be in solution as sodium ions (Na^+) and chloride ions (Cl^-). Urine contains many other ions, such as potassium (K^+) phosphate (HPO_4^{2-}) and ammonium (NH_4^+), and removes excess ions from the blood.

Notice the words **nitrogenous waste**. Urea and ammonia are two examples of nitrogenous waste. It means that they contain the element **nitrogen**. All animals have to excrete a nitrogenous waste product.

The reason behind this is quite involved. Carbohydrates and fats only contain the elements carbon, hydrogen and oxygen. Proteins, on the other hand, also contain nitrogen. If the body has too much carbohydrate or fat, these substances can be stored, for example as glycogen in the liver, or as fat under the skin and around other organs. Excess proteins, or their building blocks (called amino acids) *cannot* be stored. The amino acids are first broken down in the liver. They are converted into carbohydrate (which is stored as glycogen) and the main nitrogen-containing waste product, urea. The urea passes into the blood, to be filtered out by the kidneys during the formation of urine. Notice that the urea is made by chemical reactions in the cells of the body (the body's metabolism). 'Excretion' means getting rid of waste of this kind. When the body gets rid of solid waste from the digestive system (faeces), this is not excretion, since it contains few products of *metabolism*, just the 'left over remains' of undigested food, along with bacteria and dead cells.

So the kidney is really carrying out two functions. It is a *homeostatic* organ, controlling the water and salt (ion) concentration in the body as well as an *excretory* organ, concentrating nitrogenous waste in a form that can be eliminated.

The urinary system

The human urinary system is shown in Figure 8.2.

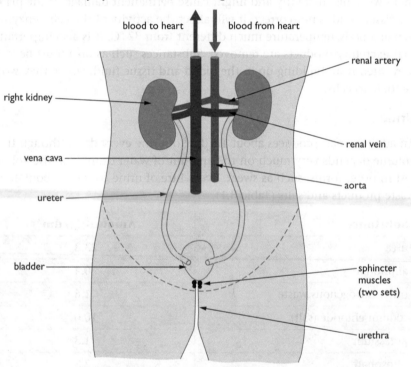

Figure 8.2 *The human urinary system.*

Each kidney is supplied with blood through a short **renal artery**. This leads straight from the body's main artery, the aorta, so the blood entering the kidney is at a high pressure. Inside each kidney the blood is filtered, and the 'cleaned' blood passes out through each **renal vein** to the main vein, or vena cava. The urine passes out of the kidneys through two tubes, the **ureters**, and is stored in a muscular bag called the **bladder**.

The bladder has a tube leading to the outside, called the **urethra**. The wall of the urethra contains two ring-like muscles, called **sphincters**. They can contract to close the urethra and hold back the urine. The lower sphincter muscle is consciously controlled, or voluntary, while the upper one is involuntary – it automatically relaxes when the bladder is full.

The kidneys

If you cut a kidney lengthwise as in Figure 8.3 you should be able to find the structures shown.

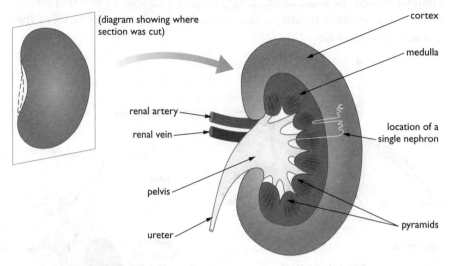

Figure 8.3 *Section through a kidney cut along the plane shown.*

There is not much that you can make out without the help of a microscope. The darker outer region is called the **cortex**. This contains many tiny blood vessels that branch from the renal artery. It also contains microscopic tubes that are not blood vessels. They are the filtering units, called **kidney tubules** or **nephrons** (from the Greek word *nephros*, meaning kidney). The tubules then run down through the middle layer of the kidney, called the **medulla**. The medulla has bulges called **pyramids** pointing inwards towards the concave side of the kidney. The tubules in the medulla eventually join up and lead to the tips of these pyramids, where they empty urine into a space called the **pelvis**. The pelvis connects with the **ureter**, carrying the urine to the **bladder**.

By careful dissection, biologists have been able to find out the structure of a single tubule and its blood supply (Figure 8.4). There are about a million of these in each kidney.

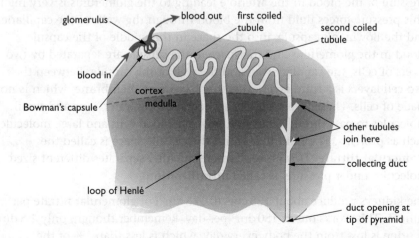

Figure 8.4 *A single nephron, showing its position in the kidney. Each kidney contains about a million of these filtering units.*

At the start of the nephron is a hollow cup of cells called the **Bowman's capsule**. It surrounds a ball of blood capillaries called a **glomerulus** (the plural is glomeruli). It is here that the blood is filtered. Blood enters the kidney through the renal artery, which divides into smaller and smaller arteries. The smallest arteries, called **arterioles**, supply the capillaries of the glomerulus (Figure 8.5).

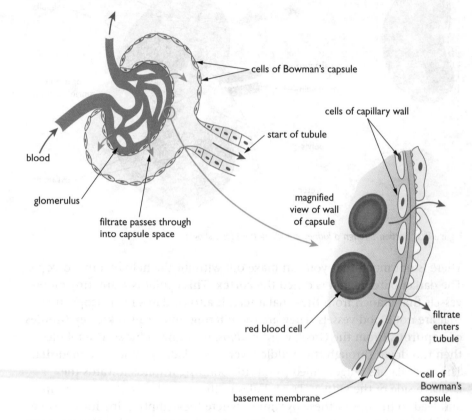

Figure 8.5 *A Bowman's capsule and glomerulus.*

The cells of the glomerulus capillaries do not fit together very tightly, there are spaces between them making the capillary walls much more permeable than others in the body. The cells of the Bowman's capsule also have gaps between them, so only act as a coarse filter. It is the basement membrane which is the fine molecular filter.

A blood vessel with a smaller diameter carries blood away from the glomerulus, leading to capillary networks which surround the other parts of the nephron. Because of the resistance to flow caused by the glomerulus, the pressure of the blood in the arteriole leading to the glomerulus is very high. This pressure forces fluid from the blood through the walls of the capillaries and the Bowman's capsule, into the space in the middle of the capsule. Blood in the glomerulus and the space in the capsule are separated by two layers of cells, the capillary wall and the wall of the capsule. Between the two cell layers is a third layer called the **basement membrane**, which is not made of cells. These layers act like a filter, allowing water, ions and small molecules to pass through, but holding back blood cells and large molecules such as proteins. The fluid that enters the capsule space is called the **glomerular filtrate**. This process, where the filter separates different sized molecules under pressure, is called **ultrafiltration**.

The kidneys produce about $125 \, cm^3$ ($0.125 \, dm^3$) of glomerular filtrate per minute. This works out at $180 \, dm^3$ per day. Remember though, only $1.5 \, dm^3$ of urine is lost from the body every day, which is less than 1% of the volume filtered through the capsules. The other 99% of the glomerular filtrate is *reabsorbed* back into the blood.

We know this because scientists have actually analysed samples of fluid from the space in the middle of the nephron. Despite the diameter of the space being only 20 μm (0.02 mm), it is possible to pierce the tubule with microscopic glass pipettes and extract the fluid for analysis. Figure 8.6 shows the structure of the nephron and the surrounding blood vessels in more detail.

There are two **coiled regions** of the tubule in the cortex, separated by a U-shaped loop that runs down into the medulla of the kidney, called the **loop of Henlé**. After the second coiled tubule, several nephrons join up to form a **collecting duct**, where the final urine passes out into the pelvis.

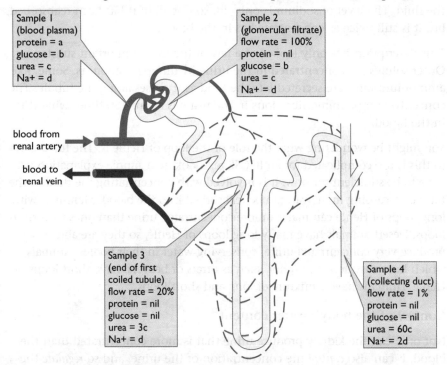

Sample 1
(blood plasma)
protein = a
glucose = b
urea = c
Na+ = d

Sample 2
(glomerular filtrate)
flow rate = 100%
protein = nil
glucose = b
urea = c
Na+ = d

blood from
renal artery

blood to
renal vein

Sample 3
(end of first
coiled tubule)
flow rate = 20%
protein = nil
glucose = nil
urea = 3c
Na+ = d

Sample 4
(collecting duct)
flow rate = 1%
protein = nil
glucose = nil
urea = 60c
Na+ = 2d

Figure 8.6 *A nephron and its blood supply. Samples 1–4 show what is happening to the fluid as it travels along the nephron.*

Samples 1–4 show the results of analysing the blood before it enters the glomerulus, and the fluid at three points inside the tubule. The flow rate is a measure of how much water is in the tubule. If the flow rate falls from 100% to 50%, this is because 50% of the water in the tubule has gone back into the blood. To make the explanation easier, the concentrations of dissolved protein, glucose, urea and sodium are shown by different letters (a to d). You can tell the relative concentration of one substance at different points along the tubule from this. For example, urea at a concentration '3c' is three times more concentrated than when it is 'c'.

In the blood (sample 1) the plasma contains many dissolved solutes, including protein, glucose, urea and salts (just sodium ions, Na+, are shown here). As we saw above, protein molecules are too big to pass through into the tubule, so the protein concentration in sample 2 is zero. The other substances are at the same concentration as in the blood.

Now look at sample 3, taken at the end of the first coiled part of the tubule. The flow rate that was 100% is now 20%. This must mean that 80% of the water in the tubule has been reabsorbed back into the blood. If no solutes were reabsorbed along with the water, their concentrations should be *five times* what they were in sample 2. Since the concentration of sodium hasn't changed, 80% of this substance must have been reabsorbed (and some of the urea too). However, the glucose concentration is now zero – *all* of the glucose is taken back into the blood in the first coiled tubule. This is necessary because glucose is a useful substance that is needed by the body.

Finally, look at sample 4. By the time the fluid passes through the collecting duct, its flow rate is only 1%. This is because 99% of the water has been reabsorbed. Protein and glucose are still zero, but most of the urea is still in the fluid. The level of sodium is only 2d, so not all of it has been reabsorbed, but it is still twice as concentrated as in the blood.

This description has only looked at a few of the more important substances. Other solutes are concentrated in the urine by different amounts. Some, like ammonium ions, are secreted *into* the fluid as it passes along the tubule. The concentration of ammonium ions in the urine is about 150 times what it is in the blood.

You might be wondering what the role of the loop of Henlé is. The full answer to this is too complicated for an IGCSE textbook, so a simple explanation will have to be sufficient for now. It is involved with concentrating the fluid in the tubule by causing more water to be reabsorbed into the blood. Mammals with long loops of Henlé can make a more concentrated urine than ones with short loops. Desert animals have many long loops of Henlé, so they are able to produce very concentrated urine, conserving water in their bodies. Animals which have easy access to water, such as otters or beavers, have short loops of Henlé. Humans have a mixture of long and short loops.

Control of the body's water content

Not only can the kidney produce urine that is more concentrated than the blood, it can also *control* the concentration of the urine, and so *regulate* the water content of the blood. This chapter began by asking you to think what would happen if you drank a litre of water. The kidneys respond to this 'upset' to the body's water balance by making a larger volume of more dilute urine. Conversely, if the blood becomes too concentrated, the kidneys produce a smaller volume of urine. These changes are controlled by a hormone produced by the pituitary gland, at the base of the brain. The hormone is called **anti-diuretic hormone**, or **ADH**.

'Diuresis' means the flow of urine from the body, so 'anti-diuresis' means producing less urine. ADH starts to work when your body loses too much water, for example if you are sweating heavily and not replacing lost water by drinking.

The loss of water means that the concentration of the blood starts to increase. This is detected by special cells in a region of the brain called the **hypothalamus** (see Chapter 6). These cells are sensitive to the solute concentration of the blood, and cause the pituitary gland to release more ADH. The ADH travels in the bloodstream to the kidney. At the kidney tubules, it causes the collecting ducts to become more permeable to water, so that more water is reabsorbed back into the blood. This makes the urine more concentrated, so that the body loses less water and the blood becomes more dilute.

When the water content of the blood returns to normal, this acts as a signal to 'switch off' the release of ADH. The kidney tubules then reabsorb less water. Similarly, if someone drinks a large volume of water, the blood will become too dilute. This leads to lower levels of ADH secretion, the kidney tubules become less permeable to water, and more water passes out of the body in the urine. In this way, through the action of ADH, the level of water in the internal environment is kept constant.

Control of body temperature

You may have heard mammals and birds described as 'warm blooded'. A better word for this is **homeothermic**. It means that they keep their body temperature constant, despite changes in the temperature of their surroundings. For example, the body temperature of humans is kept steady at about 37 °C, give or take a few tenths of a degree. This is another example of homeostasis. All other animals are 'cold blooded'. For example, if a lizard is kept in an aquarium at 20 °C, its body temperature will be 20 °C too. If the temperature of the aquarium is raised to 25 °C, the lizard's body temperature will rise to 25 °C as well. We can show this difference between homeotherms and other animals as a graph (Figure 8.8).

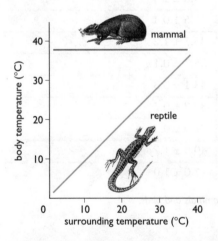

Figure 8.8 *The temperature of a homeotherm, such as a mammal, is kept constant at different external temperatures, whereas the lizard's body temperature changes.*

In the wild, lizards keep their temperature more constant than in Figure 8.8, by adapting their behaviour. For example, in the morning they may bask in the sun to warm their bodies, or at midday, if the sun is too hot, retreat to holes in the ground to cool down.

The real difference between homeotherms and all other animals is that homeotherms can keep their temperatures constant by using **physiological** changes for generating or losing heat. For this reason, mammals and birds are also called **endotherms**, meaning 'heat from inside'.

An endotherm uses heat from the chemical reactions in its cells to warm its body. It then controls its heat loss by regulating processes like sweating and blood flow through the skin. Endotherms use behavioural ways to control their temperature too. For example, penguins 'huddle' to keep warm, and humans put on extra clothes in winter.

What is the advantage of a human maintaining a body temperature of 37 °C? It means that all the chemical reactions taking place in the cells of

The action of ADH illustrates the principle of **negative feedback**. A change in conditions in the body is detected, and starts a process which works to return conditions to normal. When the conditions are returned to normal, the corrective process is switched off (Figure 8.7).

In the situation described, the blood becomes too concentrated. This switches on ADH release, which acts at the kidneys to correct the problem. The word 'negative' means that the process works to eliminate the change. When the blood returns to normal, ADH release is switched off. The feedback pathway forms a 'closed loop'. Many conditions in the body are regulated by negative feedback loops like this.

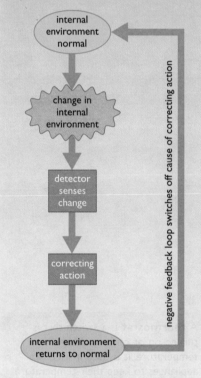

Figure 8.7 *In homeostasis, the extent of a correction is monitored by negative feedback.*

Physiology is a branch of biology that deals with how the bodies of animals or plants work, for example how muscles contract, how nerves send impulses, or how xylem carries water through plants. In this chapter you have read about kidney physiology.

the body can go on at a steady, predictable rate. The metabolism doesn't slow down in cold environments. If you watch goldfish in a garden pond, you will notice that in summer, when the pond water is warm, they are very active, swimming about quickly. In winter, when the temperature drops, the fish slow down and become very sluggish in their actions. This would happen to mammals too, if their body temperature was not kept steady.

It is also important that the body does not become *too* hot. The cells' enzymes work best at 37 °C. At higher temperatures enzymes, like all proteins, are destroyed by **denaturing** (see Chapter 1). Endotherms have all evolved a body temperature of around 40 °C (Table 8.2) and enzymes that work best at this temperature.

Species	Average and normal range of body temperature (°C)
brown bear	38.0 ± 1.0
camel	37.5 ± 0.5
elephant	36.2 ± 0.5
fox	38.8 ± 1.3
human	36.9 ± 0.7
mouse	39.3 ± 1.3
polar bear	37.5 ± 0.4
shrew	35.7 ± 1.2
whale	35.7 ± 0.1
duck	43.1 ± 0.3
ostrich	39.2 ± 0.7
penguin	39.0 ± 0.2
thrush	40.0 ± 1.7
wren	41.0 ± 1.0

Table 8.2: *The body temperatures of a range of mammals and birds.*

Monitoring body temperature

In humans and other mammals the core body temperature is monitored by a part of the brain called the **thermoregulatory centre**. This is located in the hypothalamus of the brain (see Figure 6.12, page 75). It acts as the body's thermostat.

If a person goes into a warm or cold environment, the first thing that happens is that temperature receptors in the skin send electrical impulses to the hypothalamus, which stimulates the brain to alter our behaviour. We start to feel hot or cold, and usually do something about it, such as finding shade or having a cold drink.

If changes to our behaviour are not enough to keep our body temperature constant, the thermoregulatory centre in the hypothalamus detects a change in the temperature of the blood flowing through it. It then sends signals via nerves to other organs of the body, which regulate the temperature by physiological means.

A **thermostat** is a switch that is turned on or off by a change in temperature. It is used in electrical appliances to keep their temperature steady. For example, a thermostat in an iron can be set to 'hot' or 'cool' to keep the temperature of the iron set for ironing different materials.

The skin and temperature control

The human skin has a number of functions related to the fact that it forms the outer surface of the body. These include:

- forming a tough outer layer able to resist mechanical damage
- acting as a barrier to the entry of disease-causing microorganisms
- forming an impermeable surface, preventing loss of water
- acting as a sense organ for touch and temperature changes
- controlling the loss of heat through the body surface.

Figure 8.9 shows the structure of human skin. It is made up of three layers, the epidermis, dermis and hypodermis.

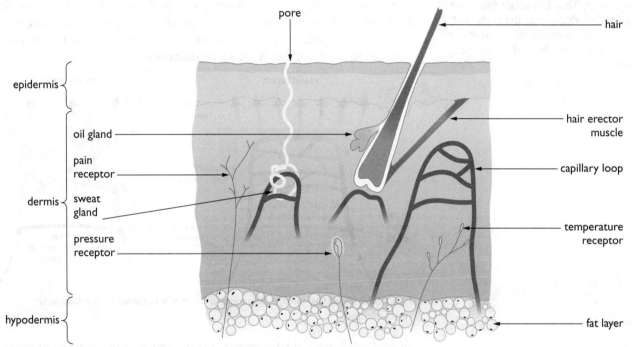

Figure 8.9 *A section through human skin.*

The outer **epidermis** consists of dead cells that stop water loss and protect the body against invasion by microorganisms such as bacteria. The **hypodermis** contains fatty tissue, which insulates the body against heat loss and is a store of energy. The middle layer, the **dermis**, contains many sensory receptors. It is also the location of sweat glands and many small blood vessels, as well as hair follicles. These last three structures are involved in temperature control.

Imagine that the hypothalamus detects a rise in the central (core) body temperature. Immediately it sends nerve impulses to the skin. These bring about changes to correct the rise in temperature.

First of all, the **sweat glands** produce greater amounts of sweat. This liquid is secreted onto the surface of the skin. When a liquid evaporates, it turns into a gas. This change needs energy, called the **latent heat of vaporisation**. When sweat evaporates, the energy is supplied by the body's heat, cooling the body down. It is not that the sweat is cool – it is secreted at body temperature. It only has a cooling action when it evaporates. In very humid atmospheres (e.g. a tropical rainforest) the sweat stays on the skin and doesn't evaporate. It then has very little cooling effect.

Secondly, hairs on the surface of the skin lie flat against the skin's surface. This happens because of the relaxation of tiny muscles called **hair erector muscles** attached to the base of each hair. In cold conditions, these contract and the hairs are pulled upright. The hairs trap a layer of air next to the skin, and since air is a poor conductor of heat, this acts as insulation. In warm conditions, the thinner layer of trapped air means that more heat will be lost. This is not very effective in humans, because the hairs over most of our body do not grow very large. It is very effective in hairy mammals like cats or dogs. The same principle is used by birds, which 'fluff out' their feathers in cold weather.

Lastly, there are tiny blood vessels called capillary loops in the dermis. Blood flows through these loops, radiating heat to the outside, and cooling the body down. If the body is too hot, small arteries (arterioles) leading to the capillary loops **dilate** (widen). This increases the blood flow to the skin's surface (Figure 8.10) and is called **vasodilation**.

> Students often describe vasodilation incorrectly. They talk about the blood vessels 'moving nearer the surface of the skin'. They don't *move* at all, it's just that more blood flows through the surface vessels.

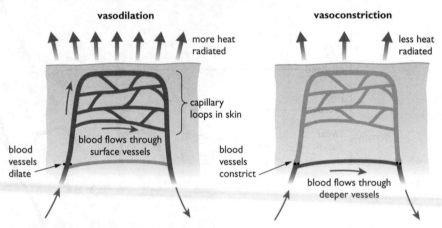

Figure 8.10 *Blood flow through the surface of the skin is controlled by vasodilation or vasoconstriction.*

In cold conditions, the opposite happens. The arterioles leading to the surface capillary loops **constrict** (become narrower) and blood flow to the surface of the skin is reduced, so that less heat is lost. This is called **vasoconstriction**. Vasoconstriction and vasodilation are brought about by tiny rings of muscles in the walls of the arterioles, called sphincter muscles, like the sphincters you met earlier in this chapter, at the outlet of the bladder.

There are other ways that the body can control heat loss and heat gain. In cold conditions, the body's **metabolism** speeds up, generating more heat. The liver, a large organ, can produce a lot of metabolic heat in this way. The hormone **adrenaline** stimulates the increase in metabolism (see Chapter 7). **Shivering** also takes place, where the muscles contract and relax rapidly. This also generates a large amount of heat.

Sweating, vasodilation and vasoconstriction, hair erection, shivering and changes to the metabolism, along with behavioural actions, work together to keep the body temperature to within a few tenths of a degree of the 'normal' 37 °C. If the difference is any bigger than this it shows that something is wrong. For instance, a temperature of 39 °C might be due to an illness.

End of Chapter Checklist

You should now be able to:

- recall that the kidneys, lungs and skin are organs of excretion
- recall the composition of urine
- understand how the kidney carries out its roles of excretion and osmoregulation
- describe the structure of the urinary system and a nephron
- describe ultrafiltration in the Bowman's capsule and the composition of the glomerular filtrate
- understand that selective reabsorption of glucose occurs in the first coiled tubule of the nephron
- understand that water is reabsorbed into the blood from the collecting duct, and describe the role of ADH in regulating the water content of the blood
- describe the role of the skin in temperature regulation.

Questions

More questions on homeostasis and excretion can be found at the end of Section B on page 108.

1 Explain the meaning of the following terms:

   a) homeostasis

   b) excretion

   c) ultrafiltration

   d) selective reabsorption

   e) endotherm.

2 The diagram below shows a simple diagram of a nephron (kidney tubule).

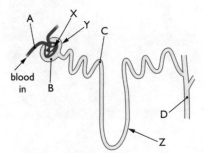

   a) What are the names of the parts labelled X, Y and Z?

   b) Four places in the nephron and its blood supply are labelled A, B and C and D. Which of the following substances are found at each of these four places?

      water   urea   protein   glucose   salt

3 The hormone ADH controls the amount of water removed from the blood by the kidneys. Write a short description of the action of ADH in a person who has lost a lot of water by sweating, but has been unable to replace this water by drinking. Explain how this is an example of negative feedback. (You need to write about half a page to answer this question fully.)

4 The bar chart shows the volume of urine collected from a person before and after drinking 1000 cm^3 (1 dm^3) of distilled water. The person's urine was collected immediately before the water was drunk and then at 30 minute intervals for four hours.

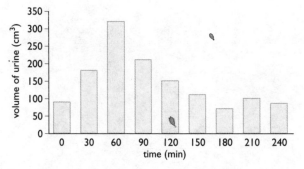

   a) Describe how the output of urine changed during the course of the experiment.

   b) Explain the difference in urine produced at 60 minutes and at 90 minutes.

c) The same experiment was repeated with the person sitting in a very hot room. How would you expect the volume of urine collected to differ from the first experiment? Explain your answer.

d) Between 90 and 120 minutes, the person produced 150 cm³ of urine. If the rate of filtration at the glomeruli during this time was 125 cm³ per minute, calculate the percentage of filtrate reabsorbed by the kidney tubules.

5 Working on a computer, construct a table to show the changes that take place when a person is put in a hot or cold environment. Your table should have three columns.

Changes taking place	Hot environment	Cold environment
sweating		
blood flow through capillary loops		Vasoconstriction decreases blood flow through surface capillaries so that less heat is radiated from the skin.
hairs in skin		
shivering		
metabolism		

6 Look at the body temperatures of mammals and birds shown in Table 8.2 on page 92. Use the information in the table to answer these questions:

a) How does the average temperature of birds differ from the average temperature of mammals? Can you suggest why this is an advantage for birds?

b) Is there a relationship between the body temperature of a mammal and the temperature of its habitat? Give an example to support your answer.

c) Polar bears have thick white fur covering their bodies. Explain two ways in which this is an adaptation to their habitat.

Chapter 9: Reproduction in Humans

One of the characteristics of living organisms that sets them apart from non-living things is their ability to produce offspring, or **reproduce**. Reproduction is all about an organism passing on its genes. This can be through special sex cells, or asexually, without the production of these cells. In this chapter we look at the differences between sexual and asexual reproduction, and study in detail the process of human reproduction.

The plural of sperm is sperm. The plural of ovum is ova.

Figure 9.1 *A sperm fertilising an ovum.*

A gene is a section of DNA that determines a particular characteristic or feature. Genes are found in the nucleus of a cell on the chromosomes.

Individuals produced asexually from the same adult organism are called **clones**.

Sexual and asexual reproduction compared

In any method of reproduction, the end result is the production of more organisms of the same species. Humans produce more humans, jellyfish produce more jellyfish and salmonella bacteria produce more salmonella bacteria. However, the way in which they reproduce differs. There are two types of reproduction: **sexual reproduction** and **asexual reproduction**.

In sexual reproduction, specialised **sex cells** called **gametes** are produced. There are usually two types, a mobile male gamete (a **sperm**) and a stationary female gamete (an **ovum**).

The sperm must move to the ovum and fuse (join) with it. This is called **fertilisation** (Figure 9.1). The single cell formed by fertilisation is called a **zygote**. This cell will divide many times by mitosis to form all the cells of the new animal.

In asexual reproduction, there are no specialised gametes and there is no fertilisation. Instead, cells in one part of the body divide by mitosis to form a structure that breaks away from the parent body and grows into a new organism. Not many animals reproduce in this way. Figure 9.2 shows *Hydra* (a small animal similar to jellyfish) reproducing by budding. Cells in the body wall divide to form a small version of the adult. This eventually breaks off and becomes a free-living *Hydra*. One animal may produce several 'buds' in a short space of time.

buds – young *Hydra* growing from the parent – they will eventually break off and become independent

parent *Hydra*

Figure 9.2 *Hydra reproducing asexually by budding.*

Asexual reproduction produces identical offspring

All the offspring produced when *Hydra* buds are genetically identical – they have exactly the same **genes**. This is because all the cells of the new individual are produced by mitosis from just one cell in the body of the adult. When cells divide by mitosis, the new cells that are produced are exact copies of the original cell (see Chapter 17 for more details of mitosis). As a result, all the cells of an organism that is produced asexually have the same genes as the cell that produced them – the original adult cell. So *all* asexually produced offspring from one adult will have the same genes as the cells of the adult. They will *all* be genetic copies of that adult and so will be identical to each other.

Asexual reproduction is useful to a species when the environment in which it lives is relatively stable. If an organism is well adapted to this stable environment, asexual reproduction will produce offspring that are also well adapted. However, if the environment changes significantly, then *all* the individuals will be affected equally by the change. It may be such a dramatic change that none of the individuals are adapted well enough to survive. The species will die out in that area.

Sexual reproduction produces offspring that show genetic variation

There are four key stages in any method of sexual reproduction.

1. Gametes (sperm and ova) are produced.

2. The male gamete (sperm) is transferred to the female gamete (ovum).

3. Fertilisation must occur – the sperm fuses with the ovum.

4. The zygote formed develops into a new individual.

Production of gametes

Sperm are produced in the male sex organs – the **testes**. Ova are produced in the female sex organs – the **ovaries**. Both are produced when cells inside these organs divide. These cells do not divide by mitosis but by **meiosis** (see Chapter 17). Meiosis produces cells that are not genetically identical and have only half the number of chromosomes as the original cell. Figure 9.3 shows how a cell with just four chromosomes divides by meiosis. These four chromosomes are in two pairs called **homologous pairs**. Homologous pairs of chromosomes carry the same genes in the same sequence.

In meiosis the cell divides twice, rather than just once as in mitosis. Also, because each of the sex cells formed only receives one chromosome from each original pair, they only have *half* the original number of chromosomes. They are **haploid** cells. Table 9.1 compares mitosis and meiosis.

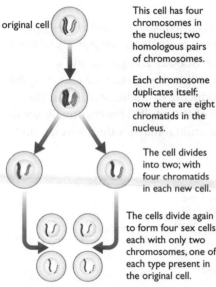

original cell

This cell has four chromosomes in the nucleus; two homologous pairs of chromosomes.

Each chromosome duplicates itself; now there are eight chromatids in the nucleus.

The cell divides into two; with four chromatids in each new cell.

The cells divide again to form four sex cells, each with only two chromosomes, one of each type present in the original cell.

Figure 9.3 *The stages of meiosis.*

Cells that have the full number of chromosomes in homologous pairs are called **diploid** cells. Cells that only have half the normal number of chromosomes are called **haploid** cells.

Feature	Mitosis	Meiosis
number of cell divisions	1	2
number of cells formed	2	4
number of chromosomes in cells formed	same as original cell (diploid)	half the number of original cell (haploid)
type of cells formed	body cells	sex cells
genetic variation in cells formed	none	variation

Table 9.1: *Mitosis and meiosis compared.*

Transfer of the sperm to the ovum

Sperm are specialised for swimming. They have a tail-like **flagellum** that moves them through water or a water-based liquid. Figure 9.4 shows the structure of a sperm.

Some male animals, such as those of most fish, release their sperm into the water in which they live. The female animals release their ova into the water and the sperm then swim through the water to fertilise the ova. This is

external fertilisation as it takes place *outside* the body. Before the release takes place, there is usually some mating behaviour to ensure that male and female are in the same place at the same time. This gives the best chance of fertilisation occurring before water currents sweep the sex cells away.

Other male animals, such as those of birds and mammals, **ejaculate** their sperm in a special fluid into the bodies of the females. **Internal fertilisation** then takes place inside the female's body. Fertilisation is much more likely as there are no external factors to prevent the sperm from reaching the ova. Some form of **sexual intercourse** precedes ejaculation.

Fertilisation

Once the sperm has reached the ovum, its nucleus must enter the ovum and fuse with the ovum nucleus. As each gamete has only half the normal number of chromosomes, the zygote formed by fertilisation will have the full number of chromosomes. In humans, sperm and ovum each have only 23 chromosomes. The zygote has 46 chromosomes, like all other cells in the body. Figure 9.5 shows the main stages in fertilisation.

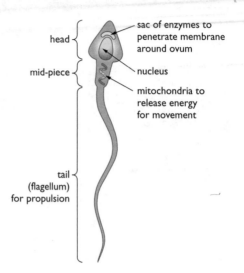

Figure 9.4 *The structure of a sperm.*

Red blood cells are exceptions. They have no nucleus, so have no chromosomes.

Sperm approach the ovum.

An extra membrane (the fertilisation membrane) now prevents any more sperm from entering.

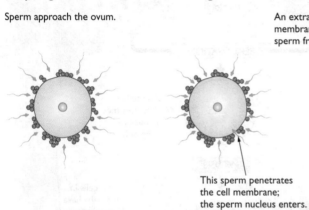

This sperm penetrates the cell membrane; the sperm nucleus enters.

The sperm nucleus and ovum nucleus fuse.

Figure 9.5 *The main stages in fertilisation.*

Fertilisation does more than just restore the diploid chromosome number, it provides an additional source of genetic variation. The sperm and ova are all genetically different because they are formed by meiosis. Therefore, each time fertilisation takes place, it brings together a different combination of genes.

Development of the zygote

Each zygote that is formed must divide to produce all the cells that will make up the adult. All these cells must have the full number of chromosomes, so the zygote divides repeatedly by mitosis. Figure 9.6 shows the importance of meiosis, mitosis and fertilisation in the human life cycle.

However, mitosis is not the only process involved in development, otherwise all that would be produced would be a ball of cells. During the process, cells move around and different shaped structures are formed. Also, different cells specialise to become bone cells, nerve cells, muscle cells, and so on.

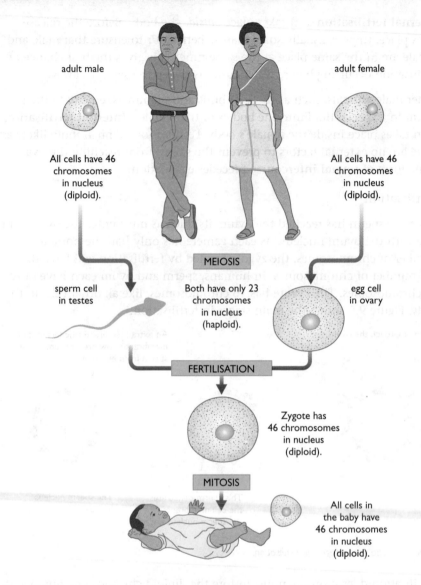

adult male

adult female

All cells have 46 chromosomes in nucleus (diploid).

All cells have 46 chromosomes in nucleus (diploid).

MEIOSIS

sperm cell in testes

Both have only 23 chromosomes in nucleus (haploid).

egg cell in ovary

FERTILISATION

Zygote has 46 chromosomes in nucleus (diploid).

MITOSIS

All cells in the baby have 46 chromosomes in nucleus (diploid).

Figure 9.6 *The importance of meiosis, mitosis and fertilisation in the human life cycle.*

Reproduction in humans

Humans reproduce sexually and fertilisation is internal. Figures 9.7 and 9.8 show the structure of the human female and male reproductive systems.

The sperm are produced in the testes by meiosis. During sexual intercourse, they pass along the sperm duct and are mixed with a fluid from the seminal vesicles. This mixture, called **semen**, is ejaculated into the vagina of the female. The sperm then begin to swim towards the Fallopian tubes.

One ovum is released into a Fallopian tube each month from an ovary. If an ovum is present in the Fallopian tubes, then it may be fertilised by sperm introduced during intercourse. The zygote formed will begin to develop into an **embryo** which will **implant** in the lining of the uterus. Here, the embryo will develop a **placenta**, which will allow the embryo to obtain materials such as oxygen and nutrients from the mother's blood. It also allows the embryo to get rid of waste products such as urea and carbon dioxide, as well as anchoring the embryo in the uterus. The placenta secretes female hormones, in particular progesterone, that maintain the pregnancy and prevent the embryo from aborting. Figure 9.9 shows the structure and position of the placenta.

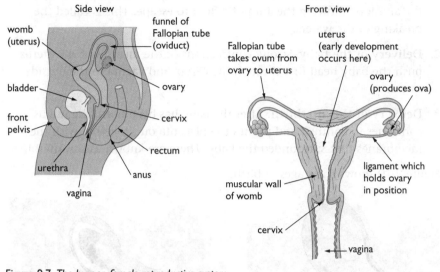

Figure 9.7 *The human female reproductive system.*

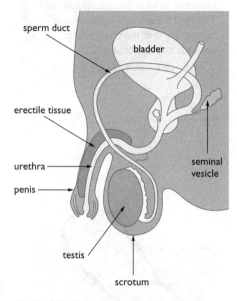

Figure 9.8 *The human male reproductive system.*

During pregnancy, a membrane called the **amnion** encloses the developing embryo. The amnion secretes a fluid called **amniotic fluid**, which protects the developing embryo against jolts and bumps. As the embryo develops, it becomes more and more complex. When it becomes recognisably human, we no longer call it an embryo but a **fetus**. At the end of nine months of development, there just isn't any room left for the fetus to grow and it sends a hormonal 'signal' to the mother to initiate birth. This is called 'going into labour'. Figure 9.9 also shows the position of a human fetus just before birth.

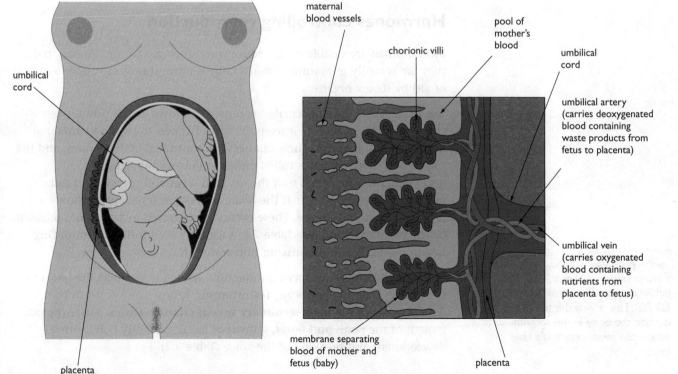

Figure 9.9 *The position of the fetus just before birth, and the structure of the placenta.*

There are three stages to the birth of a child.

1. **Dilation of the cervix.** The cervix gets wider to allow the baby to pass through. The muscles of the uterus contract quite strongly and rupture the amnion, allowing the amniotic fluid to escape. This is called the breaking of the waters.

2. **Delivery of the baby.** Strong contractions of the muscles of the uterus push the baby head first through the cervix and vagina to the outside world.

3. **Delivery of the afterbirth.** After the baby has been born, the uterus continues to contract and pushes the placenta out, together with the membranes that surrounded the baby. These are known as the afterbirth.

Figure 9.10 shows the stages of birth.

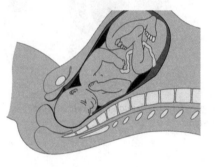

1 Baby's head pushes cervix; mucous plug dislodges and waters break.

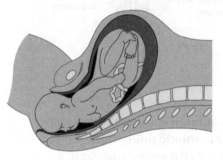

2 Uterus contracts to push baby out through the vagina.

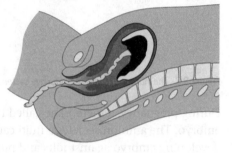

3 The placenta becomes detached from the wall of the uterus and is expelled through the vagina as the afterbirth.

Figure 9.10 *The stages of birth.*

Hormones controlling reproduction

Most animals are unable to reproduce when they are young. We say that they are sexually immature. When a baby is born, it is recognisable as a boy or girl by its sex organs.

The presence of male or female sex organs is known as the primary sex characteristics. During their teens, changes happen to boys and girls that lead to sexual maturity. These changes are controlled by hormones, and the time when they happen is called **puberty**. Puberty involves two developments. The first is that the sex cells (eggs and sperm) start to be produced. The second is that the bodies of both sexes adapt to allow reproduction to take place. These events are triggered by hormones released by the pituitary gland (see Table 7.2, page 80) called **follicle stimulating hormone (FSH)** and **luteinising hormone (LH)**.

In boys, FSH stimulates sperm production, while LH instructs the testes to secrete the male sex hormone, **testosterone**. Testosterone controls the development of the male **secondary sexual characteristics**. These include growth of the penis and testes, growth of facial and body hair, muscle development and breaking of the voice (Table 9.2).

In girls, the pituitary hormones control the release of a female sex hormone called **oestrogen**, from the ovaries. Oestrogen produces the female secondary sex characteristics, such as breast development and the beginning of menstruation ('periods').

In boys	In girls
sperm production starts	the menstrual cycle begins, and eggs are released by the ovaries every month
growth and development of male sexual organs	growth and development of female sexual organs
growth of armpit and pubic hair, and chest and facial hair (beard)	growth of armpit and pubic hair
increase in body mass; growth of muscles, e.g. chest	increase in body mass; development of 'rounded' shape to hips
voice breaks	voice deepens without sudden 'breaking'
sexual 'drive' develops	sexual 'drive' develops
	breasts develop

Table 9.2: *Changes at puberty.*

The age when puberty takes place can vary a lot, but it is usually between about 11 and 14 years in girls and 13 and 16 years in boys. It takes several years for puberty to be completed. Some of the most complex changes take place in girls, with the start of menstruation.

Hormones and the menstrual cycle

'Menstrual' means 'monthly', and in most women the cycle takes about a month, although it can vary from as little as two weeks to as long as six weeks (Figures 9.11 and 9.12). In the middle of the cycle is an event called **ovulation**, which is the release of a mature egg cell, or **ovum**.

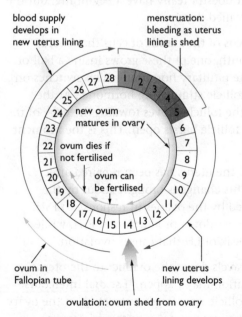

Figure 9.11 *The menstrual cycle.*

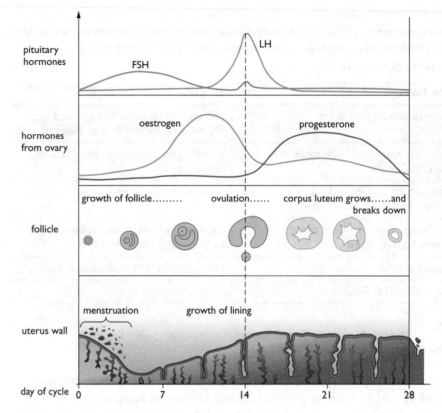

pituitary hormones

FSH

LH

hormones from ovary

oestrogen

progesterone

growth of follicle......... ovulation...... corpus luteum grows......and breaks down

follicle

menstruation   growth of lining

uterus wall

day of cycle   0   7   14   21   28

Figure 9.12 *Changes taking place during the menstrual cycle.*

One function of the cycle is to control the development of the lining of the uterus (womb), so that if the ovum is fertilised, the lining will be ready to receive the fertilised egg. If the egg is not fertilised, the lining of the uterus is lost from the woman's body as the flow of menstrual blood and cells of the lining, called a **period**.

A cycle is a continuous process, so it doesn't really have a beginning, but the first day of menstruation is usually called day 1.

Inside a woman's ovaries are hundreds of thousands of cells that could develop into mature eggs. Every month, one of these grows inside a ball of cells called a **follicle**. This is why the pituitary hormone which switches on the growth of the follicle is called 'follicle stimulating hormone'. At the middle of the cycle (about day 14) the follicle moves towards the edge of the ovary and the egg is released as the follicle bursts open. This is the moment of ovulation.

While this is going on, the lining of the uterus has been repaired after menstruation, and has thickened. This change is brought about by the hormone oestrogen, which is secreted by the ovaries in response to FSH. Oestrogen also has another job. It slows down production of FSH, while stimulating secretion of LH. It is a peak of LH that causes ovulation.

After the egg has been released, it travels down the oviduct to the uterus. It is here in the oviduct that fertilisation may happen, if sexual intercourse has taken place. What's left of the follicle now forms a structure in the ovary called the **corpus luteum**. The corpus luteum makes another hormone called **progesterone**. Progesterone completes the development of the uterus

A small percentage of women are able to feel the exact moment that ovulation happens, as the egg bursts out of an ovary.

lining, which thickens ready for the fertilised egg to sink into it and develop into an embryo. Progesterone also inhibits (prevents) the release of FSH and LH by the pituitary, stopping ovulation.

If the egg is not fertilised, the corpus luteum breaks down and stops making progesterone. The lining of the uterus is then shed through the woman's vagina, during menstruation. If, however, the egg is fertilised, the corpus luteum carries on making progesterone, the lining is not shed, and menstruation doesn't happen. The first sign that tells a woman she is pregnant is when her monthly periods stop. Later on in pregnancy, the **placenta** secretes progesterone, taking over the role of the corpus luteum.

'Corpus luteum' is Latin for 'yellow body'. A corpus luteum appears as a large yellow swelling in an ovary after the egg has been released. The growth of the corpus luteum is under the control of luteinising hormone (LH) from the pituitary.

End of Chapter Checklist

You should now be able to:

- describe the differences between sexual and asexual reproduction
- recall the structure and function of the human male and female reproductive systems
- understand that fertilisation involves the fusion of a male and female gamete to produce a zygote
- recall that a zygote undergoes cell division and develops into an embryo
- describe the role of the placenta and the amniotic fluid
- recall the roles of oestrogen and testosterone in the development of secondary sexual characteristics
- understand the roles and effects of oestrogen and progesterone in the menstrual cycle.

Questions

More questions on human reproduction can be found at the end of Section B on page 108.

1   The diagram shows a baby about to be born.

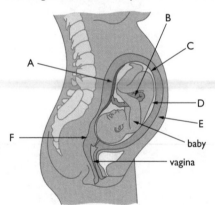

a)   Name parts A to F on the diagram.

b)   What is the function of A during pregnancy?

c)   What must happen to D and E just before birth?

d)   What must E and F do during birth?

2   The diagram shows *Hydra* (a small water animal) reproducing in two ways.

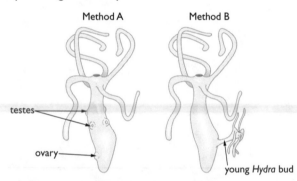

a)   Which of the two methods shows asexual reproduction? Give a reason for your answer.

b)   Explain why organisms produced asexually are genetically identical to each other and to the organism that produced them.

c)   When the surroundings do not change for long periods, *Hydra* reproduces mainly asexually. When the conditions change, *Hydra* begins to reproduce sexually. How does this pattern of sexual and asexual reproduction help *Hydra* to survive?

3 a) The diagram shows the female reproductive system.

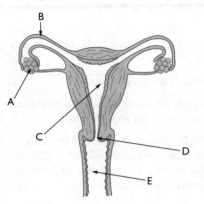

Which letter represents:

i) the site of production of oestrogen and progesterone

ii) the structure where fertilisation usually occurs

iii) the structure that must dilate when birth commences

iv) the structure that releases ova?

b) The graph shows the changes in the thickness of the lining of a woman's uterus over 100 days.

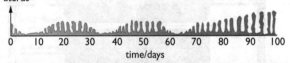

i) Name the hormone that causes the thickening of the uterine lining.

ii) Use the graph to determine the duration of *this* woman's menstrual cycle. Explain how you arrived at your answer.

iii) From the graph, deduce the approximate day on which fertilisation leading to pregnancy took place. Explain how you arrived at your answer.

iv) Why must the uterus lining remain thickened throughout pregnancy?

4 The number of sperm cells per cm³ of semen (the fluid containing sperm) is called the 'sperm count'. Some scientists believe that over the last 50 years, the sperm counts of adult male humans have decreased. They think that this is caused by a number of factors, including drinking water polluted with oestrogens and other chemicals. Carry out an Internet search to find out the evidence for this. Download information into a word processor and summarise your findings in no more than two sides of A4, including graphs.

5 The graph shows some of the changes taking place during the menstrual cycle.

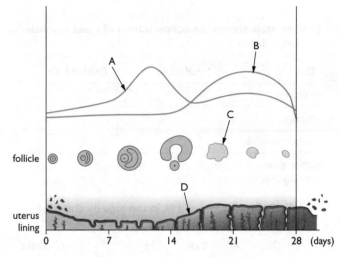

a) Identify the two hormones produced by the ovary, which are shown by the lines A and B on the graph.

b) Name the structure C.

c) What is the purpose of the thickening of the uterus lining at D?

d) When is sexual intercourse most likely to result in pregnancy, at day 6, 10, 13, 20 or 23?

e) Why is it important that the level of progesterone remains high in the blood of a woman during pregnancy? How does her body achieve this:

i) just after she becomes pregnant?

ii) later on in pregnancy?

End of Section Questions

1 The table shows the concentration of gases in inhaled and exhaled air.

Gas	Inhaled air	Exhaled air
nitrogen	78	79
oxygen		
carbon dioxide		
other gases (mainly argon)	I	I

a) Copy the table and fill in the gaps by choosing from the following numbers:

21   4   0.04   16   *(2 marks)*

b) Explain why the concentration of carbon dioxide is so different. *(2 marks)*

c) Explain why exhaling is a form of excretion. *(2 marks)*

d) The following features can be seen in the lungs:

i) thin membranes between the alveoli and the blood supply

ii) a good blood supply

iii) a large surface area.

In each case explain how the feature helps gas exchange to happen quickly. *(6 marks)*

Total 12 marks

2 Digestion is brought about by enzymes converting large insoluble molecules into smaller soluble molecules that can be more easily absorbed.

a) The activity of enzymes is influenced by pH and temperature. The graph shows the activity of two human enzymes from different regions of the gut at different pHs.

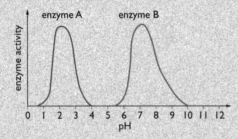

i) Suggest which regions of the gut the two enzymes come from. Explain your answer. *(4 marks)*

ii) Which nutrient does enzyme A digest? *(1 mark)*

b) Farmers sometimes include urea in cattle food. The microorganisms in the rumen can use urea to make protein.

i) In mammals, where in the body is urea made? *(1 mark)*

ii) What is urea made from? *(1 mark)*

iii) Suggest how feeding urea to cattle can result in an increased growth rate. *(1 mark)*

iv) The Bowman's capsule and the Loop of Henlé are both parts of a nephron. Explain how each of them help to remove urea from the bloodstream. *(4 marks)*

Total 12 marks

3 The circulation system carries nutrients, oxygen and carbon dioxide around the body.

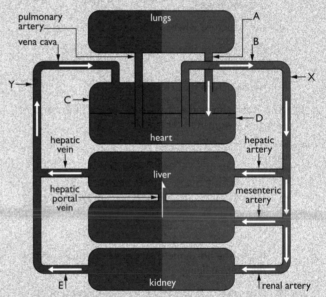

➡ direction of blood flow ■ oxygenated blood ■ deoxygenated blood

a) Write out the correct labels for A to E. *(5 marks)*

b) Give two differences between the blood vessels at point X and point Y. *(2 marks)*

c) During exercise, the adrenal gland releases the hormone adrenaline. Reflexes involving the medulla of the brain influence the heartbeat and breathing.

i) Describe two effects of adrenaline on the heartbeat. *(2 marks)*

ii) Describe two other effects of adrenaline on the body. *(2 marks)*

d) How is a reflex action different from a voluntary action? *(2 marks)*

e) Following exercise there is a recovery period in which breathing rate and heart rate gradually return to pre-exercise levels. Explain why they do not return immediately to these levels. *(3 marks)*

Total 16 marks

4 Humans and other mammals are able to maintain a constant body temperature which is usually higher than that of their surroundings.

a) Explain the advantage in maintaining a constant, high body temperature. *(1 mark)*

b) The temperature of the blood is constantly monitored by the brain. If it detects a drop in blood temperature, the following things happen: the arterioles leading to the skin capillaries constrict, less sweat is formed and shivering begins.

  i) Explain how each response helps the body to keep warm. *(2 marks)*

  ii) Explain how the structure of arterioles allows them to constrict. *(2 marks)*

c) When the weather is hot we produce less urine.

  i) What is the name of the hormone that controls the amount of urine produced by the body? *(1 mark)*

  ii) Explain why the body produces less urine in hot weather. *(1 mark)*

  iii) Explain how the hormone in *i)* works in the kidney to produce less urine. *(3 marks)*

  Total 10 marks

5 The diagram represents a typical menstrual cycle.

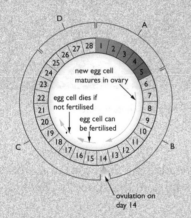

a) Using evidence from the diagram, answer the following questions.

  During which of the stages A, B, C or D does:

  i) the level of the hormone oestrogen increase in the blood

  ii) the level of the hormone progesterone increase in the blood

  iii) the uterine lining become more vascular

  iv) the levels of oestrogen and progesterone in the blood fall

  v) the uterine lining begin to break down? *(5 marks)*

b) Explain how knowledge of the menstrual cycle can be used to avoid pregnancy. *(3 marks)*

  Total 8 marks

6 Cells can divide by mitosis or by meiosis. Human cells contain 46 chromosomes. The graphs show the changes in the number of chromosomes per cell as two different human cells undergo cell division.

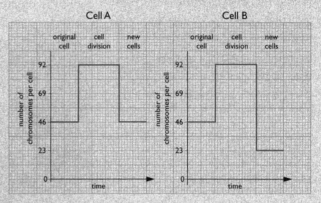

a) Which of the two cells, A or B, is dividing by meiosis? Explain how you arrived at your answer. *(3 marks)*

b) Explain the importance of meiosis, mitosis and fertilisation in maintaining the human chromosome number constant at 46 chromosomes per cell, generation after generation. *(6 marks)*

c) Give *three* differences between mitosis and meiosis. *(3 marks)*

  Total 12 marks

Chapter 10: Plants and Food

This chapter looks at photosynthesis, the process by which plants make starch, and the structure of leaves in relation to photosynthesis. It also describes the nature and method of obtaining other nutrient materials, and their uses in the plant.

Plants make starch

All the foods shown in Figure 10.1 are products of plants. Some, such as potatoes, rice and bread, form the staple diet of humans. They all contain *starch*, which is the main storage carbohydrate made by plants. Starch is a good way of storing carbohydrate because it is not soluble, is compact and can be broken down easily.

Figure 10.1 *All these foods are made by plants and contain starch.*

Testing leaves for starch

You can test for starch in food by adding a few drops of red-brown iodine solution (see Chapter 4). If the food contains starch, a blue-black colour is produced.

Leaves that have been in sunlight also contain starch, but you can't test for it by adding iodine solution to a fresh leaf. The outer waxy surface of the leaf will not absorb the solution, and besides, the green colour of the leaf would hide the colour change. To test for starch in a leaf, the outer waxy layer needs to be removed and the leaf decolourised. You can do this by placing the leaf in boiling ethanol (see Figure 10.2).

Carry out the following:
1. Set up a beaker of water on a tripod and gauze and heat the water until it boils.

2. Remove a leaf from the plant and, holding it with forceps, kill it by placing it in the boiling water for 30 seconds (this stops all chemical reactions in the leaf).

3. Turn off the Bunsen burner, place the leaf in a boiling tube containing ethanol and stand the boiling tube in a hot water bath. The tube containing ethanol *must not be heated directly, since ethanol is highly flammable*. The boiling point of ethanol (about 78 °C) is lower than that of water (100 °C) so the ethanol will boil for a few minutes until the water bath cools down. This is long enough to remove most of the **chlorophyll** from the leaf.

4. When the leaf has turned colourless or pale yellow, remove it and wash it with cold water to soften it.

5. Spread the leaf out on a white tile or Petri dish. Cover the leaf with a few drops of iodine solution and leave it for a few minutes, noting any colour change.

FLAMMABLE

USE EYE
PROTECTION

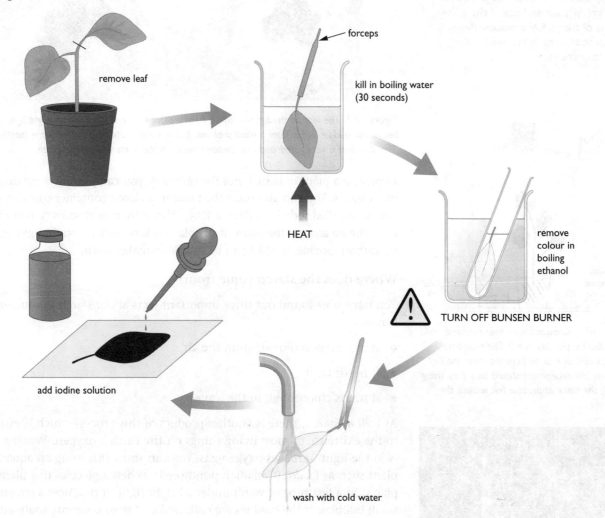

Figure 10.2 *How to test a leaf for starch.*

When you try this method, you will see that the parts of the leaf that contain starch turn a very dark 'blue-black' colour as the iodine reacts with the starch. This will only work if the plant has had plenty of light for some time before the test.

You can 'destarch' a plant by placing it in the dark for 2 or 3 days. The plant uses up the starch stores in its leaves.

You might think that the results of the test on the variegated leaf prove that chlorophyll is needed for photosynthesis. However, this is not really a 'fair test'. The leaf could have photosynthesised in the white areas and transported the sugars elsewhere in the plant. Similarly, the green areas may not be photosynthesising at all, but simply laying down starch from glucose made somewhere else. All it really shows is that starch is made in the green areas and not in the white areas of the leaf. We *assume* this is because chlorophyll is needed for photosynthesis.

Starch is only made in the parts of leaves that are green. You can show this by testing a variegated leaf which has green and white areas. The white regions, which lack the green pigment called chlorophyll, give a negative starch test. The results of the starch tests on three leaves are shown in Figure 10.3.

Figure 10.3 *The leaf on the left was taken from a plant that was left under a bright light for 48 hours. The middle leaf is from a plant that was put in a dark cupboard for the same length of time. The third leaf is variegated, and only contains starch in the parts which were green.*

Depriving a plant of light is not the only way you can prevent it making starch in its leaves. You can also place the plant in a closed container containing a chemical called soda lime (Figure 10.4). This substance absorbs carbon dioxide from the air around the plant. If the plant is kept under a bright light but with no carbon dioxide, it will again be unable to make starch.

Where does the starch come from?

You have now found out three important facts about starch production by leaves:

- it uses carbon dioxide from the air
- it needs light
- it needs chlorophyll in the leaves.

As well as starch, there is another product of this process which is essential to the existence of most living things on the Earth – oxygen. When a plant is in the light, it makes oxygen gas. You can show this using an aquatic plant such as *Elodea* (Canadian pondweed). When a piece of this plant is placed in a test tube of water under a bright light, it produces a stream of small bubbles. If the bubbles are collected and their contents analysed, they are found to contain a high concentration of oxygen (Figure 10.5).

Starch is composed of long chains of glucose (see Chapter 4). A plant does not make starch directly, but first produces glucose, which is then joined together in chains to form starch molecules. A carbohydrate made of many sugar sub-units is called a **polysaccharide**. Glucose has the formula $C_6H_{12}O_6$. The carbon and oxygen atoms of the glucose molecule come from the carbon dioxide gas in the air around the plant. The hydrogen atoms come from another molecule essential to the living plant – water.

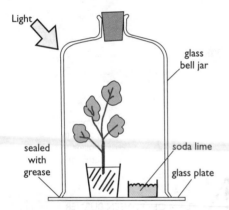

Figure 10.4 *Demonstration that carbon dioxide is needed for photosynthesis. The soda lime absorbs carbon dioxide from the air in the bell jar. A control experiment should be set up, using exactly the same apparatus but without the soda lime.*

Light

glass bell jar

sealed with grease

soda lime

glass plate

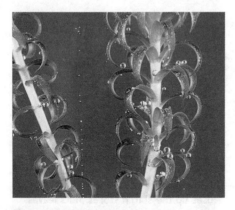

Figure 10.5 *The bubbles of gas released from this pondweed contain a higher concentration of oxygen than in atmospheric air.*

It would be very difficult in a school laboratory to show that a plant uses water to make starch. If you deprived a plant of water in the same way as you deprived it of carbon dioxide, it would soon wilt and die. However, scientists have proved that water is used in photosynthesis. They have done this by supplying the plant with water with 'labelled' atoms, for example using the 'heavy' isotope of oxygen (^{18}O). This isotope ends up in the oxygen gas produced by the plant. A summary of the sources of the atoms in the glucose and oxygen looks like this:

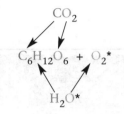

(*oxygen labelled with ^{18}O)

Photosynthesis

Plants use the simple inorganic molecules carbon dioxide and water, in the presence of chlorophyll and light, to make glucose and oxygen. This process is called **photosynthesis**.

It is summarised by the equation:

$$\text{carbon dioxide} + \text{water} \xrightarrow[\text{chlorophyll}]{\text{light}} \text{glucose} + \text{oxygen}$$

or: $6CO_2 + 6H_2O \longrightarrow C_6H_{12}O_6 + 6O_2$

The role of the green pigment, chlorophyll, is to absorb the light energy needed for the reaction to take place. The products of the reaction (glucose and oxygen) contain more energy than the carbon dioxide and water. You will probably have noticed that the equation for photosynthesis is the reverse of the one for aerobic respiration (see Chapter 1):

$$C_6H_{12}O_6 + 6O_2 \longrightarrow 6CO_2 + 6H_2O \text{ (plus energy)}$$

Respiration, which is carried out by both animals and plants, *releases* energy (but not as light) from the breakdown of glucose. The chemical energy in the glucose came originally from light 'trapped' by the process of photosynthesis.

The structure of leaves

Most green parts of a plant can photosynthesise, but the leaves are the plant organs which are best adapted for this function. To be able to photosynthesise efficiently, leaves need to have a large surface area to absorb light, many chloroplasts containing the chlorophyll, a supply of water and carbon dioxide, and a system for carrying away the products of photosynthesis to other parts of the plant. They also need to release oxygen (and water vapour) from the leaf cells. Most leaves are thin, flat structures supported by a leaf stalk which can grow to allow the blade of the leaf to be angled to receive the maximum amount of sunlight (Figure 10.6).

Chapter 10: Plants and Food

113

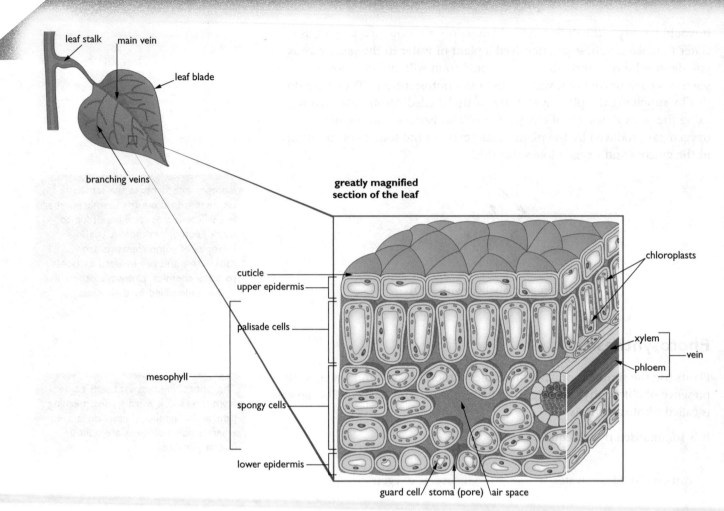

Figure 10.6 *External and internal features of a leaf.*

Inside the leaf are layers of cells with different functions.

- The two outer layers of cells (the upper and lower **epidermis**) have few chloroplasts and are covered by a thin layer of a waxy material called the **cuticle**. This reduces water loss by evaporation, and acts as a barrier to the entry of disease-causing microorganisms such as bacteria and fungi.

- The lower epidermis has many pores called **stomata** (a single pore is a **stoma**). Usually the upper epidermis contains fewer or no stomata. The stomata allow carbon dioxide to diffuse into the leaf, to reach the photosynthetic tissues. They also allow oxygen and water vapour to diffuse out. Each stoma is formed as a gap between two highly specialised cells called **guard cells**, which can alter their shape to open or close the stoma (see Chapter 11).

- In the middle of the leaf are two layers of photosynthetic cells called the **mesophyll** ('mesophyll' just means 'middle of the leaf'). Just below the upper epidermis is the **palisade** layer. This is a tissue made of elongated cells, each containing hundreds of chloroplasts, and is the main site of photosynthesis. The palisade cells are close to the source of light, and the upper epidermis is relatively transparent, allowing light to pass through to the enormous numbers of chloroplasts which lie below.

- Below the palisade layer is a tissue made of more rounded, loosely packed cells, with air spaces between them, called the **spongy** layer. These cells also photosynthesise, but have fewer chloroplasts than the palisade cells. They form the main **gas exchange surface** of the leaf, absorbing carbon dioxide and releasing oxygen and water vapour. The air spaces allow these gases to diffuse in and out of the mesophyll.

- Water and mineral ions are supplied to the leaf by vessels in a tissue called the **xylem**. This forms a continuous transport system throughout the plant. Water is absorbed by the roots and passes up through the stem and through veins in the leaves in the **transpiration stream**. In the leaves, the water leaves the xylem and supplies the mesophyll cells.

- The products of photosynthesis, such as sugars, are carried away from the mesophyll cells by another transport system, the **phloem**. The phloem supplies all other parts of the plant, so that tissues and organs that can't make their own food receive products of photosynthesis. The veins in the leaf contain both xylem and phloem tissue, and branch again and again to supply all parts of the leaf.

You can find out more about both plant transport systems in Chapter 11.

Photosynthesis and respiration

Through photosynthesis, plants supply animals with two of their essential needs – food and oxygen – as well as removing carbon dioxide from the air. But remember that living cells, including plant cells, respire *all the time*, and they need oxygen for this. When the light intensity is high, a plant carries out photosynthesis at a much higher rate than it respires. So in bright light, there is an overall uptake of carbon dioxide from the air around a plant's leaves, and a surplus production of oxygen that animals can use. A plant only produces more carbon dioxide than it uses up in dim light. We can show this as a graph of carbon dioxide exchanged at different light intensities (Figure 10.7).

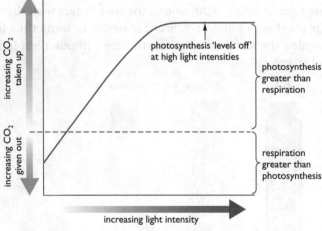

The point where the curve crosses the dashed line shows where photosynthesis is equal to respiration – there is no net gain or loss of CO_2.

Figure 10.7 *As the light intensity gets higher, photosynthesis speeds up, but eventually levels off in very bright light.*

A 'gas exchange' surface is a tissue that allows gases (usually oxygen, carbon dioxide and water vapour) to pass across it between the plant or animal and the outer environment. Gas exchange surfaces all have a large surface area in proportion to their volume, which allows large amounts of gases to diffuse across. Examples include the alveoli of the lungs, the gills of a fish and the spongy mesophyll of a leaf.

Starch is insoluble and so cannot be transported around the plant. The phloem carries only soluble substances such as sugars. These are converted into other compounds when they reach their destination.

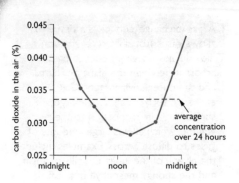

Figure 10.8 *Photosynthesis affects the concentration of carbon dioxide in the air around plants. Over a 24-hour period, the concentration rises and falls, as a result of the relative levels of photosynthesis and respiration.*

The concentration of carbon dioxide in the air around plants actually changes throughout the day. Scientists have measured the level of carbon dioxide in the air in the middle of a field of long grass in summer. They found that the air contained least carbon dioxide in the afternoon, when photosynthesis was happening at its highest rate (Figure 10.8). At night, when there was no photosynthesis, the level of carbon dioxide rose. This rise is due to less carbon dioxide being absorbed by the plants, while carbon dioxide was added to the air from the respiration of all organisms in the field.

Investigating the effect of light on gas exchange by a leaf

Hydrogencarbonate indicator solution is very sensitive to changes in carbon dioxide concentration. When the solution is made, it is equilibrated with atmospheric air, which has a CO_2 concentration of 0.04%. If extra CO_2 is added to the solution, or if CO_2 is taken away from the solution, it changes colour (Table 10.1).

Condition	Indicator colour
high concentrations of CO_2 (more than 0.04%)	yellow
CO_2 in normal air (0.04%)	orange
low concentrations of CO_2 (less than 0.04%)	purple

Table 10.1: *Changes to hydrogencarbonate indicator solution with different concentrations of carbon dioxide*

Carry out the following:

1. Place 10 cm³ of hydrogencarbonate indicator solution in the bottom of four boiling tubes.

2. Detach three large leaves from a suitable plant. Place a leaf into the top of three of the tubes. Seal each tube with a bung.

3. Place one tube in bright light, one in the dark (cover with silver foil), and cover the third with some translucent material, to restrict the intensity of light reaching the leaf. Leave the fourth tube without a leaf in the light as a control (Figure 10.9).

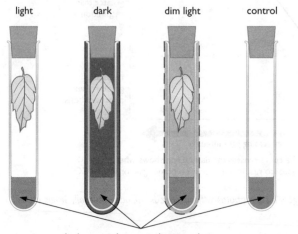

hydrogencarbonate indicator solution

Figure 10.9 *Using hydrogencarbonate indicator to test the effect of leaves on gas exchange.*

4. Leave the four tubes set up for a few hours, then record the colour of the hydrogencarbonate indicator.

5. Using your knowledge of a plant's rate of respiration and photosynthesis in the light and in the dark, explain the results.

Factors affecting the rate of photosynthesis

In Figure 10.7, you can see that when the light intensity rises, the rate of photosynthesis starts off rising too, but eventually it reaches a maximum rate. What makes the rate 'level off' like this? It is because some other factor needed for photosynthesis is in short supply, so that increasing the light intensity does not affect the rate any more. Normally, the factor which 'holds up' photosynthesis is the concentration of carbon dioxide in the air. This is only about 0.03 to 0.04%, and the plant can only take up the carbon dioxide and fix it into carbohydrate at a certain rate. If the plant is put in a closed container with a higher than normal concentration of carbon dioxide, it will photosynthesise at a faster rate. If there is both a high light intensity and a high level of carbon dioxide, the temperature may limit the rate of photosynthesis, by limiting the rate of the chemical reactions in the leaf. A rise in temperature will then increase the rate. With normal levels of carbon dioxide, very low temperatures (close to 0 °C) slow the reactions, but high temperatures (above about 35 °C) also reduce photosynthesis by denaturing enzymes in the plant cells (see Chapter 1).

Light intensity, carbon dioxide concentration and temperature can all act as what are called **limiting factors** in this way. This is easier to see as a graph (Figure 10.10).

A limiting factor is the component of a reaction that is in 'shortest supply' so that it prevents the rate of the reaction increasing, in other words sets a 'limit' to it.

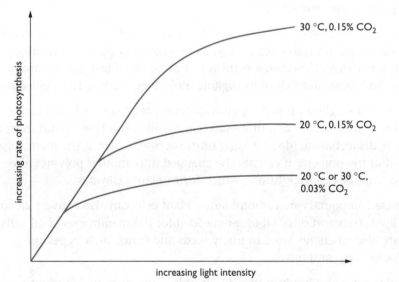

Figure 10.10 *Light intensity, carbon dioxide concentration and temperature can all act as limiting factors on the rate of photosynthesis*

Knowledge of limiting factors is used in some glasshouses (greenhouses) to speed up the growth of crop plants such as tomatoes and lettuces. Extra carbon dioxide is added to the air around the plants, by using gas burners. The higher concentration of carbon dioxide, along with the high temperature in the glasshouse, increases the rate of photosynthesis and the growth of the leaves and fruits.

Measuring the rate of photosynthesis using pondweed

You can measure the rate of photosynthesis of a plant by measuring how quickly it produces oxygen. With a land plant this is difficult, because the oxygen is released into the air, but with an aquatic plant such as *Elodea*, bubbles of oxygen are released into the water around the plant (see Figure 10.5).

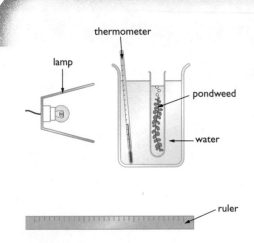

Figure 10.11 *Measuring the rate of photosynthesis in an aquatic plant.*

If you count the bubbles formed per minute, this is a measure of the rate of photosynthesis of the plant. It is easiest to count the bubbles if the cut piece of weed is placed upside down in a test tube, as in Figure 10.11. You may have to make it sink by attaching a small paper clip to the bottom of the piece of weed.

You can change the light intensity by moving the lamp and altering the distance between the lamp and the pondweed. The beaker of water keeps the temperature of the plant constant. You can check this with the thermometer.

Design an experiment to find out if the rate of photosynthesis is affected by the light intensity. In your plan you should include:

- a hypothesis – you should state what you think will happen as you alter the light intensity and why

- a systematic way of changing the light intensity

- how your experiment will be controlled so that nothing else is changed apart from the light intensity (What will you do about the background light in the laboratory?)

- a way of ensuring that your results are reliable.

When you have completed your plan, you may be able to carry out the experiment. How could you modify your plan to find the effect of changing the *temperature* on the rate of photosynthesis? What factors would you need to keep constant this time? What would be a suitable range of temperatures to try?

The plant's uses for glucose

As you have seen, some glucose that the plant makes is used in respiration to provide the plant's cells with energy. Some glucose is quickly converted into starch for storage. However, a plant is not made up of just glucose and starch, and must make all of its organic molecules, starting from glucose.

Glucose is a single sugar unit (a **monosaccharide**). Plant cells can convert it into other sugars, such as a monosaccharide called **fructose** (found in fruits) and the **disaccharide** (double sugar unit) **sucrose**, which is the main sugar carried in the phloem. It can also be changed into another polymer, the polysaccharide called **cellulose**, which forms plant cell walls.

All these compounds are carbohydrates. Plant cells can also convert glucose into lipids (fats and oils). Lipids are needed for the membranes of all cells, and are also an energy store in many seeds and fruits, such as peanuts, sunflower seeds and olives.

Carbohydrates and lipids both contain only three elements – carbon, hydrogen and oxygen – and so they can be inter-converted without the need for a supply of other elements. Proteins contain these elements too, but all amino acids (the building blocks of proteins) also contain nitrogen. This is obtained as nitrate ions from the soil, through the plant's roots (see Chapter 11). Other compounds in plants contain other elements. For example, chlorophyll contains magnesium ions, which are also absorbed from water in the soil. Some of the products that a plant makes from glucose are summarised in Figure 10.12.

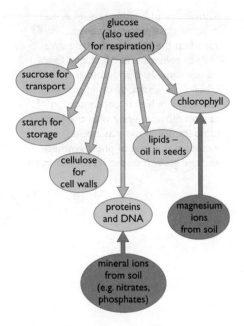

Figure 10.12 *Compounds that plant cells can make from glucose.*

Mineral nutrition

Nitrate ions are absorbed from the soil water, along with other minerals such as phosphate, potassium and magnesium ions. The element phosphorus is needed for the plant cells to make many important compounds, including DNA. Potassium ions are required for enzymes in respiration and photosynthesis to work, and magnesium forms a part of the chlorophyll molecule.

Water culture experiments

A plant takes only water and mineral ions from the soil for growth. Plants can be grown in soil-free cultures (water cultures) if the correct balance of minerals is added to the water. In the nineteenth century, the German biologist Wilhelm Knop invented one example of a culture solution. Knop's solution contains the following chemicals (per dm^3 of water):

0.8 g	calcium nitrate
0.2 g	magnesium sulphate
0.2 g	potassium nitrate
0.2 g	potassium dihydrogen phosphate
(trace)	iron(III) phosphate

Notice that these chemicals provide all of the main elements that the plant needs to make proteins, DNA and chlorophyll, as well as other compounds, from glucose. It is called a *complete* culture solution. If you were to make up a similar solution, but to replace, for example, magnesium sulphate with more calcium sulphate, this would produce a culture solution which was *deficient* (lacking) in magnesium. You could then grow plants in the complete and deficient solutions, and compare the results. There are several ways to grow the plants, such as using the apparatus shown in Figure 10.13, which is useful for plant cuttings. Seedlings can be grown by packing cotton wool around the seed, instead of using a rubber bung.

The plant is kept in bright light, so that it can photosynthesise. The covering around the flask prevents algae from growing in the culture solution, and the aeration tube is used for short periods to supply the roots with oxygen for respiration of the root cells. Using methods like this, it soon becomes clear that mineral deficiencies result in poor plant growth. A shortage of a particular mineral results in particular symptoms in the plant, called a **mineral deficiency disease**. For example, lack of magnesium means that the plant won't be able to make chlorophyll, and the leaves will turn yellow. Some of the mineral ions that a plant needs, their uses, and the deficiency symptoms are shown in Table 10.2. Compare the photographs of the mineral deficient plants to those of the control plants in Figure 10.14a.

Glucose from photosynthesis is not just used as the *raw material* for the production of molecules such as starch, cellulose, lipids and proteins. Reactions like these, which synthesise large molecules from smaller ones, also need a source of energy. This energy is provided by the plant's *respiration* of glucose.

In fact, in addition to the ions listed in Knop's solution, plants need very small amounts of other mineral ions for healthy growth. Knop's culture solution only worked because the chemicals he used to make his solutions weren't very pure, and supplied enough of these additional ions by mistake!

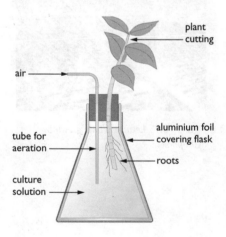

Figure 10.13 *A simple water culture method.*

Figure 10.14 *(a) A healthy bean plant*

Some commercial crops such as lettuces can be grown without soil, in culture solutions. This is called **hydroponics**. The plants' roots grow in a long plastic tube which has culture solution passing through it (Figure 10.15). The composition of the solution can be carefully adjusted to ensure the plants grow well. Pests, which might live in soil, are also less of a problem.

Figure 10.15 *Lettuce plants grown by hydroponics.*

Mineral ion	Use	Deficiency symptoms
nitrate	making amino acids, proteins, chlorophyll, DNA and many other compounds	stunted growth of plant; older leaves turn yellow Figure 10.14 *(b) A plant showing symptoms of nitrate deficiency.*
phosphate	making DNA and many other compounds; part of cell membranes	poor root growth; younger leaves turn purple Figure 10.14 *(c) A plant showing symptoms of phosphate deficiency.*
potassium	needed for enzymes of respiration and photosynthesis to work	leaves turn yellow with dead spots Figure 10.14 *(d) A plant showing symptoms of potassium deficiency.*
magnesium	part of chlorophyll molecule	leaves turn yellow Figure 10.14 *(e) A plant showing symptoms of magnesium deficiency.*

Table 10.2: *Mineral ions needed by plants.*

End of Chapter Checklist

You should now be able to:

● describe the process of photosynthesis and understand its importance in conversion of light energy to chemical energy

● recall the word equation and the balanced symbol equation for photosynthesis

● describe simple controlled experiments to investigate the need for light, carbon dioxide and chlorophyll by leaves in the production of starch

● describe a simple experiment to show the evolution of oxygen from an aquatic plant

● understand how light intensity, carbon dioxide concentration and temperature affect the rate of photosynthesis

● explain how the structure of a leaf is adapted for photosynthesis and gas exchange

● understand exchange of carbon dioxide and oxygen in flowering plants, in relation to respiration and photosynthesis in the light and in the dark

● describe simple, controlled experiments to investigate the effect of light intensity on the net gas exchange from a leaf, using hydrogencarbonate indicator

● recall that plants require mineral ions for growth, including the role of nitrate and magnesium ions.

Questions

More questions on plants and food can be found at the end of Section C on page 152.

1 A plant with variegated leaves had a piece of black paper attached to one leaf as shown in the diagram below.

The plant was kept under a bright light for 24 hours. The leaf was then removed, the paper taken off and the leaf was tested for starch.

a) Name the chemical used to test for starch, and describe the colour change if the test is positive.

b) Copy the leaf outline and shade in the areas which would contain starch.

c) Explain how you arrived at your answer to (b).

d) What is starch used for in a plant? How do the properties of starch make it suitable for this function?

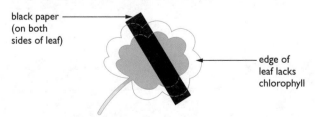

black paper (on both sides of leaf)

edge of leaf lacks chlorophyll

2 Copy and complete the following table to show the functions of different parts of a leaf. One has been done for you.

Part of leaf	Function
palisade mesophyll layer	main site of photosynthesis
spongy mesophyll layer	
stomata	
xylem	
phloem	

3 The graph shows the changes in the concentration of carbon dioxide in a field of long grass throughout a 24-hour period in summer.

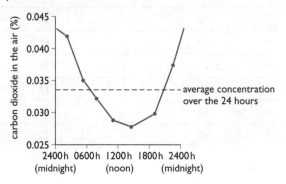

a) Explain why the levels of carbon dioxide are high at 0200 hours and low at 1200 hours.

b) What factor will limit the rate of photosynthesis at 0400 hours and at 1400 hours?

4 The table below shows some of the substances that can be made by plants. Give one use in the plant for each. The first has been done for you.

Substance	Use
glucose	oxidised in respiration to give energy
sucrose	
starch	
cellulose	
protein	
lipid	

5 The apparatus shown in the diagram was used to grow a pea seedling in a water culture experiment.

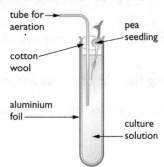

a) Explain the purpose of the aeration tube and the aluminium foil around the test tube.

b) After two weeks, the roots of the pea seedling had grown less than normal, although the leaves were well developed. What mineral ion is likely to be deficient in the culture solution?

6 A piece of Canadian pondweed was placed upside down in a test tube of water, as shown in the diagram. Light from a bench lamp was shone onto the weed, and bubbles of gas appeared at the cut end of the stem. The distance of the lamp from the weed was changed, and the number of bubbles produced per minute was recorded. The results are shown in the table below.

Distance of lamp (cm) (D)	Number of bubbles per minute
5	126
10	89
15	64
20	42
25	31
30	17
35	14
40	10

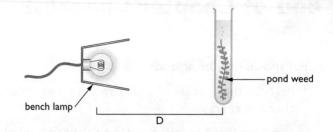

a) Plot a graph of the number of bubbles per minute against the distance of the weed from the lamp. You could do this on graph paper, or use a spreadsheet program on a computer.

b) Using your graph, predict the number of bubbles per minute that would be produced if the lamp was placed 17 cm from the weed.

c) The student who carried out this experiment arrived at the following conclusion:

'The gas made by the weed is oxygen from photosynthesis, so the faster production of bubbles shows that the rate of photosynthesis is greater at higher light intensities.'

Write down three reasons why his conclusion could be criticised (Hint: think about the bubbles, and whether the experiment was a 'fair test').

7 Write a summary account of photosynthesis. You should include a description of the process, a summary equation, an account of how a leaf is adapted for photosynthesis and a note of how photosynthesis is important to other organisms, such as animals. You must keep your summary to less than two sides. It will be easier to organise your account if you work on it using a computer.

Chapter 11: Transport in Plants

Osmosis

Osmosis is the name of a process by which water moves into and out of cells. To be able to understand how water moves through a plant, you need to understand the mechanism of osmosis. Osmosis happens when a material called a **partially permeable membrane** separates two solutions. One artificial partially permeable membrane is called Visking tubing. This is used in kidney dialysis machines. Visking tubing has microscopic holes in it, which let small molecules like water pass through (it is *permeable* to them) but is not permeable to some larger molecules, such as the sugar sucrose. This is why it is called 'partially' permeable. You can show the effects of osmosis by filling a Visking tubing 'sausage' with concentrated sucrose solution, attaching it to a capillary tube and placing the Visking tubing in a beaker of water (Figure 11.1).

The level in the capillary tube rises as water moves from the beaker to the inside of the Visking tubing. This movement is due to osmosis. You can understand what's happening if you imagine a highly magnified view of the Visking tubing separating the two liquids (Figure 11.2).

capillary tube

cotton thread tied tightly

water

sucrose solution

Visking tubing

knot tied in tubing

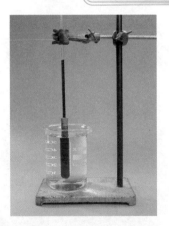

Figure 11.1 *Water enters the Visking tubing 'sausage' by osmosis. This causes the level of liquid in the capillary tube to rise. In the photograph, the contents of the Visking tubing have had a red dye added to make it easier to see the movement of the liquid.*

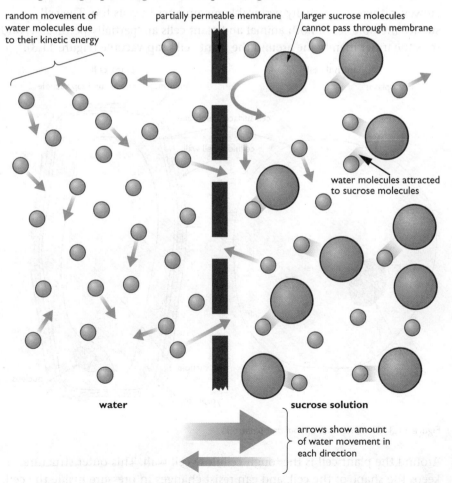

random movement of water molecules due to their kinetic energy

partially permeable membrane

larger sucrose molecules cannot pass through membrane

water molecules attracted to sucrose molecules

water

sucrose solution

arrows show amount of water movement in each direction

Figure 11.2 *In this model of osmosis, more water molecules diffuse from left to right than from right to left.*

The sucrose molecules are too big to pass through the holes in the partially permeable membrane. The water molecules can pass through the membrane in either direction, but those on the right are attracted to the sugar molecules. This slows them down and means that they are less free to move – they have less kinetic energy. As a result of this, more water molecules diffuse from left to right than from right to left. In other words, there is a greater diffusion of water molecules from the more dilute solution (in this case pure water) to the more concentrated solution.

How 'free' the water molecules are to move is called the **water potential**. The molecules in pure water can move most freely, so pure water has the highest water potential. The more concentrated a solution is, the lower is its water potential. In the model in Figure 11.2, water moves from a high to a low water potential. This is a law which applies whenever water moves by osmosis. We can bring these ideas together in a definition of osmosis.

> Osmosis is the net diffusion of water across a partially permeable membrane, from a solution with a high water potential to one with a lower water potential.

Osmosis in plant cells

So far we have only been dealing with osmosis through Visking tubing. However, there are partially permeable membranes in cells too. The cell surface membranes of both animal and plant cells are partially permeable, and so is the inner membrane around the plant cell's sap vacuole (Figure 11.3).

It is important to realise that neither of the two solutions has to be pure water. As long as there is a difference in their concentrations (and their water potentials), and they are separated by a partially permeable membrane, osmosis can still take place.

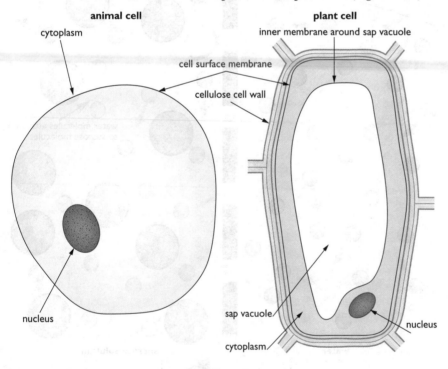

Figure 11.3 *Membranes in animal and plant cells.*

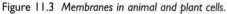

Around the plant cell is the tough cellulose cell wall. This outer structure keeps the shape of the cell, and can resist changes in pressure inside the cell. This is very important, and critical in explaining the way that plants are supported. The cell contents, including the sap vacuole, contain many dissolved solutes, such as sugars and ions.

The cell *wall* has large holes in it, making it fully permeable to water and solutes. Only the cell *membranes* are partially permeable barriers that allow osmosis to take place.

If a plant cell is put into pure water or a dilute solution, the contents of the cell have a lower water potential than the external solution, so the cell will absorb water by osmosis (Figure 11.4). The cell then swells up and the cytoplasm pushes against the cell wall. A plant cell that has developed an internal pressure like this is called **turgid**.

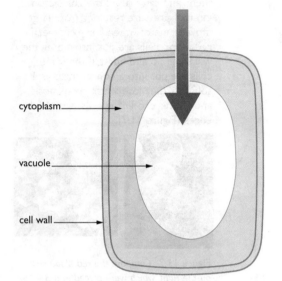
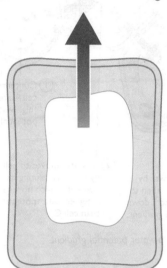
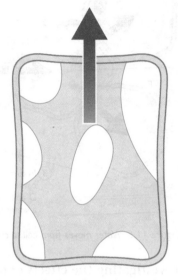

cytoplasm

vacuole

cell wall

cell placed in dilute solution, or water, absorbs water by osmosis and becomes turgid

cell placed in concentrated solution loses water by osmosis and becomes flaccid

excessive loss of water by osmosis causes the cell to become plasmolysed

Figure 11.4 *The effects of osmosis on plant cells.*

On the other hand, if the cell is placed in a concentrated sucrose solution that has a lower water potential than the cell contents, it will *lose* water by osmosis. The cell decreases in volume and the cytoplasm no longer pushes against the cell wall. In this state, the cell is called **flaccid**. Eventually the cell contents shrink so much that the membrane and cytoplasm split away from the cell wall and gaps appear between the wall and the membrane. A cell like this is called **plasmolysed**. You can see plasmolysis happening in the plant cells shown in Figure 11.5. The space between the cell wall and the cell surface membrane will now be filled with the sucrose solution.

Turgor (the state a plant is in when its cells are turgid) is very important to plants. The pressure inside the cells pushes neighbouring cells against each other, like a box full of inflated balloons. This supports the non-woody parts of the plant, such as young stems and leaves, and holds stems upright, so the leaves can carry out photosynthesis properly. Turgor is also important in the functioning of stomata. If a plant loses too much water from its cells so that they become flaccid, this makes the plant **wilt**. You can see this in a pot plant which has been left for too long without water. The leaves droop and collapse. In fact this is a protective action. It cuts down water loss by reducing the exposed surface area of the leaves and closing the stomata.

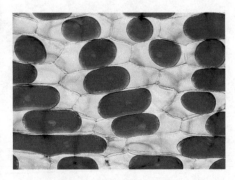

Figure 11.5 *Cells of rhubarb epidermis, showing plasmolysis. The cell membranes can be seen pulling away from the cell walls.*

Inside the plant, water moves from cell to cell by osmosis. If a cell has a higher water potential than the cell next to it, water will move from the first cell to the second. In turn, this will dilute the contents of the second cell, so that it has a higher water potential than the next cell. In this way, water can move across a plant tissue, down a gradient of water potential (Figure 11.6).

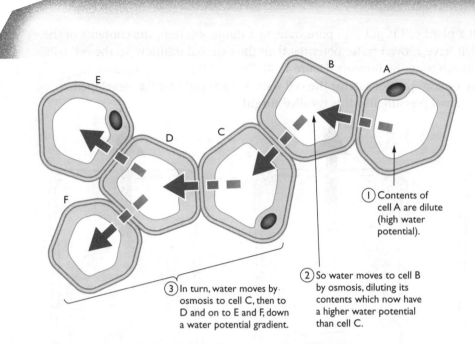

① Contents of cell A are dilute (high water potential).

② So water moves to cell B by osmosis, diluting its contents which now have a higher water potential than cell C.

③ In turn, water moves by osmosis to cell C, then to D and on to E and F, down a water potential gradient.

Figure 11.6 *Water moves from cell to cell down a water potential gradient.*

Investigating the effects of osmosis in onion epidermis cells

Carry out the following:

1. Place a drop of concentrated (Molar) sucrose solution on one microscope slide, and a drop of tap water on the other. Use a different pipette to transfer each liquid.

2. Remove two small squares of inner epidermis from one of the outer fleshy layers of an onion (Figure 11.8). Transfer one square to the tap water and the other to the sucrose solution. This should be done as quickly as possible, so that the cells do not dry out.

3. Add a drop of the correct solution to the top of each specimen, followed by a cover slip. Clean up your slide, blotting any excess liquid with tissue or filter paper.

4. Examine each slide through the microscope for several minutes. Note any differences between the cells on each slide, comparing your findings with Figures 11.4 and 11.5.

5. Make accurate labelled drawings of two or three representative cells from each slide.

6. Replace the sucrose solution of the second slide with tap water. You can do this quite easily without removing the cover slip. Place some water on one side of the cover slip and draw it across the slide using filter paper (Figure 11.8). You may have to do this for a while to ensure that all the sucrose solution is replaced by water.

7. Examine the cells again and draw a couple of cells that have been placed in water after being in sucrose solution.

8. Explain your findings in terms of osmosis.

This chapter only deals with plant cells. Osmosis also happens in animal cells, but there is much less water movement. This is because animal cells do not have a strong cell wall around them, and can't resist the changes in internal pressure resulting from large movements of water. For example, if red blood cells are put into water, they will swell up and burst. If the same cells are put into a concentrated salt solution, they lose water by osmosis and shrink, producing cells with crinkly edges (Figure 11.7).

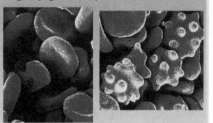

Figure 11.7 *Compare the red blood cells on the right, which were placed in a 3% salt solution, with the normal cells on the left. Blood plasma has a concentration equal to a 0.85% salt solution.*

If you use a red onion, the contents of the cells are coloured and easier to see.

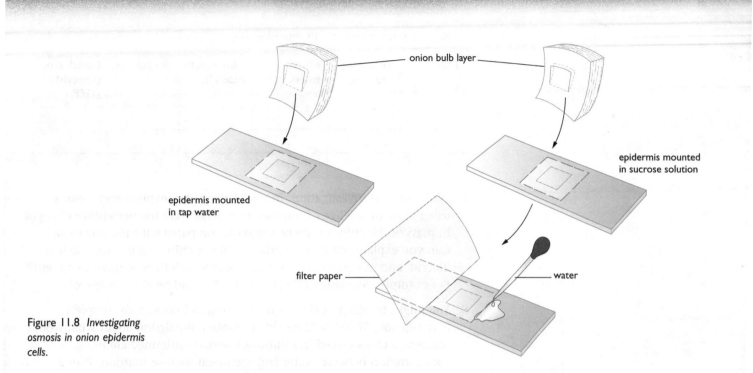

onion bulb layer

epidermis mounted
in sucrose solution

epidermis mounted
in tap water

filter paper

water

Figure 11.8 *Investigating
osmosis in onion epidermis
cells.*

Investigating the effects of osmosis on potato tuber tissue

A potato tuber is a plant storage organ. It is a convenient tissue to use to investigate the effects of osmosis on the mass of the tissue.

Carry out the following:

1. Half fill a boiling tube with tap water and a second with concentrated (Molar) sucrose solution. Leave the third empty. Mark the tubes.

2. Cut chips of potato measuring 5 cm × 1 cm × 1 cm. Make these measurements as accurate as possible so that the three chips are the same size. You should be able to measure to ±1 mm. Make sure that no skin is left on the potato tissue.

3. Gently blot each chip to remove excess moisture and find the mass of each by weighing them on a balance. Place each chip in a boiling tube. Their masses will be slightly different, so make sure you know which is which – this is best recorded in a table (see next page). Leave them for 30 minutes (Figure 11.9).

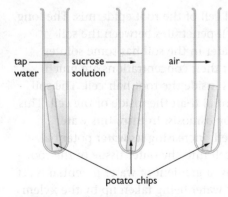

tap
water

sucrose
solution

air

potato chips

Figure 11.9 *Investigating osmosis in potato tissue.*

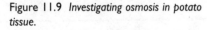

4. Remove the chips using forceps and blot them gently, then re-weigh them.

5. Feel each chip in turn to compare how flexible or stiff they are. Note the differences.

6. Calculate the change in mass (+ or –), and the percentage change from the equation:

$$\% \text{ change} = \frac{\text{change in mass}}{\text{starting mass}} \times 100$$

Record your results in a table like this.

Tube	Starting mass/g	Final mass/g	Change in mass/g	% change	Condition (flexible/ stiff)

7. Write up your investigation. In your conclusion, explain your results using your knowledge of osmosis. How large were the percentage changes in mass of the chips in the two liquids, compared with the one in air? Can you explain the final 'condition' of the chips, using terms such as 'flaccid' and 'turgid'? Can you think of any criticisms of this experiment? For example, does using one chip per tube yield reliable evidence?

8. You might be able to extend this experiment into a more complete investigation. You should be able to make a prediction about what would happen to chips placed in solutions that were intermediate in concentration between water and the molar sucrose solution. Plan a method to test your hypothesis. You should include a description of the apparatus and materials to be used, descriptions of procedures and a statement of the expected results.

You don't have to use potato. You can try other vegetables such as carrots. You can also measure the length of the chips at the end of the experiment, and compare this with their starting length, instead of weighing them. However, weighing is more accurate and gives a bigger percentage change.

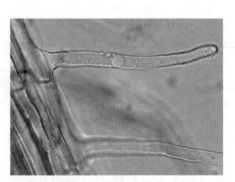

Figure 11.10 *These root hairs increase the surface area for water absorption.*

Uptake of water by roots

The regions just behind the growing tips of the roots of a plant are covered in thousands of tiny root hairs (Figure 11.10). These areas are the main sites of water absorption by the roots, where the hairs greatly increase the surface area of the root epidermis.

Each hair is actually a single, specialised cell of the root epidermis. The long, thin outer projection of the root hair cell penetrates between the soil particles, reaching the soil water. The water in the soil has some solutes dissolved in it, such as mineral ions, but their concentrations are much lower than the concentrations of solutes inside the root hair cell. The soil water therefore has a higher water potential than the inside of the cell. This allows water to enter the root hair cell by osmosis. In turn, this water movement dilutes the contents of the cell, increasing its water potential. Water then moves out of the root hair cell into the outer tissue of the root (the root cortex). Continuing in this way, a gradient of water potential is set up across the root cortex, kept going by water being taken up by the xylem in the middle of the root (Figure 11.11).

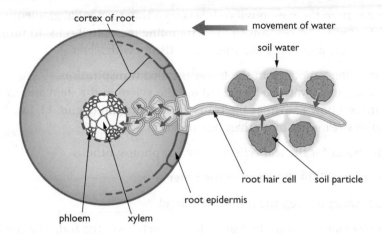

Figure 11.11 *Water is taken up by root hairs of the plant epidermis and carried across the root cortex by a water potential gradient. It then enters the xylem and is transported to all parts of the plant.*

Loss of water by the leaves – transpiration

Osmosis is also involved in the movement of water through leaves. The epidermis of leaves is covered by a waxy cuticle (see Chapter 10), which is impermeable to water. Most water passes out of the leaves as water vapour through pores called stomata (stoma is the singular of stomata). Water leaves the cells of the leaf mesophyll and evaporates into the air spaces between the spongy mesophyll cells. The water vapour then diffuses out through the stomatal pores (Figure 11.12).

Plants that live in dry habitats, such as cacti and succulents, usually have a very thick layer of waxy cuticle on their leaves, which reduces water loss as much as possible. Cacti have leaves reduced to spines, which have a low surface area and cut down water loss.

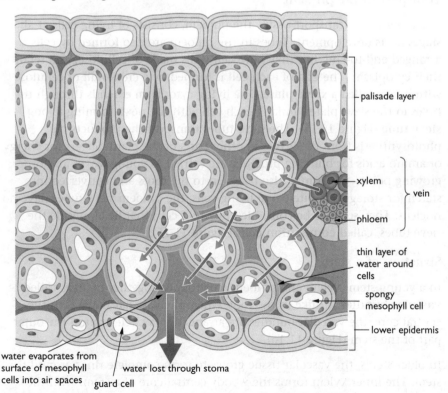

Figure 11.12 *Passage of water from the xylem to the stomatal pores of a leaf.*

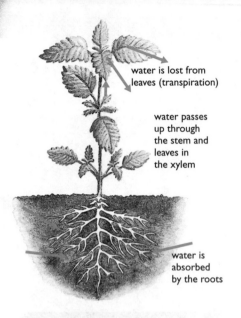

water is lost from leaves (transpiration)

water passes up through the stem and leaves in the xylem

water is absorbed by the roots

Figure 11.13 *The transpiration stream.*

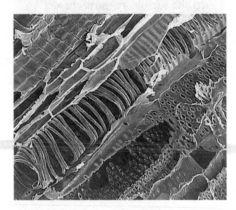

Figure 11.14 *Xylem vessels in a stem.*

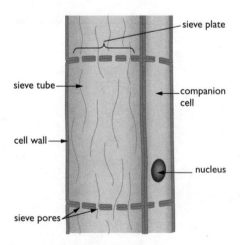

sieve plate

sieve tube

companion cell

cell wall

nucleus

sieve pores

Figure 11.15 *Phloem is living tissue, responsible for carrying the products of photosynthesis around the plant.*

Loss of water from the mesophyll cells sets up a water potential gradient which 'draws' water by osmosis from surrounding mesophyll cells. In turn, the xylem vessels supply the leaf mesophyll tissues with water.

This loss of water vapour from the leaves is called **transpiration**. Transpiration causes water to be 'pulled up' the xylem in the stem and roots in a continuous flow known as the **transpiration stream** (Figure 11.13). The transpiration stream has more than one function. It:

● supplies water for the leaf cells to carry out photosynthesis

● carries mineral ions dissolved in the water

● provides water to keep the plant cells turgid

● allows evaporation from the leaf surface, which cools the leaf, in a similar way to sweat cooling the human skin.

Xylem contains dead cells arranged end-to-end, forming continuous vessels. When they are mature, the vessels contain no cytoplasm. Instead, they have a hollow central space or **lumen** through which the water passes. The walls of the xylem vessels contain a woody material called **lignin** (Figure 11.14).

The xylem vessels begin life as living cells with normal cytoplasm and cellulose cell walls. As they develop they become elongated, and gradually their original cellulose cell walls become impregnated with lignin, made by the cytoplasm. As this happens, the cells die, forming hollow tubes. Lignification makes them very strong, and enables them to carry water up tall plants without collapsing. Lignin is also impermeable to water.

Transport in the phloem

The other plant transport tissue, the phloem, consists of living cells at all stages in its development. Tubes in the phloem are also formed by cells arranged end-to-end, but they have cell walls made of cellulose, and retain their cytoplasm. The end of each cell is formed by a cross-wall of cellulose with holes, called a **sieve plate**. The living cytoplasm extends through the holes in the sieve plates, linking each cell with the next, forming a long **sieve tube** (Figure 11.15). The sieve tubes transport the products of photosynthesis from the leaves to other parts of the plant. Sugars for energy, or amino acids for building proteins, are carried to young leaves and other growing points. Sugar may also be taken to the roots and converted into starch for storage. Despite being living cells, the phloem sieve tubes have no nucleus. They seem to be controlled by other cells that lie alongside the sieve tubes, called **companion cells** (Figure 11.15).

Structure of a stem

In a young stem, xylem and phloem are grouped together in areas called **vascular bundles**. Unlike in the root, where the vascular tissue is in the central core, the vascular bundles are arranged in a circle around the outer part of the stem (Figure 11.16).

In older stems, the vascular tissue grows to form complete rings around the stem. The inner xylem forms the woody central core of a stem, with the living layer of phloem outside this.

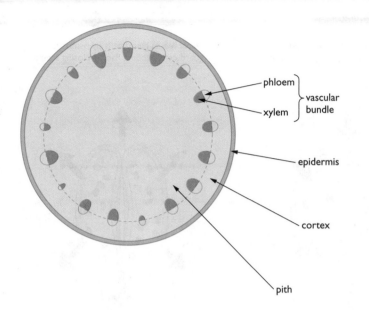

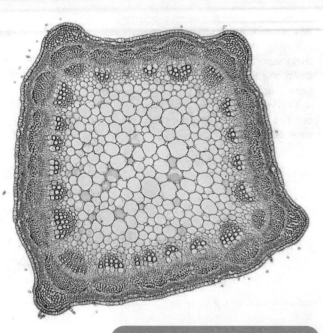

Figure 11.16 *This cross-section of a stem shows the arrangement of xylem and phloem tissue in vascular bundles.*

Control of transpiration by stomata

As you saw in Chapter 10, there are usually more stomata on the lower surface of the leaves than the upper surface in most plant species (Figure 11.17). If they were mainly on the upper leaf surface, the leaf would lose too much water. This is because the stomata would be exposed to direct sunlight, which would produce a high rate of evaporation from them. There is also less air movement on the underside of leaves. The evolution of this arrangement of stomata is an adaptation that reduces water loss.

The stomata can open and close. The guard cells that surround each stoma have an unusual 'banana' shape, and the part of their cell wall nearest the stoma is particularly thick. In the light, water enters the guard cells by osmosis from the surrounding epidermis cells. This causes the guard cells to become turgid, and, as they swell up, their shape changes. They bend outwards, opening up the stoma. In the dark, the guard cells lose water again, they become flaccid and the stoma closes. No one knows for sure how this change is brought about, but it seems to be linked to the fact that the guard cells are the only cells in the lower epidermis that contain chloroplasts. In the light, the guard cells use energy to accumulate solutes in their vacuoles, causing water to be drawn in by osmosis (Figure 11.18).

Closure of stomata in the dark is a useful adaptation. Without the sun there is no need for loss of water vapour from the stomata to cool the leaves. In addition, leaves cannot photosynthesise in the dark, so they don't need water for this purpose. Therefore, it doesn't matter if the transpiration stream is shut down by closure of the stomata. As you will see, other physical factors can also affect the rate of transpiration.

Remember: Xylem carries water and minerals up from the roots. Phloem carries products of photosynthesis away from the leaves. The contents of the phloem can travel up or down the plant.

'Vascular' means 'made of vessels'. A vascular bundle is a group of vessels or tubes (xylem and phloem).

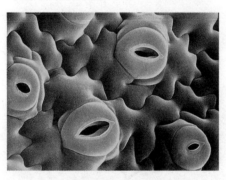

Figure 11.17 *Stomata in the surface of the lower epidermis of a leaf.*

You can make a 'mould' of a leaf surface using colourless nail varnish. Paint an area of nail varnish about 1 cm^2 on the lower surface of a leaf (privet leaves work well). Leave this to dry for half an hour and then use forceps to peel off the nail varnish. Place this on a slide and look at it through a microscope (you don't need to use a cover slip). Under medium or high power you should be able to see impressions of the stomata and guard cells.

You can model the action of a guard cell using a long balloon and some sticky tape. Stick a few pieces of tape down one side of the balloon and then blow it up. As it inflates, the balloon will curve outwards like a turgid guard cell. The tape represents the thick inner cell wall.

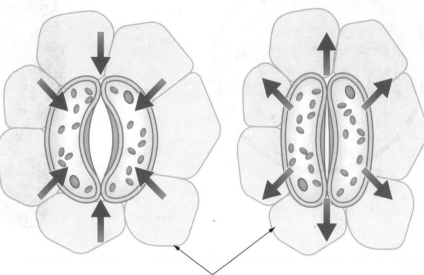

water enters guard cells by osmosis; guard cells become turgid, opening stoma

water leaves guard cells by osmosis; guard cells become flaccid, closing stoma

epidermis cells surrounding guard cells

Figure 11.18 *When the guard cells become turgid, the stoma opens. When they become flaccid, it closes.*

Measuring the rate of transpiration: potometers

A potometer is a simple piece of apparatus which measures the rate of transpiration or the rate of uptake of water by a plant. (These are not the same thing – some of the water taken up by the plant may stay in the plant cells, or be used for photosynthesis.) There are two types, 'weight' and volume potometers.

A 'weight' potometer measures the rate of loss of mass from a potted plant or leafy shoot over a longish period of time, usually several hours (Figure 11.19).

The polythene bag around the pot prevents loss of moisture by evaporation from the soil. Most of the mass lost by the plant will be due to water evaporating from the leaves during transpiration (although there will be small changes in mass due to respiration and photosynthesis, since both of these processes exchange gases with the air).

A volume potometer is used to find the rate of uptake of water by a leafy shoot, by 'magnifying' this uptake in a capillary tube. These potometers come in various shapes and sizes. The simplest is a straight vertical tube joined to the shoot by a piece of rubber tubing. More 'deluxe' versions have a horizontal capillary tube and a way of refilling the capillary to re-set the water at its starting position (Figure 11.20).

To set up a volume potometer, the whole apparatus is placed in a sink of water and any air in the tubing removed. A shoot is taken from a plant and the end of the stem cut at an angle. This makes it easier to push the stem into the rubber tubing, which is done under water to stop air entering. The apparatus is removed from the sink, and vaseline used to seal any joins. The

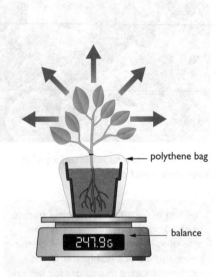

polythene bag

balance

247.9G

Figure 11.19 *A 'weight' potometer.*

movement of the water column in the capillary tube can be timed. If the water moves more quickly, this shows a faster rate of transpiration. The plant can then be exposed to different conditions to see how they affect the rate.

Factors affecting the rate of transpiration

There are four main factors which affect the rate of transpiration:

- **Light intensity** The rate of transpiration increases in the light, because of the opening of the stomata in the leaves.

- **Temperature** High temperatures increase the rate of transpiration, by increasing the rate of evaporation of water from the mesophyll cells.

- **Humidity** When the air around the plant is humid, this reduces the diffusion gradient between the air spaces in the leaf and the external air. The rate of transpiration therefore decreases in humid air and speeds up in dry air.

- **Wind speed** The rate of transpiration increases with faster air movements across the surface of the leaf. The moving air removes any water vapour which might remain near the stomata. This moist air would otherwise reduce the diffusion gradient and slow down diffusion.

It is easy to use a potometer to demonstrate these effects. For example, you can use a fan or hair drier on a plant to show the effects of moving air, or put the plant under a bright light or in the dark to find the effect of light intensity.

Uptake of mineral ions

Mineral ions are needed for plants to make a range of organic compounds from the products of photosynthesis (see Chapter 10). These mineral ions are taken up from the soil, along with the water that enters by osmosis. However, *only* water can move by osmosis. Mineral ions have to enter the root cells by other means.

One way an ion might enter the root cells would be by simple diffusion. For this to happen there needs to be a concentration gradient, with the soil water containing a higher concentration of the ion than the root hair cells. An experiment with an alga (a small plant-like organism) showed that plant cells (or, strictly speaking, algal cells) could concentrate ions in the cell sap to a much higher level than in the water surrounding the alga (Table 11.1 and Figure 11.21).

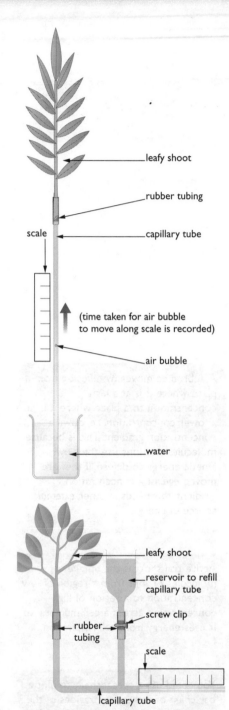

Figure 11.20 *Two types of volume potometer.*

> The concentration of water vapour inside the leaf is greater than the concentration in the air outside. This is a diffusion (or concentration) gradient. A big difference in concentration means there is a steep gradient. The molecules of water vapour will diffuse out of the leaf more quickly if the gradient is steep.

| | Concentration of ion (mg/dm^3) | | | | |
	sodium (Na$^+$)	potassium (K$^+$)	calcium (Ca^{2+})	magnesium (Mg^{2+})	chloride (Cl$^-$)
in cell sap	1980	2400	380	260	3750
in pond water	28	2	26	36	35

Table 11.1: *Concentration of ions in the cell sap of an alga and in the surrounding pond water.*

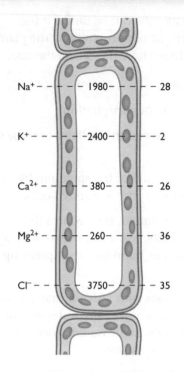

Na⁺	1980	28

Na⁺ – – – – – 1980 – – – – 28

K⁺ – – – – –2400– – – – 2

Ca²⁺ – – – – 380– – – 26

Mg²⁺ – – – 260– – – 36

Cl⁻ – – – – 3750– – – 35

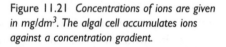

Figure 11.21 *Concentrations of ions are given in mg/dm³. The algal cell accumulates ions against a concentration gradient.*

A substance moves by diffusion from a place where it is at a high concentration to a place where it is at a lower concentration, i.e. down a concentration gradient. This is because molecules and ions use their own kinetic energy to diffuse. If they are moved *against* a concentration gradient, this needs another, *external* source of energy.

Active transport is the uptake of molecules or ions from a region of low concentration to a region of high concentration across a cell membrane. It uses energy from cell respiration.

You could use a spreadsheet to plot a bar chart of the concentrations of the ions in Table 11.1. You should be able to plot both the concentrations in the cell sap and in the pond water on the same graph. You could then use the data in the spreadsheet to calculate how much more concentrated each ion is inside the cells compared with outside.

None of these ions could have entered the cells of the alga by diffusion, because the concentration gradient for each ion is in the wrong direction.

To accumulate the ions inside its cells, the alga must have 'pumped' the ions in. Scientists now know that the cell membranes of algae and plant cells, including the root hair cell, contain molecular pumps which push the ions into the cells, against a concentration gradient. This process is called **active transport**. Unlike diffusion, which just uses the kinetic energy of the diffusing particles, active transport needs another source of energy. It uses chemical energy from respiration.

Active transport is responsible for the uptake of several mineral ions into the root hair cells. However, it depends upon their concentration in the soil water. If an ion is present in the soil water in large amounts, there may be a downward concentration gradient allowing it to enter by diffusion. For example, if nitrate fertiliser is added to the soil, active transport may not be needed for the roots to absorb the nitrate ions.

Table 11.1 shows another interesting fact about transport across the plant cell membrane. If you look at potassium ions, they are 1200 times more concentrated inside the cells than outside, whereas magnesium ions are only about 7 times more concentrated. The cell membrane is able to concentrate different ions by different amounts. Because the membrane is being 'selective' in how much of each ion it allows in, some scientists prefer to call it **selectively permeable**, rather than partially permeable.

Once inside the root, the mineral ions pass across the root cortex mainly by diffusion, and enter the xylem vessels. They are then carried all around the plant in the transpiration stream.

End of Chapter Checklist

You should now be able to:

- understand how water can move in or out of cells by osmosis

- understand the importance of turgid cells as a means of support in plants

- describe simple experiments on osmosis

- explain how water is absorbed by root hair cells

- recall the meaning and functions of transpiration

- describe the position of xylem and phloem in a stem

- describe the roles of xylem and phloem

- explain how the rate of transpiration is affected by changes in temperature, wind speed, humidity and light intensity

- describe experiments that investigate the role of environmental factors in determining the rate of transpiration from a leafy shoot

- understand that the uptake of mineral ions by root cells can be by diffusion or active transport.

Questions

More questions on transport in plants can be found at the end of Section C on page 152.

1   Three 'chips' of about the same size and shape were cut from the same potato. Each was blotted, weighed and placed in a different sucrose solution (A, B or C). The chips were left in the solutions for an hour, then removed, blotted and re-weighed. Here are the results:

	Starting mass (g)	Final mass (g)	Change in mass (%)
solution A	7.4	6.5	−12.2
solution B	8.2	8.0	
solution C	7.7	8.5	+10.4

   a)   Calculate the percentage change in mass for the chip in solution B.

   b)   Name the process that caused the chips to lose or gain mass.

   c)   Which solution was likely to have been the most concentrated?

   d)   Which solution had the highest water potential?

   e)   Which solution had a water potential most similar to the water potential of the potato cells?

   f)   The cell membrane is described as 'partially permeable'. Explain the meaning of this.

2   Explain how each of the following cells is adapted for its function:

   a)   a root hair cell

   b)   a xylem vessel

   c)   a guard cell.

3   Suggest reasons for each of the following observations.

   a)   When transplanting a small plant from a pot to the garden, it is important to dig it up carefully, leaving the roots in a ball of soil. If this is not done, the plant may wilt after it has been transplanted.

   b)   A plant cutting is more likely to grow successfully if you remove some of its leaves before planting it in compost.

   c)   Plants that live in very dry habitats often have stomata located in sunken pits in their leaves.

   d)   Greenflies feed by sticking their hollow tube-like mouthparts into the phloem of a plant stem.

4 The diagram shows a cross-section through the stem of a plant.

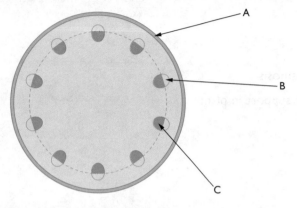

a) Identify the tissues labelled A, B and C.

b) A young stem was placed in a solution of a red dye for an hour. Which tissue in the diagram would be most likely to contain the dye? Explain your answer.

5 A simple volume potometer was used to measure the uptake of water by a leafy shoot under four different conditions. During the experiment, the temperature, humidity and light intensity were kept constant. The conditions were:

1. Leaves in still air with no vaseline applied to them.

2. Leaves in moving air with no vaseline applied to them.

3. Leaves in still air with the lower leaf surface covered in vaseline.

4. Leaves in moving air with the lower surface covered in vaseline.

The results are shown in the graph.

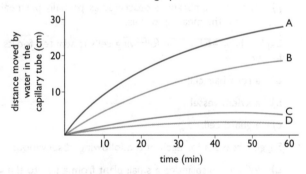

a) Complete the table below to show which condition (1, 2, 3 or 4) is most likely to produce curve A, B, C and D. One has been done for you:

Condition	Curve
1	B
2	
3	
4	

b) Explain why moving air affects the rate of uptake of water by the shoot.

6 During transpiration, water moves through the cells of a leaf and is finally lost through the stomata by evaporation.

a) Explain how water travels from one cell to another in the leaf.

b) How would the rate of transpiration be affected if the air temperature increased from 20 °C to 30 °C? Explain your answer.

c) Describe an adaptation found in plants living in dry habitats that decreases water loss from the leaves.

7 A scientist measured the uptake of sulphate ions by seedlings grown in a liquid culture. Two groups of seedlings were used. The roots of the first group were given oxygen bubbled through the culture solution. The second group had nitrogen gas bubbled through the solution, to produce anaerobic conditions around the roots. The amount of sulphate taken up by the seedlings is shown in the table below.

Time (h)	Sulphate absorbed with roots in aerobic conditions (arbitrary units)	Sulphate absorbed with roots in anaerobic conditions (arbitrary units)
0	0	0
1	108	65
2	143	93
3	176	106
4	195	112
5	216	115
6	237	125
7	249	131
8	267	137

a) Plot a graph of both sets of results on the same axes.

b) What process that uses oxygen takes place in most cells?

c) Explain why the roots in aerobic conditions absorbed more sulphate than when oxygen was not present.

8 Write a short description of how water moves from the soil through the plant. Your description must include these words: xylem, evaporation, root hair cells, water potential, stomata and osmosis.

Underline each of these words in your description.

Chapter 12: Chemical Coordination in Plants

Like animals, plants sense and respond to their environment, but the responses are usually much slower than those of animals because their movements are due to changes in the plant's growth. This chapter is about these growth responses, and the chemicals that coordinate them.

Chapter 6 explains how animals sense and respond to changes in their environment. Animals usually respond very quickly – for example the reflex action resulting from a painful stimulus (page 73) is over in a fraction of a second.

As in animals, some species of plant can respond rapidly to a stimulus, for example the Venus' flytrap (Figure 12.1). This plant has modified leaves, which close quickly around their 'prey', trapping it. The plant then secretes enzymes to digest the insect. The movement is brought about by rapid changes in turgor of specialised cells at the base of the leaves.

Figure 12.1 *The Venus' flytrap catches and digests insects to gain extra nutrients. The plant responds very quickly to a fly landing on one of its leaves.*

Tropisms

Most plants do not respond to stimuli as quickly as this, because their response normally involves changing their rate of growth. Different parts of plants may grow at different rates, and a plant may respond to a stimulus by increasing growth near the tip of its shoot or roots. Imagine a plant growing normally in a pot. Usually, most light will be falling on the plant from above. If you turn the plant on its side and leave it for a day or so, you will see that its shoot starts to grow upwards (Figure 12.2).

There are two stimuli acting on the plant in Figure 12.2. One is the direction of the light that falls on the plant. The other stimulus is gravity. Both light and gravity are **directional stimuli** (they act in a particular direction). The growth response of a plant to a directional stimulus is called a **tropism**. If the growth response is *towards* the direction of the stimulus, it is a *positive* tropism, and if it is *away* from the direction of the stimulus, it is a *negative* tropism. The stem of the plant in Figure 12.2 is showing a positive **phototropism** and a negative **geotropism**, which both make the stem grow upwards.

The aerial part of a plant (the 'shoot') needs light to carry out photosynthesis. This means that in most species, a positive phototropism is the strongest tropic response of the shoot. If a shoot grows towards the light, it ensures that

Figure 12.2 *This bean has responded to being placed horizontally. The growing shoot has started to bend upwards.*

Phototropisms are growth responses to light from one direction. Geotropisms are growth responses to the direction of gravity ('geo' refers to the Earth).

137

the leaves, held out at an angle to the stem, will receive the maximum amount of sunlight. This response is easily seen in any plant placed near a window, or another source of 'one-way' or *unidirectional* light (Figure 12.3).

In darkness or uniform light, the shoot shows a negative geotropism. As you might expect, the roots of plants are strongly positively geotropic. This response makes sure that the roots grow down into the soil, where they can reach water and mineral ions, and obtain anchorage.

The roots of some species that have been studied are also negatively phototropic, but most roots don't respond to directional light at all. In the same way, some experiments have shown that roots of a few species show positive **hydrotropism** (attraction to water). The common tropisms are summarised in Table 12.1.

Light from one direction is called 'unidirectional'. If light shines on the plant evenly from all directions, this is called 'uniform' light.

Figure 12.3 The shoots of these cress seedlings are showing a positive phototropism.

Stimulus	Name of response	Response of shoots	Response of roots
light	phototropism	grow towards light source (positive phototropism)	most species show no response; some grow away from light (negative phototropism)
gravity	geotropism	grow away from direction of gravity (negative geotropism)	grow towards direction of gravity (positive geotropism)
water	hydrotropism	none	some species may grow towards water (positive hydrotropism)

Table 12.1: *Common responses of plants to directional stimuli (tropisms).*

Detecting the light stimulus – plant hormones

Plants do not have the obvious sense organs and nervous system of animals, but since they respond to stimuli such as light and gravity, they must have some way of detecting them and coordinating the response. The detection system of phototropism was first investigated by the great English biologist Charles Darwin (see Chapter 19) in the late nineteenth century. Instead of using stems, Darwin (and later scientists) used cereal **coleoptiles**, which are easier to grow and use in experiments.

Darwin showed that the stimulus of unidirectional light was detected by the tip of the coleoptile, and transmitted to a growth zone, just behind the tip (Figure 12.5).

A coleoptile is a protective sheath that covers the first leaves of a cereal seedling. It protects the delicate leaves as the shoot emerges through the soil (Figure 12.4).

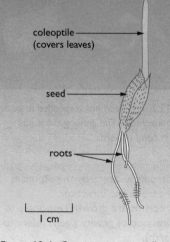

Figure 12.4 *Germinating oat seedling.*

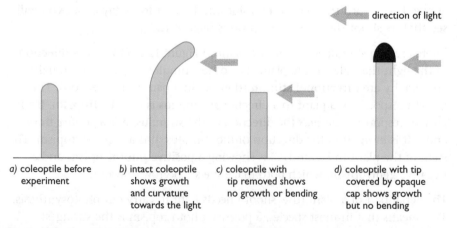

direction of light

a) coleoptile before experiment

b) intact coleoptile shows growth and curvature towards the light

c) coleoptile with tip removed shows no growth or bending

d) coleoptile with tip covered by opaque cap shows growth but no bending

Figure 12.5 *Darwin's experiments with phototropism (1880).*

Since plants don't have a nervous system, biologists began to look for a chemical messenger, or **hormone**, that might be the cause of phototropism in coleoptiles. Between 1910 and 1926 several scientists investigated this problem. Some of their results are summarised in Figure 12.6.

Experiment 1

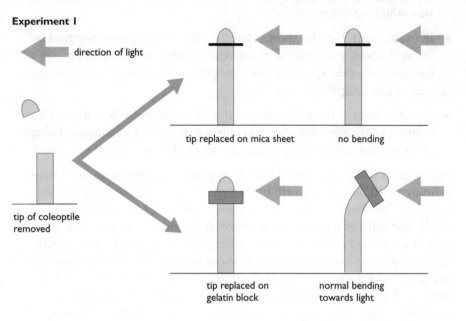

Experiment 2

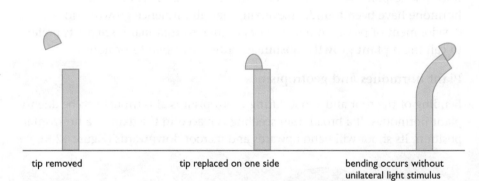

Experiment 3

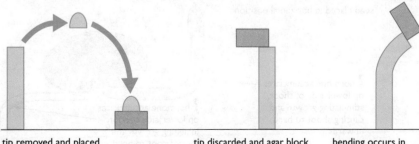

Figure 12.6 *Experiments on coleoptiles that helped to explain the mechanism of phototropism.*

- In experiment 1, the stimulus for growth was found to pass through materials such as gelatin, which absorbs water-soluble chemicals, but not through materials such as mica (a mineral) which is impermeable to water. This made biologists think that the stimulus was a chemical that was soluble in water.

- In experiment 2, it was shown that the phototropic response could be brought about, even *without* unidirectional light, by removing a coleoptile tip ('decapitating' the coleoptile) and placing the tip on one side of the decapitated stalk.

- In experiment 3, it was found that the hormone could be collected in another water-absorbing material (a block of agar jelly). Placing the agar block on one side of the decapitated coleoptile stalk caused it to bend.

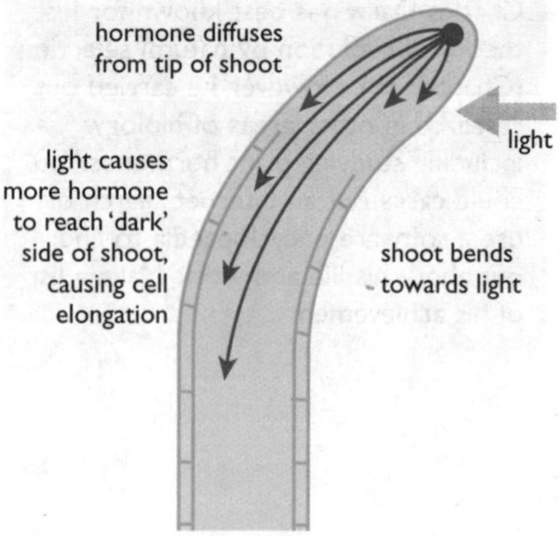

Experiments like 2 and 3 led scientists to believe that the hormone caused bending by stimulating growth on the side of the coleoptile furthest from the light. The theory is that the hormone is produced in the tip of the shoot, and diffuses back down the shoot. If the shoot is in the dark, or if light is all around the shoot, the hormone diffuses at equal rates on each side of the shoot, so it stimulates the shoot equally on all sides. However, if the shoot is receiving light from one direction, the hormone moves away from the light as it diffuses downwards. The higher concentration of hormone on the 'dark' side of the shoot stimulates cells there to grow, making the shoot bend towards the light (Figure 12.7).

Since these experiments were carried out, scientists have identified the hormone responsible. It is called **auxin**. Several other types of plant hormone have been found. Like auxin, they all influence growth and development of plants in one way or another, so that many scientists prefer to call them **plant growth substances** rather than plant hormones.

Figure 12.7 *How movement of a plant hormone causes phototropism.*

> 'Auxin' should really be 'auxins', since there are a number of chemicals with very similar structures making up a group of closely related plant hormones.

Plant hormones and geotropism

Bending of the root and shoot during geotropism is also thought to be due to plant hormones. If a broad bean seedling is placed in the dark in a horizontal position, its shoot will bend upwards and its root downwards (Figure 12.8).

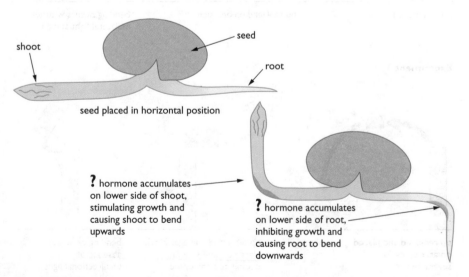

Figure 12.8 *Geotropism in a broad bean seedling. It was once thought that movement of auxin caused this response. We now know that the true explanation is not as simple as this.*

As well as auxins, there are four other main groups of plant hormones, called gibberellins, cytokinins, abscisic acid and ethene. They control many aspects of plant growth and development, apart from tropisms. These include growth of buds, leaves and fruit, fruit ripening, seed germination, leaf fall and opening of stomata, to name just a few. In addition to auxins, abscisic acid, ethene and gibberellins have all been shown to be involved in geotropisms.

It was once thought that these geotropic responses of the shoot and root were due to auxin. The auxin was supposed to be produced at the tip of the shoot, and to sink under the influence of gravity as it diffused back from the tip. A high concentration of auxin would increase growth on the lower side of the shoot, causing it to bend upwards. The downward growth of the root was supposed to be caused in a similar way, except that auxin *inhibited* growth on the lower side. We know now that these explanations are not the whole story. Although some movement of auxin happens due to the effect of gravity, it is not enough to explain geotropisms, where other hormones seem to be involved.

Investigating which part of a shoot is sensitive to light

Carry out the following:

1. Soak a number of seeds in water overnight, then allow them to germinate in Petri dishes. Leave room between the seeds so that you can measure them when they start to grow.

2. When the coleoptiles have grown to a length of about 10–15 mm, treat them as follows (Figure 12.9).

   - Cut off about 2 mm from the tip of the coleoptiles in the first dish.

   - Cover the tips of the coleoptiles in the second dish with aluminium foil.

   - Leave the coleoptiles in the third dish untreated as a control.

3. For each dish, measure the length of the coleoptiles and calculate the mean coleoptile length for each treatment group.

4. Place the dishes in the boxes with a light shining from one side (Figure 12.9). Leave them for 24–48 hours.

5. Find the new mean length of the coleoptiles in each dish, and calculate the percentage change in length. Record any change in direction of growth of the coleoptiles in the three treatment groups.

6. Write up the experiment and explain your results.

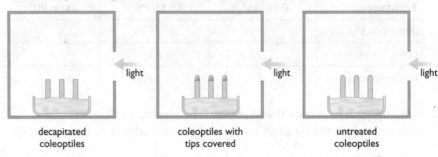

decapitated coleoptiles   coleoptiles with tips covered   untreated coleoptiles

Figure 12.9 *Investigating phototropism.*

Investigating the effects of auxin in lanolin on the growth of coleoptiles

Lanolin is a lipid substance made from wool. If it is smeared onto the surface of a coleoptile, it will stick to it. A dilute solution of auxin can be mixed with lanolin, so that the auxin can be applied to the surface with the lanolin. In this experiment you will use an auxin called indoleacetic acid, or

IAA. Lanolin will melt if it is kept in a beaker of warm water at about 40–50 °C so that it becomes easier to apply.

Carry out the following:

1. Soak a number of seeds in water overnight, then allow them to germinate in Petri dishes. Leave room between the seeds so that you can measure them when they start to grow.

2. When the coleoptiles have grown to a length of about 10–15 mm, treat them as follows (Figure 12.10).

   • Smear IAA in lanolin *along one side* of each coleoptile in the first dish. Apply the lanolin just behind the tip, for a distance of about 5 mm.

   • In the second dish, apply lanolin only, in the same way.

   • Do not treat the seedlings in the remaining dish.

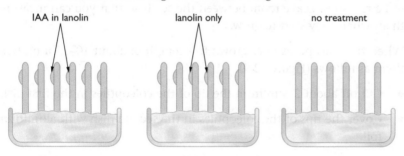

Figure 12.10

3. Label the three groups of seedlings and place them in a dark cupboard.

4. If possible, examine the coleoptiles after 4 or 5 hours, or at least by the following morning. Note down your observations. You could also record the angle of bending of each coleoptile (Figure 12.11). You can then record the number of coleoptiles in each dish that fit into different categories, as shown in the table below. (*Note*: The 'bending categories' can be adjusted to suit your results.)

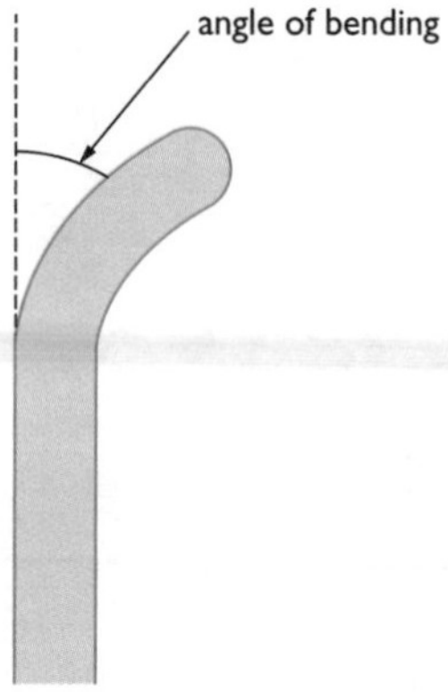

Treatment	0 to 45°	45 to 90°	over 90°
lanolin + IAA			
lanolin only			
no treatment			

Figure 12.11

5. Write up your experiment and explain the results. In the methods section, explain the controls you have used and why they are necessary.

Use of a clinostat to show geotropism in roots

A **clinostat** is a piece of apparatus consisting of an electric motor turning a cork disc. Germinating seeds can be attached to the disc. The motor turns the disc and seeds around very slowly, so that the movement eliminates any directional stimulus that may be acting on the seeds (Figure 12.12). The clinostat can be turned through 90°, so that the disc rotates either horizontally or vertically.

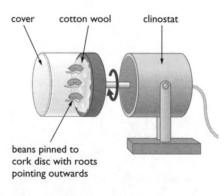

Figure 12.12 *A clinostat.*

Carry out the following:

1. Soak a few bean seeds in water overnight. Place the seeds on wet cotton wool for a day or two until the first root of each seed (called the radicle) has grown to about 2 cm in length.

2. Attach wet cotton wool to the cork disc of two clinostats. Pin three or four of the germinating bean seeds onto the discs, with their radicles pointing outwards. Place the covers over the discs to keep the air around the beans moist.

3. Turn the clinostats on their sides, as shown in Figure 12.12. Switch on one clinostat, but leave the other switched off. What is the purpose of this second clinostat?

4. Leave both clinostats set up for a few days. Make sure that you keep the cotton wool damp.

5. Observe the results. Which way do the radicles of each set of beans grow?

6. Write up your experiment and explain the results.

7. Plan an investigation using two clinostats to find out if the growing shoot of a plant responds to unidirectional light. State the hypothesis you will test, and explain how you will make sure that your experiment is controlled.

End of Chapter Checklist

You should now be able to:

- understand that plants respond to stimuli
- describe the geotropic responses of roots and stems
- describe positive phototropism of stems
- understand how phototropic responses in stems are the result of differential growth caused by auxin
- recall controlled experiments to demonstrate phototropic and geotropic plant growth responses.

Questions

More questions on chemical coordination in plants can be found at the end of Section C on page 152.

1   a) What are the main stimuli affecting the growth of

      i)   the shoot?

      ii) the root?

   b) How does a plant benefit from a positive phototropism in its stem?

2   Draw a labelled diagram to show how auxin brings about phototropism in a coleoptile that has light shining on it from one direction.

3   An experiment was carried out to investigate phototropism in a coleoptile. The diagram shows what was done. Predict the results you would expect to get in each of the experiments *a)* to *c)*. Explain your answers.

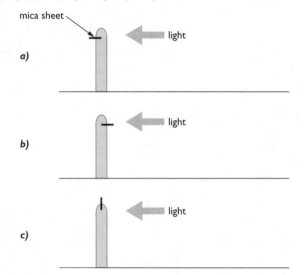

Chapter 13: Reproduction in Plants

Plants, like animals, can reproduce sexually and asexually. The sexual organs of a flowering plant are its flowers, which produce pollen and ovules containing the flower's gametes. This chapter looks at both types of reproduction in flowering plants.

As each method of asexual reproduction involves some part of the plant growing, new cells must be produced. These cells are produced by **mitosis** and so are all genetically identical. This means that all the offspring formed by asexual reproduction will also be genetically identical.

Sexual and asexual reproduction

Plants too can reproduce both sexually and asexually. Table 13.1 summarises some of the differences between the two.

Feature of the process	Sexual reproduction	Asexual reproduction
sex cells produced	yes	no
fertilisation takes place	yes	no
variation in offspring	yes	no
has survival value in:	changing environment	stable environment

Table 13.1: *Sexual and asexual reproduction compared.*

Asexual reproduction in plants

There are many different methods of asexual reproduction in plants. Most involve some part of the plant growing, and then breaking away from the parent plant before growing into a new plant (Figure 13.1).

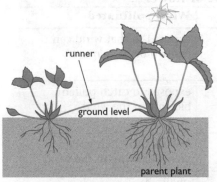
A new plant is produced where the runner touches the ground.

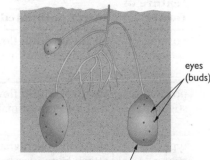
Potato tubers form underground at the ends of branches from the main stem. Each potato can produce several new plants from the 'eyes' which are buds.

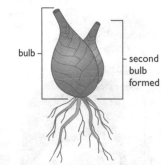
Some plants form bulbs. They are the bases of leaves which have become swollen with food. Buds in them can develop into new plants. Plants can form more than one bulb.

Figure 13.1 *Some methods of asexual reproduction in plants.*

Figure 13.2 *This geranium cutting is starting to grow roots. If planted, it will grow into a new plant.*

Gardeners often take advantage of the ways that plants can reproduce asexually. They use runners, bulbs and tubers to produce more plants. Another type of asexual reproduction is to grow plants from **cuttings**. A piece of a plant's stem, with a few leaves attached, is cut from a healthy plant. This is planted in damp compost, where it will grow roots and develop into a new plant (Figure 13.2).

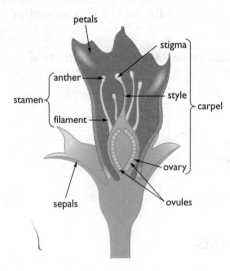

Figure 13.3 *The main structures in an insect-pollinated flower.*

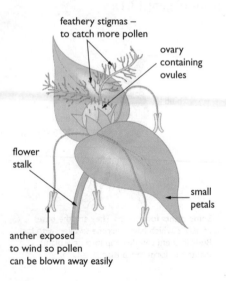

Figure 13.4 *A wind-pollinated flower.*

Haploid cells have only half the number of chromosomes of other body cells of that species.

Sexual reproduction in plants

Plants produce specialised, haploid sex cells in their flowers. The male sex cells are the **pollen grains** and the female sex cells are **ova**. Just as in animals, the male sex cells must be transferred to the female sex cells. This is called **pollination**. Pollination is normally carried out either by wind or insects. Following pollination, **fertilisation** takes place and the **zygote** formed develops into a **seed**, which, in turn, becomes enclosed in a **fruit**.

Production of sex cells and pollination

The sex cells are produced by meiosis in structures in the flowers. Pollen grains are produced in the **anthers** of the **stamens**. The ova are produced in **ovules** in the **ovaries**.

In pollination, pollen grains are transferred from the anthers of a flower to the stigma. If this occurs within the same flower it is called **self-pollination**. If the pollen grains are transferred to a different flower, it is called **cross-pollination**. Pollination can occur by wind or by insect in either case.

Plants that are wind-pollinated produce flowers with a different structure to those of insect-pollinated flowers. These differences are related to the different methods of pollination of the flowers. Figure 13.3 shows the structure of a typical insect-pollinated flower and Figure 13.4 shows the structure of a typical wind-pollinated flower. Table 13.2 summarises the main differences between insect-pollinated flowers and wind-pollinated flowers.

Feature of flower	Type of flower	
	Insect pollinated	**Wind pollinated**
position of stamens	enclosed within flower so that insect must make contact	exposed so that wind can easily blow pollen away
position of stigma	enclosed within flower so that insect must make contact	exposed to catch pollen blowing in the wind
type of stigma	sticky so pollen grains attach from insects	feathery, to catch pollen grains blowing in the wind
size of petals	large to attract insects	small
colour of petals	brightly coloured to attract insects	not brightly coloured
nectaries	present – nectar is a 'reward' for insects	absent
pollen grains	small, sticky grains to stick to insects' bodies	larger, inflated grains to carry in the wind

Table 13.2: *Differences between insect-pollinated and wind-pollinated flowers.*

Fertilisation

Pollination transfers the pollen grain to the stigma. However, for fertilisation to take place, the nucleus of the pollen grain must fuse with the nucleus of the ovum, which is inside an ovule in the ovary. To transfer the nucleus to the ovum, the pollen grain grows a tube, which digests its way through the tissue of the style and into the ovary. Here it grows around to the opening in an ovule. The tip of the tube dissolves and allows the pollen grain nucleus to move out of the tube and into the ovule. Here it fertilises the ovum (egg cell) nucleus. These events are summarised in Figure 13.5.

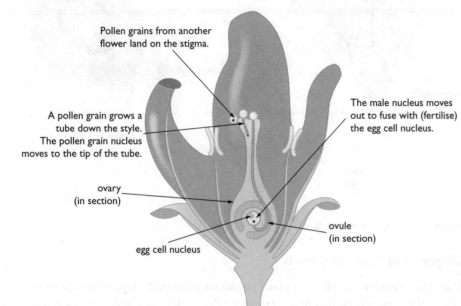

Pollen grains from another flower land on the stigma.

A pollen grain grows a tube down the style. The pollen grain nucleus moves to the tip of the tube.

The male nucleus moves out to fuse with (fertilise) the egg cell nucleus.

ovary (in section)

ovule (in section)

egg cell nucleus

Figure 13.5 *Pollination and fertilisation.*

Seed and fruit formation

Once fertilisation has occurred, a number of changes take place in the ovule and ovary that will lead to the fertilised ovule becoming a seed and the ovary in which it is found becoming a fruit. Different flowers produce different types of fruits, but in all cases the following four changes take place.

1. The zygote develops into an embryonic plant with small root (**radicle**) and shoot (**plumule**).

2. The other contents of the ovule develop into **cotyledons** which will be a food store for the young plant when the seed **germinates**.

3. The ovule wall becomes the seed coat or **testa**.

4. The ovary wall becomes the fruit coat; this can take many forms depending on the type of fruit.

Figure 13.6 summarises these changes as they occur in the plum flower. A coconut fruit forms in the same way, but the outer coat is fibrous rather than fleshy as it is in the plum.

Any structure that contains seeds is a fruit. A pea pod is a fruit. The 'pod' is the fruit wall, formed from the ovary wall, and the peas are individual seeds. Each one was formed from a fertilised ovule.

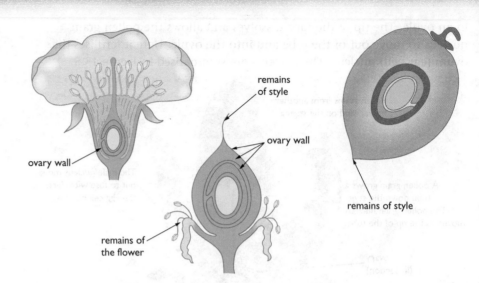

Figure 13.6 *How a plum fruit forms.*

Dispersal of fruits and seeds

If all the seeds produced by a plant began to **germinate** (grow) in the same place, there would be too much competition for the available resources such as water, mineral ions and oxygen. To avoid this, plants **disperse** their seeds. Some are dispersed still inside the fruits; others are dispersed as seeds. Some seeds are dispersed by wind and others by animals. Figure 13.7 shows some wind-dispersed seeds and fruits. Figure 13.8 shows some seeds and fruits dispersed by animals.

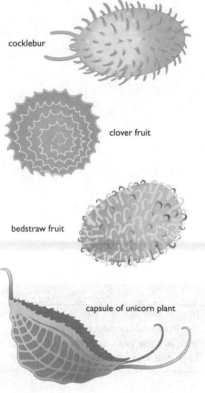

cocklebur

clover fruit

bedstraw fruit

capsule of unicorn plant

Figure 13.8 *These seeds are dispersed by animals. They have hairs or hooks that catch in the animal's fur. Seeds can also be dispersed by animals that eat the fruits and pass the undigested seeds out in their faeces.*

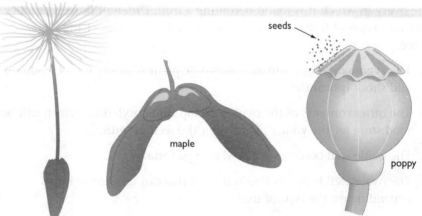

dandelion

maple

seeds

poppy

Figure 13.7 *These seeds are dispersed by wind. They are either very small and light or their fruits have 'wings' or a 'parachute' to catch the wind.*

The fruits of coconut palms are dispersed by water. They can float many hundreds of miles before reaching a beach where they can germinate. Figure 13.9 shows a coconut palm beginning to grow from the fruit on a beach where it has landed.

Figure 13.9 *A coconut palm growing from a fruit on a beach.*

Germination

A seed contains a plant embryo, consisting of a root (radicle), shoot (plumule) and one or two seed leaves, called **cotyledons**. It also contains a food store. During germination, the food store is used up, providing the nutrients to allow the radicle and plumule to grow. The radicle grows down into the soil, where it will absorb water and mineral ions. The plumule grows upwards towards the light, where it can start the process of photosynthesis (Figure 13.10). Once the small plant (seedling) is able to photosynthesise, germination is over.

The seeds of plants such as peas or beans have two cotyledons. They are called **dicotyledonous** plants, or **dicots**. Seeds of grasses and other narrow-leaved plants, such as irises and orchids have only one cotyledon. They are **monocotyledonous** plants, or **monocots**.

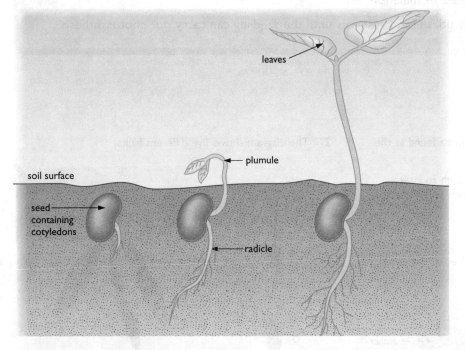

Figure 13.10 *Germination in the broad bean. In this species, the cotyledons remain below the ground when the seed germinates. In other species (e.g. the French bean), they are carried above the ground during germination.*

The food store of peas or beans is present in the cotyledons. It consists mainly of starch and protein. In monocots such as maize, there is a separate food store of starch.

The conditions needed for germination

When seeds are dispersed from the parent plant they are usually very dry, containing only about 10% water. This low water content restricts a seed's metabolism, so that it can remain alive but **dormant** for a long time, sometimes for many years.

When a seed germinates, dormancy is broken. The seed's food store is broken down by enzymes and respired aerobically (see Chapter 1). This means that germination needs the following conditions:

- **warm temperatures**, so that enzymes can act efficiently (see Chapter 1)

- **water**, for chemical reactions to take place in solution

- **oxygen**, for respiration.

> There is a well-known story that wheat seeds taken from ancient Egyptian tombs of the Pharaohs can germinate after being dormant for 6000 years. Unfortunately, this is a myth. Scientists have shown that many cereals can be stored for centuries if they are kept in cool, dry conditions. However, all attempts to revive 'mummy wheat' have failed.

End of Chapter Checklist

You should now be able to:

- describe the differences between sexual and asexual reproduction
- understand that plants can reproduce asexually by natural and artificial methods
- describe the structures of an insect-pollinated and a wind-pollinated flower and explain how each is adapted for pollination
- describe pollination and the growth of the pollen tube
- understand that fertilisation involves the fusion of a male and female gamete and leads to seed and fruit formation
- recall the conditions needed for seed germination
- understand how germinating seeds utilise food reserves until the seedling can carry out photosynthesis.

Questions

More questions on reproduction in plants can be found at the end of Section C on page 152.

1   The diagram below shows a section through an insect pollinated flower. Pollination happens when pollen grains land on part X.

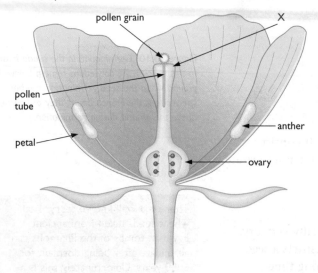

a)   Name part X.

b)   How are insects attracted to a flower like this? Give two ways.

c)   Copy the diagram and extend the pollen tube to show where it would go when fully grown.

2   The diagram shows five different fruits.

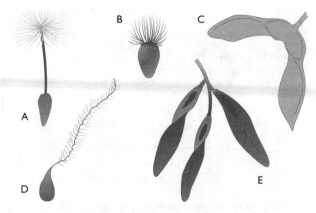

a)   i)   How are these fruits dispersed from their parent plants? Give reasons for your answer.

ii)   Describe *two* other ways in which fruits can be dispersed. Give an example for each method of dispersal.

b)   Explain the benefit of fruits being dispersed from their parent plant.

c)   Would the plants that grew from the fruits in the diagram be identical to the parent plants? Explain your answer.

3 The diagram shows a potato plant producing new tubers (potatoes). Buds on the parent plant grow into stems that grow downwards, called stolons. The ends of each stolon develop into a new tuber.

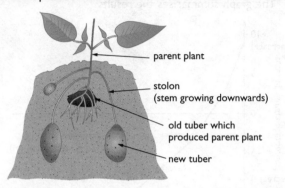

parent plant

stolon
(stem growing downwards)

old tuber which
produced parent plant

new tuber

a) Give *two* pieces of evidence which show that this is an asexual method of reproduction.

b) Explain why all the new tubers will be genetically identical.

c) Even though the tubers are genetically identical, the plants that grow from them may not be the same height. Explain why.

d) Why do wild plants need to reproduce sexually as well as asexually?

4 The drawing shows a wind-pollinated flower.

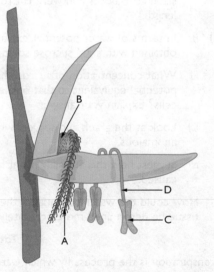

B

A

D

C

a) Name the structures labelled A, B, C and D.

b) Give *three* pieces of evidence *visible in the diagram*, which show that this flower is wind-pollinated.

c) Describe how fertilisation takes place once a flower has been pollinated.

d) Describe *four* ways in which you would expect an insect-pollinated flower to be different from the flower shown.

5 The drawing shows a strawberry plant reproducing in two ways.

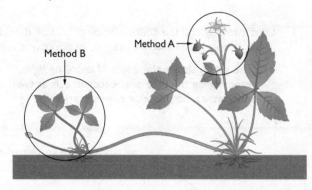

Method A

Method B

a) Which of the two methods of reproduction shown will result in offspring that show genetic variation? Explain your answer.

b) Is the strawberry flower likely to be wind-pollinated or insect-pollinated? Give reasons for your answer.

c) Many animals eat strawberry fruits. How does this help to disperse the strawberry seeds?

6 All banana plants are reproduced asexually. Biologists are concerned for their future, as a new strain of fungus has appeared which is killing all the banana plants in some plantations.

a) Explain why the fungus is able to kill *all* the banana plants in some plantations.

b) Explain why this would be less likely to happen if banana plants reproduced sexually.

c) Describe the benefits of reproducing banana plants asexually.

End of Section Questions

1   Light intensity and the concentration of carbon dioxide in the atmosphere influence the rate of photosynthesis.

a)   The graph shows the effect of changing light intensity on the rate of photosynthesis at two different carbon dioxide concentrations.

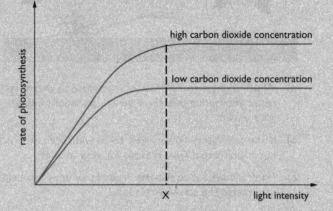

i)   Describe the effect of light intensity on the rate of photosynthesis at each concentration of carbon dioxide up to light intensity X and beyond light intensity X. *(8 marks)*

ii)   Which factor limits the rate of photosynthesis up to light intensity X and beyond light intensity X? *(2 mark)*

Explain your answer in each case. *(3 marks)*

b)   **i)**   Describe two other factors which influence the rate of photosynthesis. *(2 marks)*

ii)   Explain why each is a limiting factor. *(4 marks)*

c)   'Photosynthesis is a means of transducing light energy into chemical energy.'

Explain what this statement means. *(2 marks)*

Total 21 marks

2   In an investigation to determine the water potential of potato cells, the following procedure was adopted.

●   Cylinders of potato tissue were obtained using a cork borer and each was cut to a length of 5 cm.

●   Each was dried and then weighed.

●   Three potato cylinders were placed in each of seven different concentrations of sucrose solution and left for 2 hours.

●   The cylinders were then removed from the solutions, dried and reweighed. The percentage change in mass for each was calculated, and then an average percentage change in mass calculated for each solution.

The graph summarises the results.

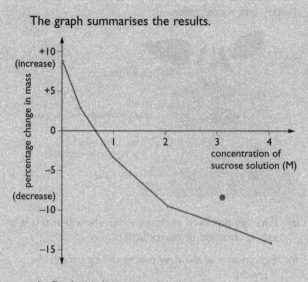

a)   Explain why:

i)   the cylinders were dried before and after being placed in the sucrose solutions *(1 mark)*

ii)   three cylinders were used for each solution *(1 mark)*

iii)   all the cylinders were obtained with the same sized cork borer and were cut to the same length. *(1 mark)*

b)   **i)**   In terms of water potential, explain the result obtained with a 3M sucrose solution. *(3 marks)*

ii)   What concentration of sucrose has a water potential equivalent to that of the potato cells? Explain your answer. *(3 marks)*

iii)   Look at the graph and suggest which result is anomalous. *(1 mark)*

iv)   Suggest how this anomaly might have been caused. *(2 marks)*

c)   How could the water potential of the potato tissue be determined more accurately? *(2 marks)*

Total 14 marks

3   Transpiration is the process by which water moves through plants from roots to leaves. Eventually, it is lost through the stomata.

a)   The diagram shows the main stages in the movement of water through a leaf.

i)   Name the tissues labelled A and B. Explain your answers. *(4 marks)*

ii)   Describe how water is being moved at each of the stages 1, 2, 3 and 4. *(4 marks)*

b)   Describe two ways, visible in the diagram, in which this leaf is adapted to photosynthesise efficiently. *(4 marks)*

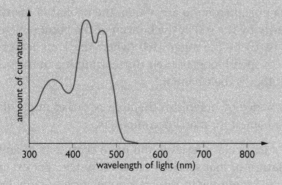

cuticle

upper
epidermis

palisade
mesophyll

spongy
mesophyll

lower
epidermis

cuticle

guard cell   stoma   air spaces

c) For plants living in dry areas, explain a possible conflict between the need to obtain carbon dioxide for photosynthesis and the need to conserve water. *(2 marks)*

Total 14 marks

4 Plants can respond to a range of stimuli.

a) Plant shoots detect and grow towards light.

   i) What is this process called? *(1 mark)*

   ii) Explain how a plant bends towards the light. *(3 marks)*

   iii) Explain the advantage to the plant of this response. *(1 mark)*

b) In an investigation, young plant shoots were exposed to light from one side. The wavelength of the light was varied. The graph summarises the results of the investigation.

   i) Describe the results shown in the graph. *(2 marks)*

   ii) Suggest why the results show this pattern. *(2 marks)*

c) *i)* Name two other stimuli that produce growth responses in plants. *(2 marks)*

   ii) For each stimulus you name, describe the way that both roots and shoots respond. *(4 marks)*

   iii) What is the benefit to the plant of these responses. *(2 marks)*

Total 17 marks

5 The diagram below shows a flower

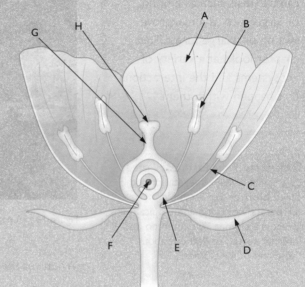

a) Give the letter of the structure which:

   i) produces pollen grains

   ii) becomes the seed

   iii) becomes the fruit wall. *(3 marks)*

b) Write down two ways (that you can see in the diagram) that this flower is adapted for insect pollination. *(2 marks)*

c) Give the letter of the structure which is:

   i) the stigma

   ii) the style

   iii) the filament. *(3 marks)*

d) Explain the difference between:

   i) pollination and fertilisation

   ii) self-pollination and cross-pollination. *(4 marks)*

Total 12 marks

Chapter 14: Ecosystems

An **ecosystem** is a distinct, self-supporting system of organisms interacting with each other and with a physical environment. An ecosystem can be small, such as a pond, or large, such as a mangrove swamp or a large forest. This chapter looks at a variety of ecosystems and the interactions that happen within them.

Large areas of the Earth dominated by a specific type of vegetation are called **biomes**. For example, temperate woodland and tropical rain forest are biomes. You could do an Internet search to find out about these and other biomes.

You may be asked to explain the terms in **bold type** in an examination.

The components of ecosystems

Figure 14.1 *A pond is a small ecosystem.*

Figure 14.2 *A mangrove swamp is a larger ecosystem.*

Whatever their size, ecosystems usually have the same components:

- **producers** – plants which photosynthesise to produce food

- **consumers** – animals that eat plants or other animals

- **decomposers** – decay dead material and help to recycle nutrients

- a physical **environment** – the sum total of the non-biological components of the ecosystem; for example, the water and soil in a pond or the soil and air in a forest.

Within each ecosystem there is a range of **habitats** – these are the places where specific organisms live. Some are provided by the physical environment. For example, in a pond ecosystem, the habitat of many of the plants is provided partly by the soil at the bottom of the pond (where the roots penetrate) and partly by the water itself (where the stem, leaves and flowers grow). Tadpoles spend most of their time swimming in the surface waters of a pond and that is their habitat.

Other habitats are provided by organisms themselves. For example, dead vegetation provides a habitat for many decomposers.

All the organisms of a particular species found in an ecosystem at any one time form the **population** of that species in that ecosystem. For example, in a pond, all the tadpoles swimming in it form a population of tadpoles; all the *Elodea* plants growing in it make up a population of *Elodea*.

The populations of *all* species (all the animals, plants and decomposers) found in a particular ecosystem at any one time form the **community** in that ecosystem. Figure 14.3 illustrates the main components of a pond ecosystem.

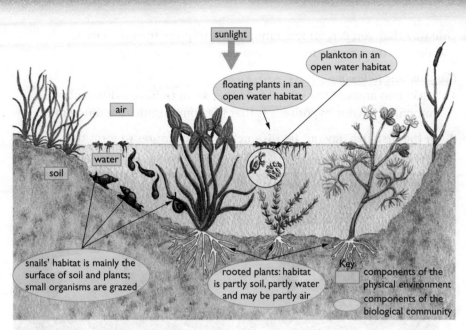

Figure 14.3 *A pond ecosystem.*

Using quadrats to sample from a habitat

When an ecologist wants to know how many organisms there are in a particular habitat, it would not be feasible for him to count them all. Instead, he would be forced to count a smaller representative part of the population, called a **sample**. Sampling of plants, or animals that do not move much (such as snails), can be done using a sampling square called a **quadrat**. A quadrat is usually made from metal, wood or plastic. A suitable size for the quadrat depends on the size of the organisms being sampled. For example, to count plants growing on a school field, you could use a quadrat with sides 0.5 or 1 metre in length (Figure 14.4).

It is important that sampling in an area is carried out **at random**, to avoid **bias**. For example, if you were sampling from a school field, but for convenience only placed your quadrats next to a path, this might not give you a sample that was representative of the whole field. It would be an unrepresentative, or biased, sample.

People often mistakenly call quadrats 'quadrants'. A quadrant is quite different: it is a quarter of a circle.

Figure 14.4 *Students sampling with a quadrat.*

One way that you can sample randomly is to place the quadrats at coordinates on a numbered grid. You can try this for yourself.

Carry out the following:

1. Select two areas of the school field that seem to have a different plant community (your hypothesis is that the communities are different).

2. In the first area, lay out two 10-metre tape measures to form the sides of a square (Figure 14.5).

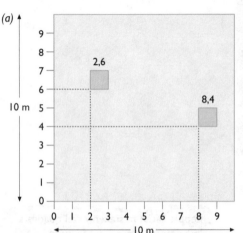

Figure 14.5 (a) A 10-m² grid with 1-m² quadrats positioned at coordinates 2,6 and 8,4. (b) Students using quadrats positioned at coordinates on a grid, placed on a school field, to sample herbaceous plants.

Some books (and teachers!) talk about 'throwing' quadrats. The idea is that you stand in the middle of a field and throw the quadrat over your shoulder. This is supposed to be random, but it isn't! The place where the quadrat falls will depend on where you stand, how hard you throw it, etc. It is wrong to use this method.

3. Generate a pair of random numbers using the random number function on a calculator.

4. Use the pair of numbers as coordinates to position the quadrat in the large square.

5. Count the numbers of each plant species in the quadrat.

6. Repeat for nine more quadrats in the first area of the field, then move the tapes to the second part of the field and use the same method to carry out ten quadrat samples there.

7. Summarise your results as a table and plot them as two bar charts showing the total numbers of each species in the two areas of the field. Do the results support your hypothesis?

Interactions in ecosystems

The organisms in an ecosystem are continually interacting with each other and with their physical environment. Interactions include the following.

- Feeding among the organisms – the plants, animals and decomposers are continually recycling the same nutrients through the ecosystem.

- Competition among the organisms – animals compete for food, shelter, mates, nesting sites; plants compete for carbon dioxide, mineral ions, light and water.

- Interactions between organisms and the environment – plants absorb mineral ions, carbon dioxide and water from the environment; plants

Don't forget that plants take in carbon dioxide and give out oxygen only when there is sufficient light for photosynthesis to occur efficiently. When there is little light, plants take in oxygen and give out carbon dioxide. You should be able to explain why – if not see Chapter 10.

156

also give off water vapour and oxygen into the environment; animals use materials from the environment to build shelters; the temperature of the environment can affect processes occurring in the organisms; processes occurring in organisms can affect the temperature of the environment (all organisms give off some heat).

Feeding relationships

The simplest way of showing feeding relationships within an ecosystem is a **food chain** (Figure 14.6).

In any food chain, the arrow (→) means 'is eaten by'. In the food chain illustrated, the grass is the **producer**. It is a plant so it can photosynthesise and produce food materials. The grasshopper is the **primary consumer**. It is an animal which eats the producer and is also a **herbivore**. The lizard is the **secondary consumer**. It eats the primary consumer and is also a **carnivore**. The different stages in a food chain (producer, primary consumer and secondary consumer) are called **trophic levels**.

Many food chains have more than three links in them. Here are two examples of longer food chains:

filamentous algae → mayfly nymph → caddis fly larvae → salmon

In this freshwater food chain, the extra link in the chain makes the salmon a **tertiary consumer**.

plankton → crustacean → fish → ringed seal → polar bear

In this marine food chain, the fifth link makes the polar bear a **quaternary consumer**. Because nothing eats the polar bear, it is also called the **top carnivore**.

Food chains are a convenient way of showing the feeding relationships between a few organisms in an ecosystem, but they oversimplify the situation. The marine food chain above implies that only crustaceans feed on plankton, which is not true. Some whales and other mammals also feed on plankton. For a fuller understanding, you need to consider how the different food chains in an ecosystem relate to each other. Figure 14.7 gives a clearer picture of the feeding relationships involved in a freshwater ecosystem in which salmon are the top carnivores. This is the **food web** of the salmon.

This is still a simplification of the true situation, as some feeding relationships are still not shown. It does, however, give some indication of the interrelationships that exist between food chains in an ecosystem. With a little thought, you can predict how changes in the numbers of an organism in one food chain in the food web might affect those in another food chain. For example, if the leech population were to decline through disease, there could be several possible consequences:

- the stonefly nymph population could increase as there would be more midge larvae to feed on

- the stonefly nymph population could decrease as the mature salmon might eat more of them as there would be fewer leeches

- the numbers could stay static due to a combination of the above.

grass

grasshopper

Figure 14.6 *A simple food chain.*

Although food webs give us more information than food chains, they don't give any information about how many, or what mass of organisms is involved. Neither do they show the role of the decomposers. To see this, we must look at other ways of presenting information about feeding relationships in an ecosystem.

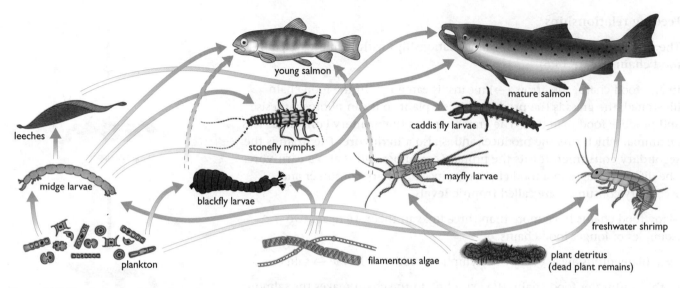

Figure 14.7 *The food web of the salmon. As you can see, young salmon have a slightly different diet to mature salmon.*

Ecological pyramids

Ecological pyramids are diagrams that represent the relative amounts of organisms at each trophic level in a food chain. There are two main types:

- **pyramids of numbers**, which represent the numbers of organisms in each trophic level in a food chain, irrespective of their mass

- **pyramids of biomass**, which show the total mass of the organisms in each trophic level, irrespective of their numbers.

> **Biomass** is the total amount of living material in an organism.

Consider these two food chains:

grass → grasshopper → frog → bird   oak tree → aphid → ladybird → bird

Figures 14.8 and 14.9 show the pyramids of numbers and biomass for these two food chains.

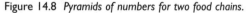

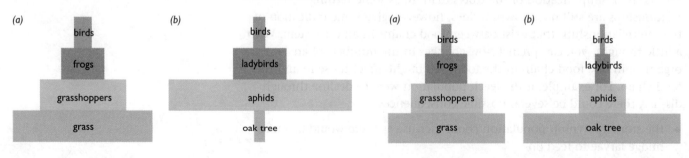

Figure 14.8 *Pyramids of numbers for two food chains.*

Figure 14.9 *Pyramids of biomass for the two food chains.*

The two pyramids for the 'grass' food chain look the same – the numbers at each trophic level decrease. The *total* biomass also decreases along the food chain – the mass of *all* the grass plants in a large field would be more than that of *all* the grasshoppers which would be more than that of *all* the frogs, and so on.

The two pyramids for the 'oak tree' food chain look different because of the size of the oak trees. Each oak tree can support many thousands of aphids, so the numbers *increase* from first to second trophic levels. But each ladybird will need to eat many aphids and each bird will need to eat many ladybirds, so the numbers *decrease* at the third and fourth trophic levels. However, the total biomass *decreases* at each trophic level – the biomass of one oak tree is much greater than that of the thousands of aphids it supports. The total biomass of all these aphids is greater than that of the ladybirds, which is greater than that of the birds.

Suppose the birds in the second food chain are parasitised by nematode worms. The food chain now becomes:

oak tree → aphid → ladybird → bird → nematode worm

The pyramid of numbers now takes on a very strange appearance (Figure 14.10a) because of the large numbers of parasites on each bird. The pyramid of biomass, however, has a true pyramid shape because the total biomass (Figure 14.10b) of the nematode worms must be less than that of the birds they parasitise.

Why do diagrams of feeding relationships give a pyramid shape?

The explanation is relatively straightforward (Figure 14.11). When a rabbit eats grass, not all of the materials in the grass plant end up as rabbit! There are losses:

- some parts of the grass are not eaten (the roots for example)

- some parts are not digested and so are not absorbed – even though rabbits have a very efficient digestive system

- some of the materials absorbed form excretory products

- many of the materials are respired to release energy, with the loss of carbon dioxide and water.

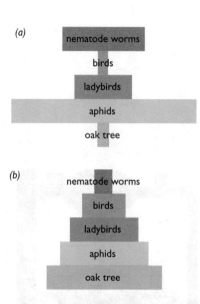

(a)

(b)

Figure 14.10 *(a) A pyramid of numbers and (b) a pyramid of biomass for the parasitised food chain.*

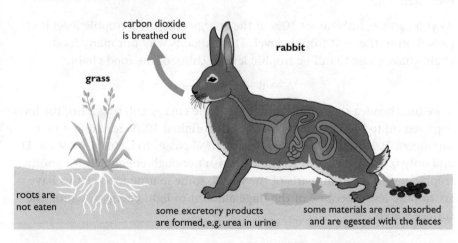

Figure 14.11 *Not all the grass eaten by a rabbit ends up as rabbit tissue.*

In fact, only a small fraction of the materials in the grass ends up in new cells in the rabbit. Similar losses are repeated at each stage in the food chain, so smaller and smaller amounts of biomass are available for growth at successive trophic levels. The shape of pyramids of biomass reflects this.

Feeding is a way of transferring energy between organisms. Another way of modelling ecosystems looks at the energy flow between the various trophic levels.

The flow of energy through ecosystems

This approach focuses less on individual organisms and food chains and rather more on energy transfer between trophic levels (producers, consumers and decomposers) in the whole ecosystem. There are a number of key ideas that you should understand at the outset.

- Photosynthesis 'fixes' sunlight energy into chemicals such as glucose and starch.

- Respiration releases energy from organic compounds such as glucose.

- Almost all other biological processes (e.g. muscle contraction, growth, reproduction, excretion, active transport) use the energy released in respiration.

- If the energy released in respiration is used to produce new cells (general body cells in growth and sex cells in reproduction) then the energy remains 'fixed' in molecules in that organism. It can be passed on to the next trophic level through feeding.

- If the energy released in respiration is used for other processes then it will, once used, eventually escape as heat from the organism. Energy is therefore lost from food chains and webs at each trophic level.

This can be shown in an **energy flow diagram**. Figure 14.12 shows the main ways in which energy is transferred in an ecosystem. It also gives the amounts of energy transferred between the trophic levels of a grassland ecosystem.

As you can see, only about 10% of the energy entering a trophic level is passed on to the next trophic level. This explains why not many food chains have more than five trophic levels. Think of the food chain:

$$A \rightarrow B \rightarrow C \rightarrow D \rightarrow E$$

If we use the idea that only about 10% of the energy entering a trophic level is passed on to the next level, then, of the original 100% reaching A (a producer), 10% passes to B, 1% (10% of 10%) passes to C, 0.1% passes to D and only 0.001% passes to E. There just isn't enough energy left for another trophic level. In certain parts of the world, some marine food chains have six trophic levels because of the huge amount of light energy reaching the surface waters.

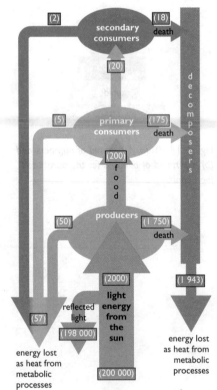

All figures given are kilojoules ($\times 10^5$)/m²/year.

Figure 14.12 *The main ways in which energy is transferred in an ecosystem. The amounts of energy transferred through 1 m² of a grassland ecosystem per year are shown in brackets.*

Cycling nutrients through ecosystems

The chemicals that make up our bodies have all been around before – probably many times! You may have in your body some carbon atoms that were part of the body of Mahatma Gandhi or were in carbon dioxide molecules breathed out by Winston Churchill. This constant recycling of substances is all part of the cycle of life, death and decay.

Microorganisms play a key role in recycling. They break down complex organic molecules in the bodies of dead animals and plants into simpler substances, which they release into the environment.

The carbon cycle

Carbon is a component of all major biological molecules. Carbohydrates, lipids, proteins, nucleic acids, vitamins and many other molecules all contain carbon. The following processes are important in cycling carbon through ecosystems.

- Photosynthesis 'fixes' carbon atoms from carbon dioxide into organic compounds.

- Feeding and assimilation pass carbon atoms already in organic compounds along food chains.

- Respiration produces inorganic carbon dioxide from organic compounds (mainly carbohydrates) as they are broken down to release energy.

- Fossilisation – sometimes living things do not decay fully when they die due to the conditions in the soil (decay is prevented if it is too acidic) and fossil fuels (coal, oil, natural gas and peat) are formed.

- Combustion releases carbon dioxide into the atmosphere when fossil fuels are burned.

Figures 14.13 and 14.14 show the role of these processes in the carbon cycle in different ways.

> Organic compounds all contain carbon and hydrogen. Starch and glucose are organic molecules, but carbon dioxide (CO_2) isn't.

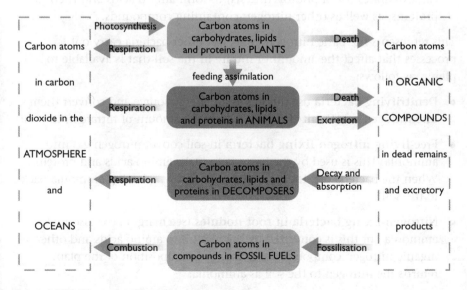

Figure 14.13 *The main stages in the carbon cycle.*

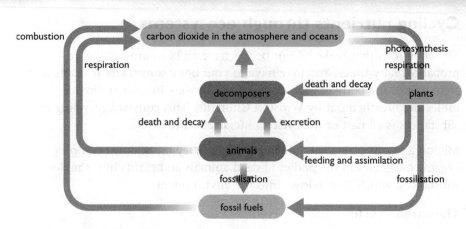

Figure 14.14 *A typical illustration of the carbon cycle.*

The nitrogen cycle

Nitrogen is a key element in many biological compounds. It is present in proteins, amino acids, most vitamins, DNA (see Chapter 16), RNA and adenosine triphosphate (ATP). Like the carbon cycle, the nitrogen cycle involves feeding, assimilation, death and decay. Photosynthesis and respiration are not directly involved in the nitrogen cycle as these processes fix and release carbon, not nitrogen. The following processes are important in cycling nitrogen through ecosystems.

- Feeding and assimilation pass nitrogen atoms already in organic compounds along food chains.

- Decomposition (putrefaction) by decomposers produces ammonia from the nitrogen in compounds like proteins, DNA and vitamins.

- The ammonia is oxidised first to nitrite and then to nitrate by **nitrifying bacteria**. This overall process is called **nitrification**.

- Plant roots can absorb the nitrates. They are combined with carbohydrates (from photosynthesis) to form amino acids and then proteins, as well as other nitrogen-containing compounds.

This represents the basic nitrogen cycle, but other bacteria carry out processes that affect the amount of nitrate in the soil that is available to plants, as follows:

- **Denitrifying bacteria** use nitrates as an energy source and convert them into nitrogen gas. **Denitrification** *reduces* the amount of nitrate in the soil.

- **Free-living nitrogen-fixing bacteria** in soil convet nitrogen gas into ammonia. This is used by the bacteria to make amino acids and proteins. When the bacteria die, their proteins decompose, releasing ammonia back to the soil.

- **Nitrogen-fixing bacteria in root nodules** (see margin box) also make ammonia but this is converted by the plant into amino acids and other organic nitrogen compounds. Death and decomposition of the plant returns the nitrogen to the soil as ammonia.

these nodules contain millions of nitrogen-fixing bacteria

roots of the clover plant

Figure 14.15 *Root nodules on a clover plant.*

Instead of entering the soil, the ammonia that the bacteria make by fixing nitrogen is passed to the plant which uses it to make amino acids. In return, the plant provides the bacteria with organic nutrients. This is an example of **mutualism**, where both organs benefit from the relationship. This nitrogen fixation enriches the soil with nitrates when the plants die and are decomposed.

In addition to all the processes described so far, lightning converts nitrogen gas in the air into various oxides of nitrogen. These dissolve in rainwater and enter the soil to be converted into nitrates by nitrifying bacteria. Figure 14.16 shows the role of these processes in the nitrogen cycle.

> To remember if an organic compound contains nitrogen, check to see if the letter **N** (symbol for nitrogen) is present.
>
> Protei**N**s, ami**N**o acids and **DNA** all contain nitrogen. Carbohydrates and fats don't – they have no **N**.

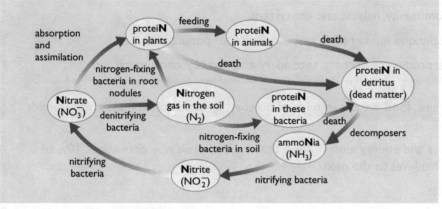

Figure 14.16 *The main stages in the nitrogen cycle.*

The water cycle

A supply of water is essential for all living organisms. The Earth from space is known as the 'blue planet', since nearly three-quarters of its surface is covered with water or ice. Most water (96%) is present in the oceans. This water is constantly being cycled between the atmosphere, rivers and lakes, organisms and back to the sea. This is called the **water cycle** (Figure 14.17).

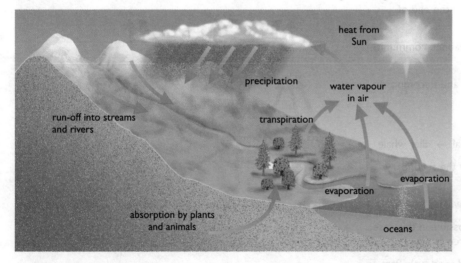

Figure 14.17 *The water cycle.*

The cycle is driven by heat from the Sun, which evaporates water from the surface of the oceans, lakes and rivers. Plant transpiration (see Chapter 11) and respiration of organisms also releases water vapour into the air. When clouds rise over mountains and high ground, they cool and water condenses to form rain or snow. This **precipitation** falls on the Earth, where it is taken up by animals or plants, or enters rivers and flows to the sea to start the cycle again.

End of Chapter Checklist

You should now be able to:

- understand the terms population, community, habitat and ecosystem

- describe the use of quadrats as a technique for sampling and estimation of population size

- recall the meanings of trophic levels; producers; primary, secondary and tertiary consumers; and decomposers

- understand the concepts of food chains, food webs, pyramids of number, pyramids of biomass and pyramids of energy transfer

- understand the transfer of substances and energy along a food chain, and explain why only about 10% of energy is transferred from one trophic level to the next

- describe the stages in the water cycle

- describe the stages in the carbon cycle

- describe the stages in the nitrogen cycle, including the roles of nitrogen-fixing bacteria, decomposers, nitrifying bacteria and denitrifying bacteria.

Questions

More questions on ecosystems can be found at the end of Section D on page 183.

1 **a)** Explain what is meant by the terms habitat, community, environment and population.

   b) What are the roles of plants, animals and decomposers in an ecosystem?

2 A marine food chain is shown below.

   plankton → small crustacean → krill → seal → killer whale

   a) Which organism is *i)* the producer, *ii)* the secondary consumer?

   b) What term best describes the killer whale?

   c) Suggest why five trophic levels are possible in this case, when many food chains only have three or four.

3 Part *(a)* of the diagram shows a woodland food web. Part *(b)* shows a pyramid of numbers and a pyramid of biomass for a small part of this wood.

   a) Write out **two** food chains (from the food web) containing four organisms, both involving moths.

   b) Name **one** organism in the food web which is both a primary consumer and a secondary consumer.

   c) Suggest how a reduction in the dead leaves may lead to a reduction in the numbers of voles.

   d) In part *(b)* of the diagram, explain why level Y is such a different width in the two pyramids.

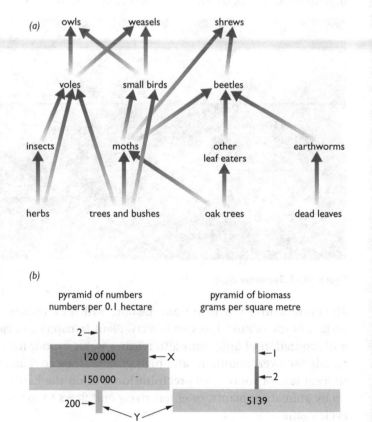

4 The diagram shows part of the nitrogen cycle.

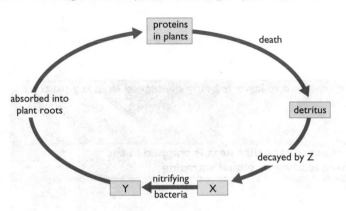

a) What do X, Y and Z represent?

b) Name the process by which plant roots absorb nitrates.

c) What are nitrogen-fixing bacteria?

d) Give **two** ways, not shown in the diagram, in which animals can return nitrogen to the soil.

5 In a year, 1 m² of grass produces 21 500 kJ of energy. The diagram below shows the fate of the energy transferred to a cow feeding on the grass.

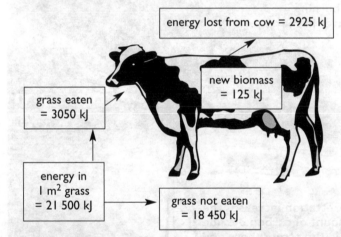

a) Calculate the energy efficiency of the cow from the following equation.

Energy efficiency =

$$\frac{\text{energy that ends up as part of cow's biomass}}{\text{energy available}} \times 100$$

b) State two ways that energy is lost from the cow.

c) Suggest what may happen to the 18 450 kJ of energy in the grass that was not eaten by the cow.

6 Read the following description of the ecosystem of a mangrove swamp.

Pieces of dead leaves (detritus) from mangrove plants in the water are fed on by a range of crabs, shrimps and worms. These, in turn, are fed on by young butterfly fish, angelfish, tarpon, snappers and barracuda. Mature snappers and tarpon are caught by fishermen as the fish move out from the swamps to the open seas.

a) Use the description to construct a food web of the mangrove swamp ecosystem.

b) Write out two food chains, each containing four organisms from this food web. Label each organism in each food chain as producer, primary consumer, secondary consumer or tertiary consumer.

c) Decomposers make carbon in the detritus available again to mangrove plants.

   i) In what form is this carbon made available to the mangrove plants?

   ii) Explain how the decomposers make the carbon available.

Chapter 15: Human Influences on the Environment

Humans have intelligence far beyond that of any other animal on Earth. This chapter looks at the ways in which we have used our intelligence to influence natural environments.

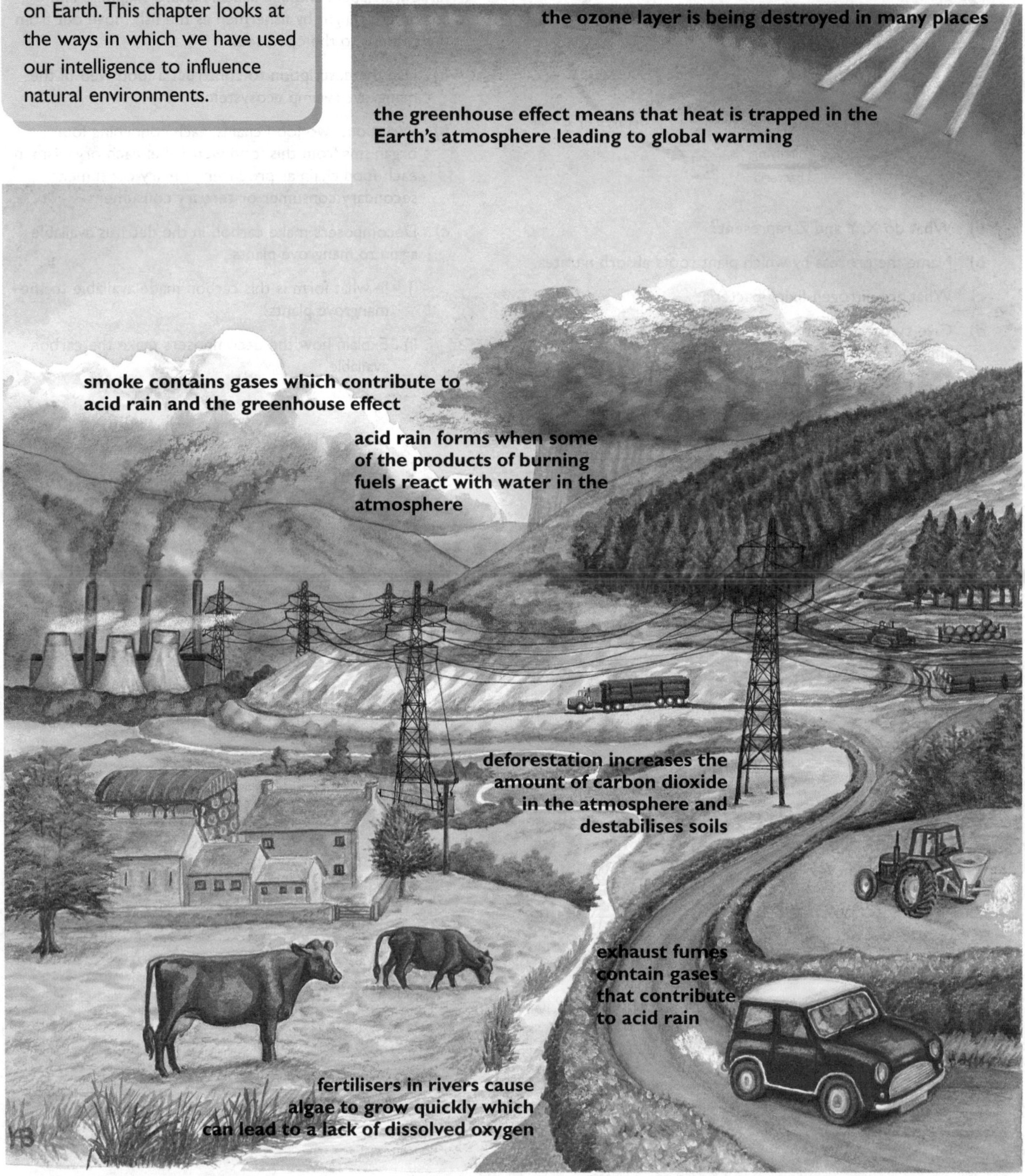

the ozone layer is being destroyed in many places

the greenhouse effect means that heat is trapped in the Earth's atmosphere leading to global warming

smoke contains gases which contribute to acid rain and the greenhouse effect

acid rain forms when some of the products of burning fuels react with water in the atmosphere

deforestation increases the amount of carbon dioxide in the atmosphere and destabilises soils

exhaust fumes contain gases that contribute to acid rain

fertilisers in rivers cause algae to grow quickly which can lead to a lack of dissolved oxygen

Figure 15.1 *How the actions of humans influence the environment.*

Since humans first appeared on Earth, our numbers have grown dramatically (Figure 15.2). The secret of our success has been our intelligence. Unlike other species, we have not adapted to one specific environment, we have changed many environments to suit us.

As our numbers have grown, so has the sophistication of our technology. Early humans made tools from materials readily to hand. Today's technology involves much more complex processes. As a result, we produce ever-increasing amounts of materials that pollute our air, soil and waterways.

Early humans influenced their environment, but the sheer size of the population today and the extent of our industries mean that we affect the environment much more significantly. We make increasing demands on the environment for:

- food to sustain an ever-increasing population

- materials to build homes, schools, industries, etc.

- fuel to heat homes and power vehicles

- space in which to build homes, schools and factories, as well as for our leisure facilities

- space in which to dump our waste materials.

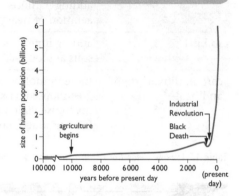

You can find out more about selection, variation and the evolution of modern humans (*Homo sapiens*) in Chapter 19. Chapter 13 gives more information on adaptation.

Figure 15.2 *Human population growth.*

Modern agriculture – producing the food we need

A modern farm can be thought of as a managed ecosystem. Many of the interactions are the same as in natural ecosystems. Crop plants depend on light and mineral ions from the soil as well as other factors in the environment. Stock animals (sheep, cattle and pigs) depend on crop plants or plant products for food (see Figure 15.3).

Farmers must make a profit from their farms. To do this, they try to control the environment in such a way as to maximise the yield from crop plants and livestock.

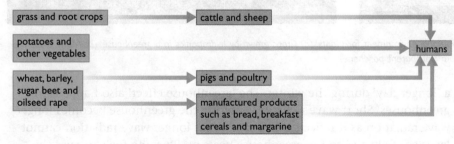

Figure 15.3 *A food web on a farm.*

Improving yields from crop plants

Table 15.1 summaries various agricultural features that can be controlled by the farmer in order to maximise yield from crops.

Greenhouses provide the right conditions for plants to grow for several reasons. The transparent material allows sufficient natural light in for photosynthesis during the summer months, while additional lighting gives

Soil pH can vary between 3.0 and 8.0. Soil pH can be tested using indicator kits and soil can be made more alkaline by adding lime or more acidic by adding peat.

Chapter 15: Human Influences on the Environment

167

Feature controlled	How it is controlled	Reason for controlling the feature
soil ions (e.g. nitrates)	adding fertilisers (organic or inorganic) to the soil or growing in a hydroponic culture (Figure 15.4a)	extra mineral ions can be taken up and used to make proteins and other compounds for growth
soil structure	ploughing fields to break up compacted soil; adding manure to improve drainage and aeration of heavy, clay soils	good aeration and drainage allow better uptake of mineral ions and water
soil pH	adding lime (calcium salts) to acidic soils; few soils are too alkaline to need treatment	an unsuitable soil pH can affect crop growth as it reduces uptake of mineral ions
carbon dioxide, light and heat	these cannot be controlled for field crops but in a greenhouse (glasshouse), all can be influenced to maximise yield of crops (Figure 15.4b); burning fuels produces both carbon dioxide and heat	all influence the rate of photosynthesis and so influence the production of the organic substances needed for growth

Table 15.1: *How yields from crop plants can be controlled.*

Figure 15.4 *Any kind of greenhouse maintains a favourable environment for plants. (a) Crops grown by hydroponics in a greenhouse. (b) Many crops are produced in huge greenhouses or in tunnels made from transparent polythene.*

By heating greenhouses to the **optimum** temperature for photosynthesis for a crop, a farmer can maximise his yield. Heating above this temperature is a waste of money as there is no further increase in yield.

a 'longer day' during the winter. The 'greenhouse effect' also happens in greenhouses! Short wave radiation entering the greenhouse becomes longer wave radiation as it reflects off surfaces. This longer wave radiation cannot leave as easily and so the greenhouse heats up. Burning fuels to raise the temperature when the external temperature is too low also produces carbon dioxide and water vapour. The water vapour maintains a moist atmosphere and so reduces water loss by transpiration (see Chapter 11). The carbon dioxide is a raw material of photosynthesis.

In addition, growing plants in a hydroponic culture provides *exactly* the right balance of mineral ions for the specific crop being grown.

Cycling nutrients on a farm

Chapter 14 describes how the elements nitrogen and carbon are cycled in nature. On a farm, the situation is quite different, particularly with regard to the circulation of nitrogen.

Nitrates from the soil become part of proteins in the plants. Some of these are crops to be sold, others are used as fodder for the stock animals. When the crops are sold, the nitrogen in the proteins goes with them and is lost from the farm ecosystem. Similarly, when livestock is sold, the nitrogen in their proteins (gained from the fodder) goes with them and is lost from the farm ecosystem. To replace the lost nitrogen, a farmer usually adds some kind of fertiliser. Figure 15.5 summarises the circulation of nitrogen on a farm.

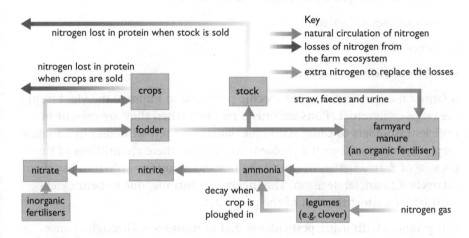

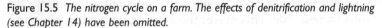

Figure 15.5 *The nitrogen cycle on a farm. The effects of denitrification and lightning (see Chapter 14) have been omitted.*

Fertilisers on the farm

There are two main types of fertilisers – **organic** and **inorganic**. Many organic fertilisers (such as farmyard manure) are made from the faeces of a range of animals mixed with straw. Inorganic fertilisers are simply inorganic compounds (like potassium nitrate or ammonium nitrate), carefully formulated to yield a specific amount of nitrate (or some other ion) when applied according to the manufacturer's instructions.

Adding farmyard manure returns some of the nitrogen to the soil. But, as farmyard manure is made from livestock faeces and indigestible fodder, it can only replace a portion of the lost nitrogen. Most farmers apply inorganic fertilisers to replace the nitrates and other mineral ions lost. Whilst this can replace *all* the lost ions, it can also lead to problems such as **eutrophication**, which we will discuss later in the chapter on page 177. Inorganic fertilisers can also damage soil structure. This is because they do not replace the organic matter lost to soils that is an essential part of the structure.

Another way to replace lost nitrates is to grow a legume crop (such as clover) in a field one year in four. Legumes have nitrogen-fixing bacteria in nodules on their roots (see Chapter 14). These bacteria convert nitrogen gas in the soil air to ammonium ions. Some of this is passed to the plants, which use it to make proteins. At the end of the season, the crop is ploughed in and the nitrogen in the proteins is decayed (putrefied) to ammonia. This is then oxidised to nitrate by nitrifying bacteria and is available to next year's crops.

In Britain, about 30% of the potential maize crop is lost to weeds, insects and fungal diseases (Figure 15.6).

Figure 15.6 *Damage to a maize plant by a caterpillar.*

A weed is a plant that is growing where it is not wanted. Weeds can be controlled mechanically or chemically. Mechanical control involves physically removing the weeds. Chemical control uses chemical weedkillers that are selective.

Pests on the farm

Pests are organisms that reduce the yield of crop plants or stock animals. By doing this, they cause economic damage to the farmer. Any type of organism – plants, animals, bacteria, fungi or protoctistans, as well as viruses – can be a pest. Pests can be controlled in a number of ways. Chemicals called **pesticides** can be used to kill them, or their numbers can be reduced by using **biological control**. Some agricultural practices, such as monoculture (see page 171), can encourage the build-up of pests. Avoiding these practices can reduce pest damage.

Pesticides are named according to the type of organism they kill:

- **herbicides** kill plant pests (they are weedkillers)

- **insecticides** kill insects

- **fungicides** kill fungi

- **molluscicides** kill molluscs.

A farmer uses pesticides to kill specific pests and so improve the yield from the crops or livestock. Pests are only a problem when they are present in sufficient numbers to cause economic damage – a few whiteflies in a tomato crop are not a problem; the problem arises when there are millions of them. Because of this, whether or not to use pesticides and how often to use them is largely a financial decision. The increase in income, due to better yields, must be set against the cost of the pesticides.

One problem with using pesticides is that of resistance. Through chance **mutation** and natural selection (see Chapter 19), a population of a pest can become resistant to a pesticide. This makes the existing pesticide useless and another must be found. In addition, the use of pesticides can cause environmental damage, as some persist in the soil and can be accumulated along food chains (see page 179).

Another option sometimes open to a farmer is the **biological control** of pests. Biological control uses another organism, rather than a toxic chemical, to reduce the numbers of a pest. We have already mentioned whiteflies as pests of tomatoes. One way of controlling them in large glasshouses is to introduce a parasite that will kill the whiteflies. A tiny wasp called *Encarsia* parasitises and kills their larvae, so reducing the numbers of whitefly.

A feature of biological control is that it never eradicates a pest. If the control organism killed off all the pests, then it, too, would die out as there would be no food. Biological control aims to reduce pest numbers to a level where they no longer cause significant economic damage (Figure 15.7).

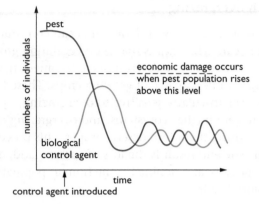

Figure 15.7 *Biological control.*

Methods of biological control include the following.

- Introducing a natural predator – ladybirds can be used to control the populations of aphids in orange groves.

- Introducing a herbivore – a moth was introduced from South America to control the prickly pear cactus that was becoming a serious weed in grazing land in Australia.

- Introducing a parasite – the wasp *Encarsia* is used to control whitefly populations in glasshouse tomato crops.

- Introducing a pathogenic (disease-causing) microorganism – the myxomatosis virus was deliberately released in Australia to control the rabbit population.

- Introducing sterile males – these mate with the females but no offspring are produced from these matings, so numbers fall.

- Using pheromones – these animal sex hormones are used to attract the males or females, which are then destroyed, reducing the reproductive potential of the population. Male-attracting pheromones are used to control aphids in plum crops.

Some agricultural practices encourage the build-up and spread of pests, whereas others discourage their spread. **Monoculture** involves giving over vast areas of land to a single crop. In the USA, big agricultural companies plant wheat and maize by the square mile. This makes for efficient harvesting as huge machinery can harvest large amounts of crop in a short period of time. However, it also makes for very efficient spread of pests. If the crop becomes infested, there are millions of crop plants to which the pest can spread. If the same crop is grown year after year in the same field, pests can lie dormant in the soil over winter. The timing of emergence in spring is often closely linked to planting time of the crop and so the pest causes damage from the moment the crop is planted. Over a number of years, the level of the pests builds up, causing increasing economic damage.

Crop rotation involves planting different crops in fields on a rotation basis. Usually, a new crop is grown in each field each year. Figure 15.8 shows a three-year crop rotation. Rotation of crops means that when over-wintering pests emerge, their 'favourite food' is no longer there! This stops the build-up of pests in one particular place.

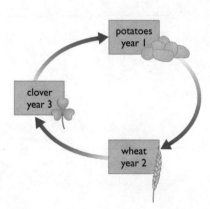

Figure 15.8 *A three-year crop rotation.*

171

Problems with overgrazing

In some very dry areas of the world, droughts can continue for many months or even years. This means that little vegetation grows in these **desert** areas. On the edges of a desert, the environment may gradually change to a moister one, capable of growing crops. These fringe areas around deserts are particularly sensitive to **overgrazing**, by sheep, goats or camels. They are very fragile ecosystems, and overgrazing can severely damage them, turning them into deserts proper. This process is called **desertification**. The end result is the loss of pasture land, death of animals, and eventually poverty and famine for the human populations that inhabit these areas (Figure 15.9).

Figure 15.9 *Overgrazing may be a major cause of desertification.*

Overgrazing, along with removal of trees and bushes for fuel, leaves the soil unprotected against erosion by wind or rain. The exposed soil may be blown or washed away, leaving infertile soil or rock. Many ecologists think that overgrazing, along with deforestation and global warming (see page 174), are working together to turn fertile land into desert.

Problems with overfishing

Over the last 50 years, the world's population has demanded an increasing amount of fish to eat. To achieve this end, the tonnage of fish caught by ships has increased steadily, until the Earth's stock of many fish species has decreased to nearly nothing. The reduction can often happen very suddenly (Figure 15.10).

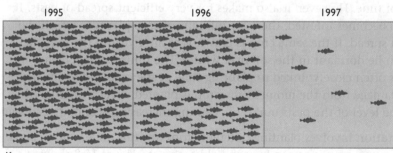

Key ➤ = 30 cod

Figure 15.10 *The numbers of cod caught per hour in the North Sea, near the United Kingdom, between 1995 and 1997.* Source: The Little Earth Book, *James Bruges.*

In a similar way, the productive cod fisheries off the east coast of Newfoundland collapsed in 1992. Fishing was suspended there for several years until the cod stocks began to revive.

Modern fishing methods are also very destructive to the environment. Trawling for fish in deep waters involves dragging a net along the seabed to catch cod, shellfish and flatfish. Unfortunately, it also kills invertebrate animals by crushing them or burying them beneath a layer of sediment. Any unwanted species of fish or other animals are killed, such as the dolphins caught in the nets of tuna fishermen.

Fish farming

Increasingly, **fish farming** is meeting the shortfall in fish. The most commonly farmed fish are the more commercial species, such as salmon, trout, tuna, sea bream and cod, as well as various types of crustacea, such as lobsters and prawns. They are not all used for human food: about one-quarter of farmed fish is used to make animal feed.

Fish farming has a number of advantages. The fish are kept in large seawater enclosures or 'tanks' in which the water quality can be carefully monitored (Figure 15.11). In some farms, temperature and oxygenation of the water can be controlled. The diet of the fish is also carefully controlled in both its quality and the frequency of feeding. The fish are protected against predators, and pesticides are used to kill parasites. Selective breeding programs (see Chapter 20) can be used to improve the quality of the fish. For example, they are bred to produce faster growth and to be more 'placid' fish than the wild types.

However, fish farming has many features in common with the 'factory' farming of chickens. In any intensive production system, the potential for the spread of disease is greater than normal because the animals are so close together. Antibiotics are often used to treat disease. This is a cause for concern because the antibiotics may not have been degraded by the time the fish are eaten by humans. Fish farms also cause a pollution problem with organic material from the animals' faeces and food pellets, which can cause eutrophication of the water (see page 177). The pesticides used to kill fish parasites are sometimes highly toxic to other non-harmful species of invertebrates.

In fact, there is good evidence that fish farming is having an adverse effect on world 'wild' fish stocks. The problem is that most farmed species are carnivores, and are fed with pellets made from other fish! It has been calculated that, in 2001, on average about 1.4 kg of wild fish needed to be used to produce 1 kg of farmed fish. The wild fish used for fishmeal are less marketable species, such as herrings and sardines.

If you eat tuna, always buy 'dolphin-friendly' tuna, which has been caught without killing dolphins.

Figure 15.11 *Feeding the fish at a fish farm.*

In any one year, there is a peak and a trough in the levels of carbon dioxide. This is shown more clearly in Figure 15.12.

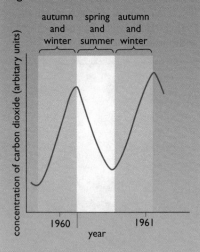

Figure 15.12 *Seasonal fluctuations in carbon dioxide levels.*

In the autumn and winter, trees lose their leaves. They photosynthesise much less and so absorb little carbon dioxide. They still respire, which produces carbon dioxide, so in the winter months, they give out carbon dioxide and the level in the atmosphere rises. In the spring and summer, with new leaves, the trees photosynthesise faster than they respire. As a result, they absorb carbon dioxide from the atmosphere and the level decreases. However, because there are fewer trees overall, it doesn't quite get back to the low level of the previous summer.

Figure 15.13 *Deforestation.*

Pollution – the consequences of our actions

Pollution means releasing substances into the environment in amounts that cause harmful effects and which natural biological processes cannot easily remove. A key feature is the *amount*. Small amounts of sulphur dioxide and carbon dioxide would easily be absorbed by the environment and, over time, made harmless. It is the sheer mass of the pollutants that poses the problem.

Modern agricultural practices, building and other industries, as well as individual actions, release many pollutants into the environment. We pollute the air, land and water with a range of chemicals and heat.

Air pollution

We pollute the air with many gases. The main ones are carbon dioxide, carbon monoxide, sulphur dioxide, nitrogen oxides, methane and CFCs (chlorofluorocarbons).

Carbon dioxide

The levels of carbon dioxide have been rising for several hundred years. Over the last 100 years alone, the level of carbon dioxide in the atmosphere has increased by nearly 30%. This recent rise has been due mainly to the increased burning of fossil fuels, including petrol and diesel in vehicle engines. It has been made worse by cutting down large areas of tropical rainforest (Figure 15.13). These extensive forests have been called 'the lungs of the Earth' because they absorb such vast quantities of carbon dioxide and produce equally large amounts of oxygen. Extensive deforestation means that less carbon dioxide is being absorbed. Figure 15.14 shows changes in the level of carbon dioxide in the atmosphere (in parts per million) from 1960 to 1990.

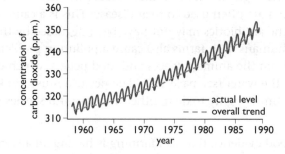

Figure 15.14 *The changes in levels of CO_2 at Mauna Loa, Hawaii from 1960 to 1990.*

The increased levels of carbon dioxide contribute to **global warming**. Carbon dioxide is just one of the so-called 'greenhouse gases' that form a layer in the Earth's atmosphere.

Short wave radiation from the sun strikes the planet. Some is absorbed and some is reflected as longer wave radiation. The greenhouse gases absorb then re-emit towards the Earth some of this long wave radiation, which would otherwise escape into space. This is the '**greenhouse effect**' and is a major factor in global warming (Figure 15.15).

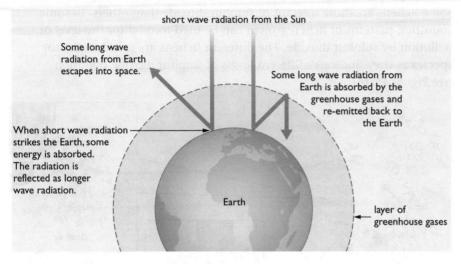

short wave radiation from the Sun

Some long wave radiation from Earth escapes into space.

Some long wave radiation from Earth is absorbed by the greenhouse gases and re-emitted back to the Earth

When short wave radiation strikes the Earth, some energy is absorbed. The radiation is reflected as longer wave radiation.

Earth

layer of greenhouse gases

Figure 15.15 *The greenhouse effect.*

A rise in the Earth's temperature of only a few degrees would have many effects.

- Polar ice caps would melt and sea levels would rise.

- A change in the major ocean currents would result in warm water being redirected into previously cooler areas.

- A change in global rainfall patterns could result. With all the extra water in the seas, there would be more evaporation from the surface and so more rainfall in most areas.

- It could change the nature of many ecosystems. If species could not migrate quickly enough to a new, appropriate habitat, or adapt quickly enough to the changed conditions in their current habitat, they could become extinct.

- Changes in agricultural practices would be necessary as some pests became more abundant. Higher temperatures might allow some pests to complete their life cycles more quickly.

Carbon monoxide

When substances containing carbon are burned in a limited supply of oxygen, carbon monoxide (CO) is formed. This happens when petrol and diesel are burned in vehicle engines. Exhaust gases contain significant amounts of carbon monoxide. It is a dangerous pollutant as it is colourless, odourless and tasteless and can cause death by asphyxiation. Haemoglobin binds more strongly with carbon monoxide than with oxygen. If a person inhales carbon monoxide for a period of time, more and more haemoglobin becomes bound to carbon monoxide and so cannot bind with oxygen. The person may lose consciousness and, eventually, may die as a result of a lack of oxygen.

Sulphur dioxide

Sulphur dioxide (SO_2) is an important pollutant as it is a major constituent of **acid rain** (see below). It is formed when fossil fuels are burned, and it can be carried hundreds of miles in the atmosphere before finally combining with rainwater to form acid rain.

Other greenhouse gases include methane (CH_4), nitrous oxide (N_2O) and chlorofluorocarbons (CFCs).

If there were no greenhouse gases and no global warming, the Earth would be the same temperature as the Moon. Life, as we know it, would be impossible.

Deforestation is thought to contribute to problems other than destruction of habitats and global warming. After the trees in an area have been cut down, the soil lacks a protective canopy, and is not held together by tree roots, so that tropical storms can produce soil erosion on a grand scale. As well as this, the trees were a source of atmospheric water vapour from transpiration (see Chapter 11). Deforestation, through disruption of the water cycle, may lead to changing rainfall patterns and drought.

In Europe there are now strict laws controlling the permitted levels of carbon monoxide in the exhaust gases produced by newly designed engines. These levels are lower than those allowed in the M.O.T. test of road-worthiness of vehicles three or more years old.

Some lichens are more tolerant of sulphur dioxide than others. In some countries, patterns of lichen growth can be used to monitor the level of pollution by sulphur dioxide. The different lichens are called **indicator species** as they 'indicate' different levels of sulphur dioxide pollution (see Figure 15.16).

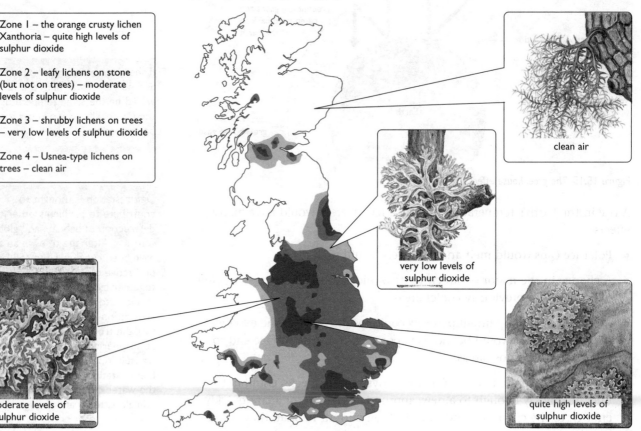

Zone 1 – the orange crusty lichen Xanthoria – quite high levels of sulphur dioxide

Zone 2 – leafy lichens on stone (but not on trees) – moderate levels of sulphur dioxide

Zone 3 – shrubby lichens on trees – very low levels of sulphur dioxide

Zone 4 – Usnea-type lichens on trees – clean air

clean air

very low levels of sulphur dioxide

moderate levels of sulphur dioxide

quite high levels of sulphur dioxide

Figure 15.16 *Lichens are sensitive to pollution levels.*

The map in Figure 15.16 shows zones in Britain colonised by different types of lichen.

Nitrogen oxides

Nitrogen oxides (NO_x) are also constituents of acid rain. They are formed when petrol and diesel are burned in vehicle engines.

Acid rain

Rain normally has a pH of about 5.5 – it is slightly acidic due to the carbon dioxide dissolved in it. Both sulphur dioxide and nitrogen oxides dissolve in rainwater to form a mixture of acids, including sulphuric acid and nitric acid. As a result, the rainwater is more acidic with a much lower pH than normal rain (Figure 15.17).

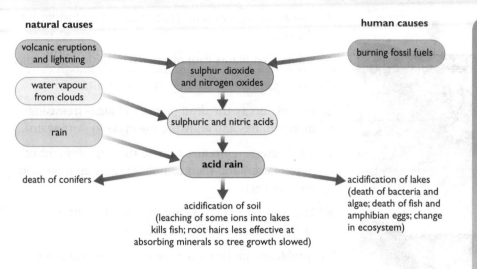

natural causes

human causes

volcanic eruptions and lightning

water vapour from clouds

rain

burning fossil fuels

sulphur dioxide and nitrogen oxides

sulphuric and nitric acids

acid rain

death of conifers

acidification of soil
(leaching of some ions into lakes
kills fish; root hairs less effective at
absorbing minerals so tree growth slowed)

acidification of lakes
(death of bacteria and
algae; death of fish and
amphibian eggs; change
in ecosystem)

Figure 15.17 *The formation of acid rain and its effects on living organisms.*

Methane

Methane (CH_4) is an organic gas. It is produced when microorganisms ferment larger organic molecules to release energy. The most significant origins of these microorganisms are:

- decomposition of waste in landfill sites by microorganisms

- fermentation by microorganisms in the rumen of cattle and other ruminants

- fermentation by bacteria in rice paddy fields.

Methane is a greenhouse gas, with effects similar to carbon dioxide. Although there is less methane in the atmosphere than carbon dioxide, each molecule has a bigger greenhouse effect.

Freshwater pollution

The three main pollutants of freshwater are nitrates from fertilisers, organic waste and detergents.

Nitrates from fertilisers

Farmers add inorganic fertilisers to soils to replace mineral ions lost when crops are removed. The ions in these fertilisers (particularly nitrates) are very soluble. As a result they are easily **leached** (carried out with water) from the soils and can enter waterways. The level of nitrates (and other ions) can rise rapidly in these lakes and rivers. This increase in mineral ions is called **eutrophication**, which is a natural process in nearly all waterways (Figure 15.19). What is *not* natural is the speed with which it happens due to leaching of ions in fertilisers from soils. Rapid eutrophication can have disastrous consequences for a waterway.

1. As nitrate levels rise, algae reproduce rapidly. They use the nitrates to make extra proteins for growth, just like the crop plants for which the nitrates were intended.

2. The algae form an **algal bloom** – a kind of algal pea soup if the algae are unicellular, or a mass of filaments if the algae are filamentous.

Besides its effects on living things, acid rain causes damage to stonework by reacting with carbonates and other ions in the stone (Figure 15.18).

Figure 15.18 *The features of this stone lion have been dissolved by acid rain.*

Herds of cattle can produce up to 40 dm³ of methane per animal per hour. This adds up to a lot of methane being belched and farted into the atmosphere!

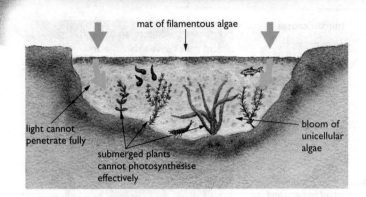

mat of filamentous algae

light cannot penetrate fully

submerged plants cannot photosynthesise effectively

bloom of unicellular algae

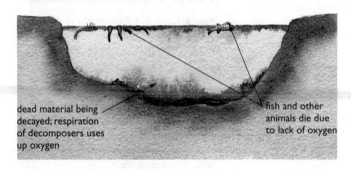

algae die due to lack of nitrates

submerged plants cannot photosynthesise and die

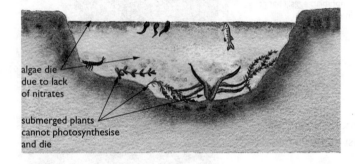

dead material being decayed; respiration of decomposers uses up oxygen

fish and other animals die due to lack of oxygen

Figure 15.19 *Stages in eutrophication in a pond.*

3. The algae prevent light from penetrating further into the water.

4. Submerged plants cannot photosynthesise and so die.

5. The algae also die as they run out of nitrates.

6. Bacteria decay the dead plants and algae (releasing more nitrates and allowing the cycle to start again).

7. The bacteria reproduce (due to the large amount of dead matter) and their respiration uses up more and more oxygen.

8. The water may become totally **anoxic** (without oxygen) and all life in the water will die.

The problems can be more severe in hot weather because the nitrates can become more concentrated as the heat evaporates water. All the processes are speeded up due to increased enzyme activity. The problems are less severe in moving water because the nitrates are rapidly diluted and the water is continually being re-oxygenated.

Rapid eutrophication is less likely when farmers use organic fertilisers (like manure). The organic nitrogen-containing compounds in manure are less soluble and so are leached less quickly from the soil. However, water can sometimes be polluted with large amounts of organic matter, for example when untreated sewage is released into waterways. Bacteria and fungi decay this and use up oxygen as they respire. The water becomes anoxic in the same way as in eutrophication. Fish and other animals die due to a lack of oxygen.

The level of organic water pollution can be monitored by the 'indicator species' present. Figure 15.20 shows some of these.

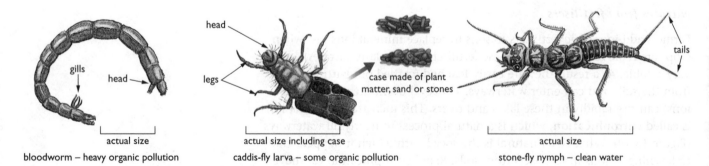

head

gills   head

actual size

bloodworm – heavy organic pollution

legs

case made of plant matter, sand or stones

actual size including case

caddis-fly larva – some organic pollution

tails

actual size

stone-fly nymph – clean water

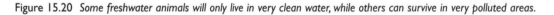

Figure 15.20 *Some freshwater animals will only live in very clean water, while others can survive in very polluted areas.*

When organic matter pollutes moving water, the point of the polluting outlet becomes very low in oxygen, as bacteria decompose the organic material. Only those species adapted to such conditions can survive. As the water moves away from the outlet, it becomes oxygenated again as it mixes with the air at the surface. The increase in oxygen levels allows more species of 'clean water' animals to survive. Figure 15.21 shows the changes in oxygen content, numbers of clean water animals and bloodworms at, and just downstream from, a sewage outlet into a river.

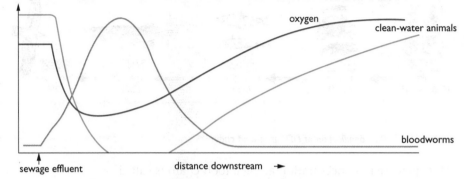
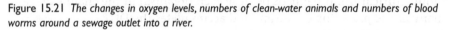

Figure 15.21 *The changes in oxygen levels, numbers of clean-water animals and numbers of blood worms around a sewage outlet into a river.*

Other forms of pollution

We pollute our air with poisonous gases and our water with organic pollutants and nitrates. We also pollute our environment in a number of other ways.

Thermal pollution

Water is used as a coolant in power stations and in other industrial plants. As water removes the heat, it becomes warmer and its ability to dissolve oxygen decreases. This can affect the number of animals able to survive in the water. Besides the effects of decreasing oxygen content, the direct effect of changing temperature may also kill animals and plants. Many animals cannot regulate their body temperature (as mammals and birds can). Their temperature changes with that of the environment. There have been cases reported in North America of river water being heated to over 80 °C and being completely lifeless. This is thermal pollution of water at its worst.

Pesticide pollution

Farmers frequently use pesticides to control many different types of pests (see page 170). Many of these have no serious side effects, but some are persistent – they are not degraded (decomposed) easily. Traces of some herbicides (weedkillers) can remain on or in the crops that were sprayed, with the risk that they could then be eaten with the food. A single, small 'dose' of herbicide is unlikely to cause any harm, but if the dose is repeated many times then the amount may accumulate and begin to have more serious consequences. Pesticides are sometimes stored in fatty tissue where the amount builds up over a period of time. This is called **bioaccumulation**.

Sometimes the effects of bioaccumulation can be *magnified* as a pesticide is passed along a food chain. The best documented cases of this happening involve the insecticide **DDT**. DDT is an extremely effective insecticide and was widely used after the Second World War. It prevented millions of deaths from malaria in some areas by significantly reducing the mosquito population. However, DDT was passed along food chains and accumulated in harmful amounts in the top carnivores. This happened because DDT is extremely persistent (a single application can take over 20 years to degrade)

An ideal pesticide should:

- control the pest effectively
- be biodegradable, so that no toxic products are left in the soil or on crops
- be specific, so that only the pest is killed
- not accumulate in organisms
- be safe to transport and store
- be easy and safe to apply.

Chapter 15: Human Influences on the Environment

179

and is fat soluble, so easily stored in living tissue. The food chain in Figure 15.22 shows the extent to which DDT can be accumulated. The amounts in brackets are parts per million of DDT.

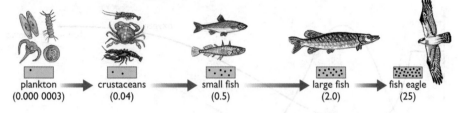

plankton   crustaceans   small fish   large fish   fish eagle
(0.000 0003)   (0.04)   (0.5)   (2.0)   (25)

Figure 15.22 *Biomagnification of DDT in a food chain.*

This increase in concentration along a food chain is called **biomagnification**. It happens because each organism in the chain eats many of the preceding organisms and accumulates the DDT (bioaccumulation). The effects of bioaccumulation are therefore magnified at each stage in the food chain.

The use of DDT has been restricted since 1972 because of its ecological effects.

Reducing the effects of pollution

Table 15.2 shows some possible courses of action to reduce the effects of pollution.

Problem	Possible individual action	Possible government/industrial action
global warming (greenhouse gases, CO_2, CH_4)	use as little energy as possible – less then needs to be generated; reduce use of private transport as far as possible	international agreements to set acceptable levels of CO_2 emissions; reduce deforestation: encourage sustainable felling and replanting schemes; encourage use of more recycled metals
acid rain (SO_2, NO_x)	reduce use of private transport as far as possible; reduce use of electricity where possible	legislation to enforce desulphurisaton of emissions from power stations; encourage use of 'cleaner' fuels such as natural gas (methane) and low-sulphur petrol
ozone depletion (overuse of CFCs)	reduce use of any aerosol containing CFCs	international legislation to restrict the use of CFCs
organic pollution of water	individual farmers can ensure safe storage and use of organic fertiliser (manure)	legislation to enforce treatment of sewage before discharge into waterways
nitrate pollution of water	individual farmers can make more use of 'organic' farming practices – use of crop rotations and organic manure; we can encourage organic farming by buying more organic produce	increase monitoring of waterways; legislation to limit levels of nitrates in water
pesticide pollution of soils	individual farmers can reduce use of pesticides and use biological control and crop rotation to limit pest build up	encourage development of 'safer' pesticides

Table 15.2: *Problems associated with pollution and possible solutions.*

End of Chapter Checklist

You should now be able to:

- describe how glasshouses and polythene tunnels can be used to increase the yield of crops
- understand the effects on crop yield of increased carbon dioxide and increased temperature in glasshouses
- understand the use of fertiliser to increase crop yield
- understand the reasons for pest control and the advantages and disadvantages of using pesticides and biological control with crop plants
- understand the biological consequences of pollution of air by sulphur dioxide and carbon monoxide
- recall that water vapour, carbon dioxide, nitrous oxide, methane and CFCs are greenhouse gases
- understand how human activities contribute to greenhouse gases
- understand how an increase in greenhouse gases results in an enhanced greenhouse effect and that this may lead to global warming and its consequences
- understand the biological consequences of pollution of water by sewage
- understand that eutrophication can result from leached minerals from fertiliser
- understand the effects of deforestation
- explain the biological consequences of overgrazing and overfishing
- explain the methods used in fish farming.

Questions

More questions on human influences on the environment can be found at the end of Section D on page 183.

1   Why are humans having much more of an impact on their environment now than they did 500 years ago?

2   The graph shows the changing concentrations of carbon dioxide at Mauna Loa, Hawaii over a number of years.

   a) Describe the overall trend shown by the graph.

   b) Explain the trend described in *a)*.

   c) In any one year, the level of atmospheric carbon dioxide shows a peak and a trough. Explain why.

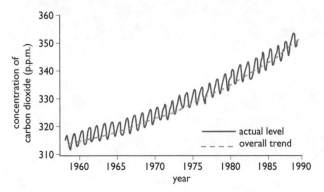

3   The diagram shows how the greenhouse effect is thought to operate.

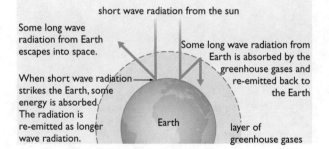

   a) Name two greenhouse gases.

   b) Explain one benefit to the Earth of the greenhouse effect.

   c) Suggest why global warming may lead to malaria becoming more common in Europe.

4 Several factories on an industrial estate burn fossil fuels. As a result, a considerable amount of sulphur dioxide is produced. Describe how you could use the patterns of lichen growth to estimate the changing levels of sulphur dioxide in the air at different distances from the industrial estate. You need not give full practical details.

5 The diagram shows the profile of the ground on a farm either side of a pond.

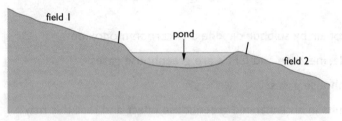

The farmer applies nitrate fertiliser to the two fields in alternate years. When he applies the fertiliser to Field 1, the pond often develops an algal bloom. This does not happen when fertiliser is applied to Field 2.

a) Explain why an algal bloom develops when he applies the fertiliser to Field 1.

b) Explain why no algal bloom develops when he applies the fertiliser to Field 2.

c) Explain why the algal bloom is more pronounced in hot weather.

6 Some untreated sewage is accidentally discharged into a small river. A short time afterwards, a number of dead fish are seen at the spot. Explain, as fully as you can, how the discharge could lead to the death of the fish.

7 Some farmers use pesticides and fertilisers to improve crop yields. Those practising 'organic' farming techniques do not use any artificial products.

a) Describe how the use of pesticides and fertilisers can improve crop yields.

b) Explain how organic farmers can maintain fertile soil and keep their crops pest free.

End of Section Questions

1 The diagram shows a simplified food web of the adult herring.

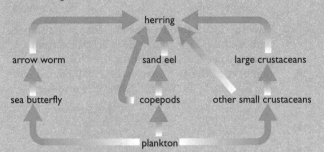

a) i) Write out a food chain from the above food web containing four organisms.   *(1 mark)*

   ii) From your food chain, name the primary consumer and secondary consumer. *(2 marks)*

   iii) Name one organism in the web that is both a secondary consumer and a tertiary consumer. Explain your answer.   *(2 marks)*

b) The amount of energy in each trophic level has been provided for the following food chain. The units are kJ/m^2/yr.

   plankton (8869) → copepod (892) → herring (91)

   i) Sketch a pyramid of energy for this food chain.   *(1 mark)*

   ii) Calculate the percentage of energy entering the plankton that passes to the copepod.   *(2 marks)*

   iii) Calculate the percentage of energy entering the copepod that passes to the herring.   *(2 marks)*

   iv) Calculate the amount of energy that enters the food chain per year if the plankton use 0.1% of the available energy.   *(2 marks)*

   v) Explain two ways in which energy is lost in the transfer from the copepod to the herring.
                                                    (2 marks)

                                            Total 14 marks

2 Nitrate fertiliser is added to their wheat crops to increase yield. The table below shows the amount of wheat yield when different amounts of nitrate fertiliser were added.

Fertiliser added (kg per hectare)	Wheat yield (tonnes per hectare)
0	15
50	18
100	22
150	31
200	30
250	31

a) Use the information in the table to draw a line graph showing the effects of fertiliser on wheat yield.   *(4 marks)*

b) What amount of fertiliser would you advise the farmer to use on his wheat crop? Explain your answer.   *(3 marks)*

c) Why is nitrate needed to help plants grow?
                                                    (1 mark)

d) Excess nitrate can be washed into rivers. Explain the effects that this could have on the river ecosystem.   *(5 marks)*

                                            Total 13 marks

3 Insecticides are used by farmers to control the populations of insect pests. New insecticides are continually being developed.

a) A new insecticide was trialled over three years to test its effectiveness in controlling an insect pest of potato plants. Three different concentrations of the insecticide were tested. Some results are shown in the table.

Concentration of insecticide	Percentage of insect pest killed each year		
	Year 1	Year 2	Year 3
1 (weakest)	95	72	18
2 (intermediate)	98	90	43
3 (strongest)	99	91	47

   i) Describe, and suggest an explanation for, the change in the effectiveness of the insecticide over the three years.   *(3 marks)*

   ii) Which concentration would a farmer be most likely to choose to apply to potato crops? Explain your answer.   *(3 marks)*

b) The trials also showed that there was no significant bioaccumulation of the insecticide.

 i) What is bioaccumulation? *(1 mark)*

 ii) Give an example of bioaccumulation of an insecticide and describe its consequences. *(2 marks)*

 iii) Explain why it is particularly important that there is no bioaccumulation of *this* insecticide. *(1 mark)*

Total 10 marks

4 Carbon is cycled through ecosystems by the actions of plants, animals and decomposers. Humans influence the cycling of carbon more than other animals.

a) Explain the importance of plants in the cycling of carbon through ecosystems. *(2 marks)*

b) Describe two human activities that have significant effects on the global cycling of carbon. *(2 marks)*

c) The graph shows the activity of decomposers acting on the bodies of dead animals under different conditions.

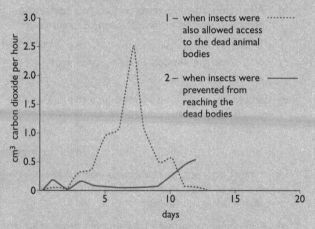

 i) Why was carbon dioxide production used as a measure of the activity of the decomposers? *(2 marks)*

 ii) Describe and explain the changes in decomposer activity when insects were also allowed access to the dead bodies (1) *(3 marks)*

 iii) Describe two differences between curves (1) and (2). Suggest an explanation for the differences you describe. *(4 marks)*

Total 13 marks

5 In natural ecosystems, there is competition between members of the same species as well as between different species.

a) Explain how competition between members of the same species helps to control population growth. *(3 marks)*

b) Crop plants must often compete with weeds for resources. Farmers often control weeds by spraying herbicides (weedkillers).

 i) Name two factors that the crop plants and weeds may compete for and explain the importance of each. *(4 marks)*

 ii) Farmers usually prefer to spray herbicides on weeds early in the growing season. Suggest why. *(2 marks)*

c) Two species of the flour beetle, *Tribolium*, compete with each other for flour. Both are parasitised by a protozoan. The graphs show the changes in numbers of the two species over 900 days when the parasite is absent and when it is present.

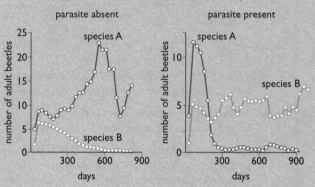

 i) Which species is the most successful when the parasite is absent? Justify your answer. *(2 marks)*

 ii) What is the effect of the parasite on the relative success of the two beetles? Suggest an explanation for your answer. *(4 marks)*

Total 15 marks

6 The table gives information about the pollutants produced in extracting aluminium from its ore (bauxite) and in recycling aluminium.

Pollutants	Amount (g per kg aluminium produced)	
Air	**Extraction from bauxite**	**Recycling aluminium**
sulphur dioxide	88 600	886
nitrogen oxides	139 000	6 760
carbon monoxide	34 600	2 440
Water		
dissolved solids	18 600	575
suspended solids	1 600	175

a) Calculate the percentage reduction in sulphur dioxide pollution by recycling aluminium. *(2 marks)*

b) Explain how extraction of aluminium from bauxite may contribute to the acidification of water hundreds of miles from the extraction plant. *(3 marks)*

c) Suggest two reasons why there may be little plant life in water near an extraction. *(4 marks)*

Total 9 marks

Chapter 16: Chromosomes, Genes and DNA

This chapter looks at the structure and organisation of genetic material, namely chromosomes, genes and DNA.

DNA is short for deoxyribonucleic acid. It gets its 'deoxyribo' name from the sugar in the DNA molecule. This is deoxyribose – a sugar containing five carbon atoms.

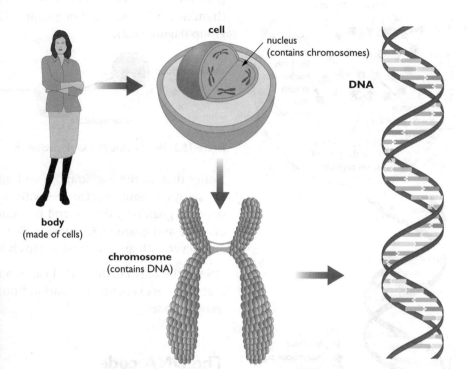

Figure 16.1 *Our genetic make-up.*

Figure 16.2 *(a) Watson and Crick with their double-helix model.*

The chemical that is the basis of inheritance in nearly all organisms is **DNA**. DNA is usually found in the nucleus of a cell, in the **chromosomes** (Figure 16.1). A small section of DNA that determines a particular feature is called a **gene**. Genes determine features by instructing cells to produce particular proteins which then lead to the development of the feature. So a gene can also be described as a section of DNA that codes for a particular protein.

DNA can replicate (make an exact copy of) itself. When a cell divides by mitosis (see Chapter 17), each new cell receives exactly the same type and amount of DNA. The cells formed are genetically identical.

The structure of DNA

Who discovered it?

James Watson and Francis Crick, working at Cambridge University, discovered the structure of the DNA molecule in 1953 (Figure 16.2a). Both were awarded the Nobel prize in 1962 for their achievement. However, the story of the first discovery of the structure of DNA goes back much further. Watson and Crick were only able to propose the structure of DNA because of the work of others – Rosalind Franklin (Figure 16.2b) had been researching the structure of a number of substances using a technique called X-ray diffraction.

Watson and Crick were able to use her results, together with other material, to propose the now-familiar double helix structure for DNA. Rosalind Franklin died of cancer and so was unable to share in the award of the Nobel Prize (it cannot be awarded posthumously).

Figure 16.2 *(b) Rosalind Franklin (1920–1958).*

DNA

adenine is always
opposite thymine

P—S—A-T—S—P

P—S—G-C—S—P

P—S—C-G—S—P

P—S—T-A—S—P

phosphate
groups
hold the
nucleotides
in each
strand
together

cytosine is
always opposite
guanine

hydrogen bonds
hold the pairs of
bases together

Key
P phosphate
S deoxyribose sugar
A adenine
T thymine
G guanine
C cytosine

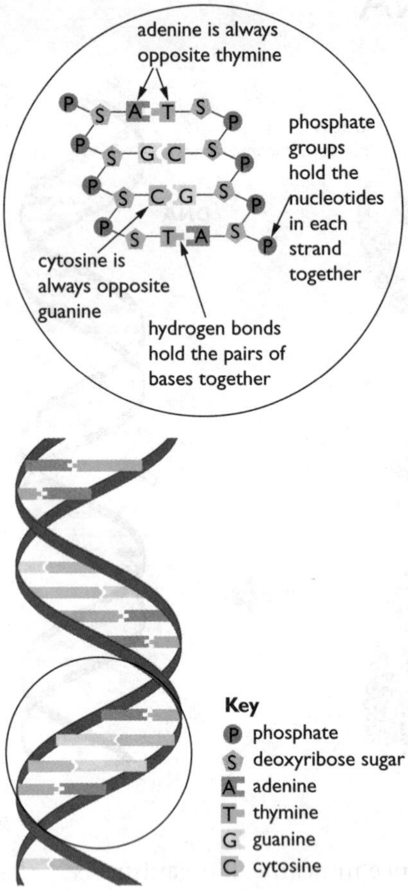

Figure 16.4 *Part of a molecule of DNA.*

Not only is the DNA code universal,
but the actual DNA in different
organisms is very similar. 98% of our
DNA is the same as that of a
chimpanzee; 50% of it is the same as
that of a banana!

A molecule of DNA is made from two strands of **nucleotides**, making it a **polynucleotide**. Each nucleotide contains a nitrogenous base (adenine (A), thymine (T), cytosine (C) or guanine (G)), a sugar molecule and a phosphate group (Figure 16.3).

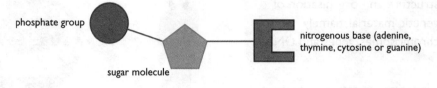

phosphate group

sugar molecule

nitrogenous base (adenine, thymine, cytosine or guanine)

Figure 16.3 *The structure of a single nucleotide.*

Notice that, in the two strands (see Figure 16.4), nucleotides with adenine are always opposite nucleotides with thymine, and cytosine is always opposite guanine. Adenine and thymine are **complementary bases**, as are cytosine and guanine. Complementary bases always bind with each other and never with any other base. This is known as the **base-pairing rule**.

DNA is the only chemical that can replicate itself exactly. Because of this, it is able to pass genetic information from one generation to the next as a 'genetic code'.

The DNA code

Only one of the strands of a DNA molecule actually codes for the manufacture of proteins in a cell. This strand is called the **sense strand**. The other strand is called the **anti-sense** strand. The proteins manufactured can be **intracellular enzymes** (enzymes that control processes within the cell), **extracellular enzymes** (enzymes that are secreted from the cell to have their effect outside the cell), **structural proteins** (e.g. used to make hair, haemoglobin, muscles, cell membranes) or **hormones**.

Proteins are made of chains of amino acids. A sequence of *three* nucleotides in the sense strand of DNA codes for one amino acid. As the sugar and phosphate are the same in all nucleotides, it is actually the bases that code for the amino acid. For example, the base sequence TGT codes for the amino acid cysteine. Because three bases are needed to code for one amino acid, the DNA code is a **triplet code**. The sequence of bases that codes for *all* the amino acids in a protein is a gene (Figure 16.5).

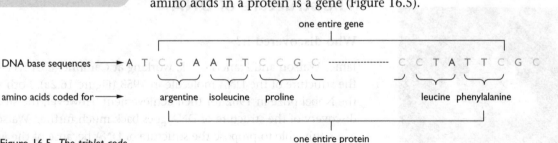

one entire gene

DNA base sequences ⟶ A T C G A A T T C C G C --------------- C C T A T T C G C

amino acids coded for ⟶ argentine isoleucine proline   leucine phenylalanine

one entire protein

Figure 16.5 *The triplet code.*

One consequence of the base-pairing
rule is that, in each molecule of DNA,
the amounts of adenine and thymine
are equal, as are the amounts of
cytosine and guanine.

The triplets of bases that code for individual amino acids are the same in all organisms. The base sequence TGT codes for the amino acid cysteine in humans, bacteria, bananas, monkfish, or in any other organism you can think of – the DNA code is a **universal code**.

DNA replication

When a cell is about to divide (see Mitosis, Chapter 17) it must first make an exact copy of each DNA molecule in the nucleus. This process is called **replication**. As a result, each cell formed receives exactly the same amount and type of DNA. Figure 16.6 summarises this process.

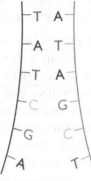 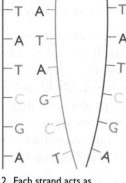 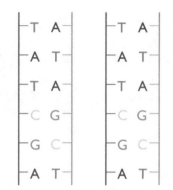

1 The polynucleotide strands of DNA separate.

2 Each strand acts as a template for the formation of a new strand of DNA.

3 DNA polymerase assembles nucleotides into two new strands according to the base-pairing rule.

4 Two identical DNA molecules are formed – each contains a strand from the parent DNA and a new complementary strand.

Figure 16.6 *How DNA replicates itself.*

Gene mutations – when DNA makes mistakes

A **mutation** is a change in the DNA of a cell. It can happen in individual genes or in whole chromosomes. Sometimes, when DNA is replicating, mistakes are made and the wrong nucleotide is used. The result is a **gene mutation** and it can alter the sequence of the bases in a gene. In turn, this can lead to the gene coding for the wrong protein. There are several ways in which gene mutations can occur (Figure 16.7).

In **duplication**, Figure 16.7 (a), the nucleotide is inserted twice instead of once. Notice that the entire base sequence is altered – each triplet after the point where the mutation occurs is changed. The whole gene is different and will now code for an entirely different protein.

In **deletion**, Figure 16.7 (b), a nucleotide is missed out. Again, the entire base sequence is altered. Each triplet after the mutation is changed and the whole gene is different. Again, it will code for an entirely different protein.

In **substitution**, Figure 16.7 (c), a different nucleotide is used. The triplet of bases in which the mutation occurs is changed and it *may* code for a different amino acid. If it does, the structure of the protein molecule will be different. This may be enough to produce a significant alteration in the *functioning* of a protein or a total lack of function. However, the new triplet may not code for a different amino acid as most amino acids have more than one code.

In **inversions**, Figure 16.7 (d), the sequence of the bases in a triplet is reversed. The effects are similar to substitution. Only one triplet is affected and this may or may not result in a different amino acid and altered protein stucture.

(a) ATT TCC GTT ATC
↑
duplication here

ATT TTC CGT TAT C
extra T becomes first base of next triplet

(b) ATT TCC GTT ATC
↑
deletion here

ATT CCG TTA TC
↑
replaced by first base of next triplet

(c) ATT TCC GTT ATC
↑
original base

ATG TCC GTT ATC
substituted base

(d) ATT TCC GTT ATC
inversion here

ATT CCT GTT ATC

Figure 16.7 *Gene mutations (a) duplication, (b) deletion, (c) substitution, (d) inversion.*

Mutations that occur in body cells, such as those in the heart, intestines or skin, will only affect that particular cell. If they are very harmful, the cell will die and the mutation will be lost. If they do not affect the functioning of the cell in a major way, the cell may not die. If the cell then divides, a group of cells containing the mutant gene is formed. When the organism dies, however, the mutation is lost with it; it is not passed to the offspring. Only mutations in the sex cells or in the cells that divide to form sex cells can be passed on to the next generation. This is how genetic diseases begin.

Sometimes a gene mutation can be advantageous to an individual. For example, as a result of random mutations, bacteria can become resistant to antibiotics. Resistant bacteria obviously have an advantage over non-resistant types if an antibiotic is being used. They will survive the antibiotic treatment and reproduce. All their offspring will be resistant and so the proportion of resistant types in the population of bacteria will increase as this happens in each generation. This is an example of **natural selection** (see Chapter 19). Pests can become resistant to pesticides in a similar way.

Gene mutations are random events that occur in all organisms. The rate at which they occur can be increased by a number of agents called **mutagens**. Mutagens include:

- ionising radiation (such as ultraviolet light, X-rays and gamma rays)
- chemicals including mustard gas and nitrous oxide, many of the chemicals in cigarette smoke and the tar from cigarettes, and some of the chemicals formed when food is charred in cooking.

The structure of chromosomes

Each chromosome contains one double-stranded DNA molecule. The DNA is folded and coiled so that it can be packed into a small space. The DNA is coiled around proteins called **histones** (Figure 16.8).

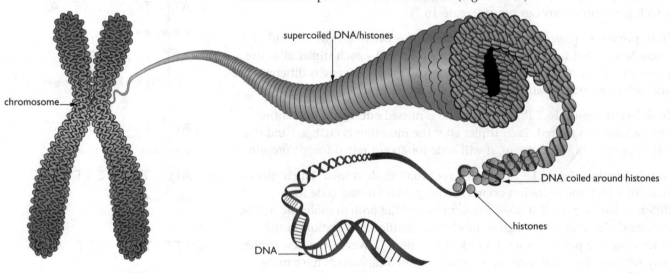

Figure 16.8 *The structure of a chromosome.*

Because a chromosome contains a particular DNA molecule, it will also contain the genes that make up that DNA molecule. Another chromosome will contain a different DNA molecule, and so will contain different genes.

How many chromosomes?

Nearly all human cells contain 46 chromosomes. The photographs in Figure 16.9 show the 46 chromosomes from the body cells of a human male and female.

> Red blood cells have no nucleus, therefore no chromosomes. This gives them more room for carrying oxygen.

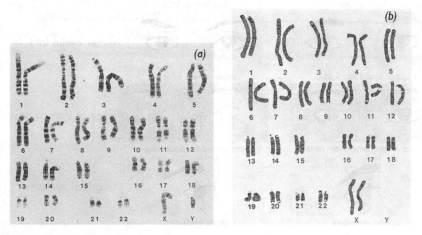

Figure 16.9 *Chromosomes of a human male (a) and female (b). A picture of all the chromosomes in a cell is called a karyotype.*

The chromosomes are not arranged like this in the cell. The original photograph has been cut up and chromosomes of the same size and shape 'paired up'. The cell from the male has 22 pairs of chromosomes and two that do not form a pair – the X and Y chromosomes. A body cell from a female has 23 matching pairs including a pair of X chromosomes.

Pairs of matching chromosomes are called **homologous pairs**. They carry genes for the same features in the same sequence (Figure 16.10). Cells with chromosomes in pairs like this are **diploid** cells.

Not all human cells have 46 chromosomes. Red blood cells have no nucleus and so have none. Sex cells have only 23 – just half the number of other cells. They are formed by a cell division called **meiosis** (see Chapter 17). Each cell formed has one chromosome from each homologous pair, and one of the sex chromosomes. Cells with only half the normal diploid number of chromosomes, and therefore only half the DNA content of other cells, are **haploid** cells.

When two sex cells fuse in **fertilisation**, the two nuclei join to form a single diploid cell (a **zygote**). This cell has, once again, all its chromosomes in homologous pairs and two copies of every gene. It has the normal DNA content.

Genes and alleles

Genes are sections of DNA that control the production of proteins in a cell. Each protein contributes towards a particular body feature. Sometimes the feature is visible, such as eye colour or skin pigmentation. Sometimes the feature is not visible, such as the type of haemoglobin in red blood cells or the type of blood group antigen on the red blood cells.

> The X and the Y chromosomes are the **sex chromosomes**. They determine whether a person is male or female.

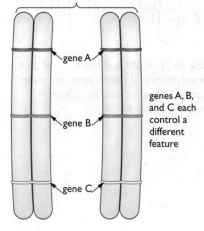

Figure 16.10 *Both chromosomes in an homologous pair have the same sequence of genes.*

Some genes have more than one form. For example, the genes controlling several facial features have alternate forms, which result in alternate forms of the feature (Figure 16.11).

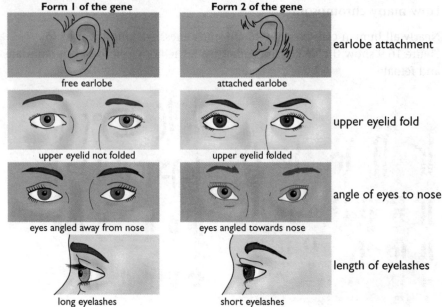

Figure 16.11 *The alternate forms of four facial features.*

The gene for earlobe attachment has the forms 'attached earlobe' and 'free earlobe'. These different forms of the gene are called **alleles**. Homologous chromosomes carry genes for the same features in the same sequence, but the alleles of the genes may not be the same (Figure 16.12). The DNA in the two chromosomes is not quite identical.

Each cell with two copies of a chromosome also has two copies of the genes on those chromosomes. Suppose that, for the gene controlling earlobe attachment, a person has one allele for attached earlobes and one for free earlobes. What happens? Is one ear free and the other attached? Are they both partly attached? Neither. In this case, both earlobes are free. The 'free' allele is **dominant** and 'switches off' the 'attached' allele, which is **recessive**. See Chapter 18 for more detail on how genes are inherited.

Chromosome mutations

When cells divide, they do not always divide properly. Bits of chromosomes can sometimes break off one chromosome and become attached to another. Sometimes one daughter cell ends up with both chromosomes of an homologous pair whilst the other has none. These 'mistakes' are called **chromosome mutations** and usually result in the death of the cells formed.

Sometimes sex cells do not form properly and they contain more (or less) chromosomes than normal. One relatively common chromosome mutation results in ova (female sex cells) containing two copies of chromosome 21. When an ovum like this is fertilised by a normal sperm, the zygote will have three copies of chromosome 21. This is called trisomy (three copies) of chromosome 21. Unlike some other chromosome mutations, the effects of this mutation are usually non-fatal and the condition that results is **Down's syndrome** (Figure 16.13).

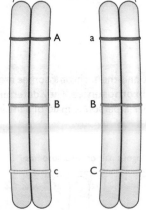

Figure 16.12 **A** and **a**, **B** and **b**, **C** and **c** are *different alleles of the same gene. They control the same feature but code for different expressions of that feature.*

Down's syndrome children sometimes die in infancy, as heart and lung defects are relatively common. Those that survive have a near normal life span. Individuals with Down's syndrome can now live much more normal lives than was thought possible just 20 years ago. They require much care and attention during childhood, and particularly in adolescence, but, given this care, they can achieve good social and intellectual growth. Most importantly, they achieve personal self-sufficiency. Trisomy of chromosome 21 is more common in women over 40 years of age. As a result, they have more babies with Down's syndrome than younger women.

Figure 16.13 *This boy has Down's syndrome. His teacher is helping him to develop his full potential.*

End of Chapter Checklist

You should now be able to:

- recall that the nucleus of a cell contains chromosomes on which genes are located

- understand that a gene is a section of a molecule of DNA

- describe the structure of a DNA molecule

- understand the meaning of alleles of a gene (see also Chapter 18)

- understand the function of meiosis (see also Chapter 17)

- recall that, in human cells, the diploid number of chromosomes is 46 and the haploid number is 23

- recall that mutation is a rare, random change in genetic material that can be inherited

- understand that many mutations are harmful but some are neutral and a few are beneficial (see also Chapter 19)

- understand that the incidence of mutations can be increased by mutagens such as ionising radiation and some chemicals.

Questions

More questions on DNA can be found at the end of Section E on page 230.

1 The diagram represents part of a molecule of DNA.

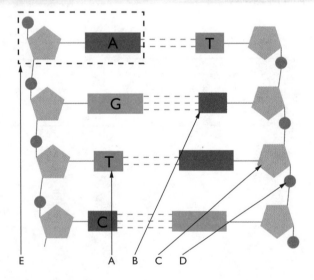

a) Name the parts labelled A, B, C, D and E.

b) What parts did James Watson, Frances Crick and Rosalind Franklin play in discovering the structure of DNA?

c) Use the diagram to explain the base-pairing rule.

2 a) What is:

i) a gene

ii) an allele?

b) Describe the structure of a chromosome.

c) How are the chromosomes in a woman's skin cells:

i) similar to

ii) different from those in a man's skin cells?

3 DNA is the only molecule capable of replicating itself. Sometimes mutations occur during replication.

a) Describe how DNA replicates itself.

b) Explain how a single gene mutation can lead to the formation of a protein in which:

   i) many of the amino acids are different from those coded for by the non-mutated gene

   ii) only one amino acid is different from those coded for by the non-mutated gene.

4 The graph shows the numbers and relative frequency of births of Down's syndrome babies in women aged between 20 and 50.

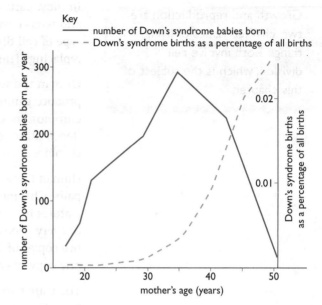

a) What is Down's syndrome?

b) How do the *numbers* of Down's syndrome births change with the age of the mother?

c) Suggest why the trend shown by the frequency of Down's syndrome births is different from that shown by the actual numbers.

Chapter 17: Cell Division

> Growth and reproduction are two characteristics of living things. Both involve cell division, which is the subject of this chapter.

In most parts of the body, cells need to divide so that organisms can grow and replace worn out or damaged cells. The cells that are produced in this type of cell division should be exactly the same as the cells they are replacing. This is the most common form of cell division.

Only in the sex organs is cell division different. Here, some cells divide to produce gametes (sex cells), which contain only half the original number of chromosomes. This is so that when male and female gametes fuse together (fertilisation) the resulting cell (zygote) will contain the full complement of chromosomes and can then divide and grow into a new individual.

Human body cells have 46 chromosomes in 23 pairs called homologous pairs. Chromosomes in an homologous pair carry genes for the same features in the same sequence. They do not necessarily have the same *alleles* of every gene (see Chapter 16). These body cells are **diploid** cells – they have *two* copies of each chromosome. The sex cells, with 23 chromosomes (only one copy of each chromosome), are **haploid** cells.

There are two kind of cell division: **mitosis** and **meiosis**. When cells divide by mitosis, two cells are formed. These have the same number and type of chromosomes as the original cell. Mitosis forms all the cells in our bodies except the sex cells.

> Meiosis is sometimes called **reduction division.** This is because it produces cells with only half the number of chromosomes of the original cell.

When cells divide by meiosis, four cells are formed. These have only half the number of chromosomes of the original cell. Meiosis forms sex cells.

Mitosis

When a **parent cell** divides it produces **daughter cells**. Mitosis produces two daughter cells that are genetically identical to the parent cell – both daughter cells have the same number and type of chromosomes as the parent cell. To achieve this, the dividing cell must do two things.

- It must copy each chromosome before it divides. This involves the DNA replicating and more proteins being added to the structure. Each daughter cell will then be able to receive a copy of each chromosome (and each molecule of DNA) when the cell divides.

- It must divide in such a way that each daughter cell receives one copy of every chromosome. If it does not do this, both daughter cells will not contain all the genes.

These two processes are shown in Figure 17.1.

A number of distinct stages occur when a cell divides by mitosis. These are shown in Figure 17.2. Figure 17.3 is a photograph of some cells from the root tip of an onion. Cells in this region of the root divide by mitosis to allow growth of the root.

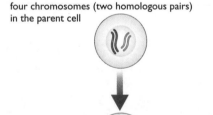

four chromosomes (two homologous pairs) in the parent cell

each chromosome copies itself

The cell divides into two; each new cell has a copy of each of the chromosomes.

Figure 17.1 *A summary of mitosis.*

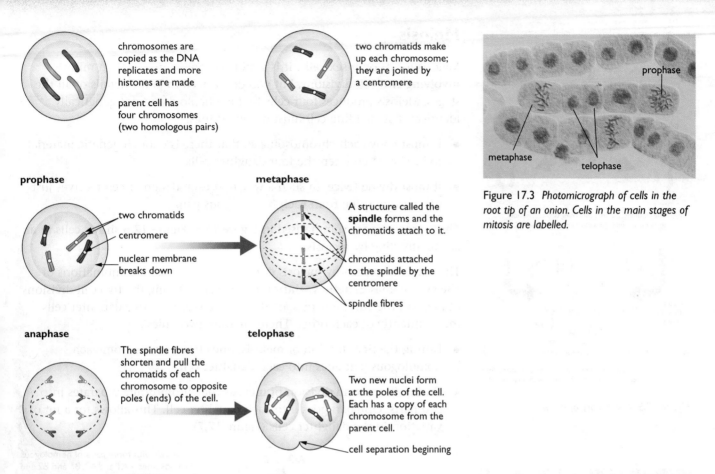

chromosomes are copied as the DNA replicates and more histones are made

parent cell has four chromosomes (two homologous pairs)

two chromatids make up each chromosome; they are joined by a centromere

prophase

two chromatids

centromere

nuclear membrane breaks down

metaphase

A structure called the **spindle** forms and the chromatids attach to it.

chromatids attached to the spindle by the centromere

spindle fibres

anaphase

The spindle fibres shorten and pull the chromatids of each chromosome to opposite poles (ends) of the cell.

telophase

Two new nuclei form at the poles of the cell. Each has a copy of each chromosome from the parent cell.

cell separation beginning

Figure 17.2 *The main stages in mitosis.*

Figure 17.3 *Photomicrograph of cells in the root tip of an onion. Cells in the main stages of mitosis are labelled.*

prophase

metaphase

telophase

Each daughter cell formed by mitosis receives a copy of every chromosome, and therefore every gene, in the parent cell. Each daughter cell is genetically identical to the others. All the cells in our body (except the sex cells) are formed by mitosis from the zygote (single cell formed at fertilisation). They all, therefore, contain copies of all the chromosomes and genes of that zygote. They are all genetically identical.

Whenever cells need to be replaced in our bodies, cells divide by mitosis to make them. This happens more frequently in some regions than in others.

- The skin loses thousands of cells every time we touch something. This adds up to millions every day that need replacing. A layer of cells beneath the surface is constantly dividing to produce replacements.

- Cells are scraped off the lining of the gut as food passes along. Again, a layer of cells beneath the gut lining is constantly dividing to produce replacement cells.

- Cells in our spleen destroy worn out red blood cells at the rate of 100 000 000 000 per day! These are replaced by cells in the bone marrow dividing by mitosis. In addition, the bone marrow forms all our new white blood cells and platelets (Figure 17.4).

- Cancer cells divide by mitosis. The cells formed are exact copies of the parent cell, including the mutation in the genes that makes the cells divide uncontrollably.

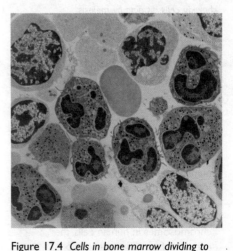

Figure 17.4 *Cells in bone marrow dividing to produce blood cells.*

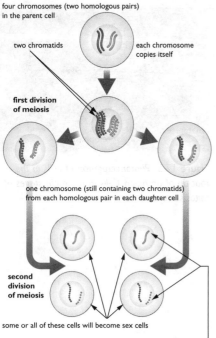

four chromosomes (two homologous pairs) in the parent cell

two chromatids

each chromosome copies itself

first division of meiosis

one chromosome (still containing two chromatids) from each homologous pair in each daughter cell

second division of meiosis

some or all of these cells will become sex cells

chromatids are separated and one chromatid from each chromosome ends up in each daughter cell

Figure 17.5 *A summary of meiosis.*

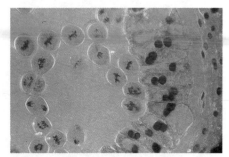

Figure 17.6 *Photomicrograph of an anther showing cells dividing by meiosis.*

There is a mathematical rule for predicting how many combinations of chromosomes there can be. The rule is:

number of possible combinations = 2^n

where n = number of *pairs* of chromosomes.

With two pairs of chromosomes, the number of possible combinations = 2^2 = 4. With three pairs of chromosomes, the number of possible combinations = 2^3 = 8. With the 23 pairs of chromosomes in human cells, the number of possible combinations = 2^{23} = 8 388 608!

Meiosis

Meiosis forms only sex cells. It is a more complex process than mitosis involving two cell divisions, but you don't need to know details of all the stages. Meiosis produces four cells that are haploid and not genetically identical. The dividing cell must do two things.

- It must copy each chromosome so that there is enough genetic material to be shared between the four daughter cells.

- It must divide twice, in such a way that each daughter cell receives just one chromosome from each homologous pair.

These processes are summarised in Figure 17.5. Figure 17.6 shows cells in an anther dividing by meiosis.

The sex cells formed by meiosis don't all have the same combinations of alleles – there is **genetic variation** in the cells. During the two cell divisions of meiosis, the chromosomes are divided between the two daughter cells independently of each other. There are only two 'rules'.

- During the first division of meiosis, one chromosome from each homologous pair goes into each daughter cell.

- During the second division of meiosis the chromosome separates into two parts. One part goes into each daughter cell. This allows for a lot of variation in the daughter cells (Figure 17.7).

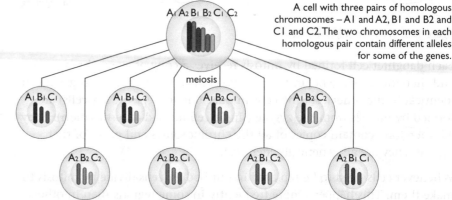

A cell with three pairs of homologous chromosomes – A1 and A2, B1 and B2 and C1 and C2. The two chromosomes in each homologous pair contain different alleles for some of the genes.

meiosis

As a result of the two divisions of meiosis, each sex cell formed contains one chromosome from each homologous pair. This gives eight combinations. As A1 and A2 contain different alleles (as do B2 and B2, and C1 and C2) the eight possible sex cells will be genetically different.

Figure 17.7 *How meiosis produces variation.*

The features of mitosis and meiosis are show in Table 17.1.

Feature of the process	Mitosis	Meiosis
Do the chromosomes duplicate before division begins?	yes	yes
How many cell divisions are there?	one	two
How many cells are formed by the process?	two	four
Are the cells formed haploid or diploid?	diploid	haploid
Is there genetic variation in the cells formed?	no	yes

Table 17.1: *Comparison of meiosis and mitosis.*

Sexual reproduction and variation

Sexual reproduction in any multicellular organism involves the fusion of two sex cells to form a zygote. The offspring from sexual reproduction vary genetically for a number of reasons. One reason is because of the huge variation in the sex cells. The other main reason is because of the random way in which fertilisation takes place. In humans, any one of the billions of sperm formed by a male during his life could, potentially, fertilise any one of the thousands of ova formed by a female.

This variation applies to both male and female sex cells. So, just using our 'low' estimate of about 8.5 million different types of human sex cells means that there can be 8.5 million different types of sperm and 8.5 million different types of ova. When fertilisation takes place, any sperm could fertilise any ovum. The number of possible combinations of chromosomes (and genes) in the zygote is 8.5 million × 8.5 million = 72 trillion! And remember, this is using our 'low' number!

This means that every individual is likely to be genetically unique. The only exceptions are **identical twins** (and identical triplets and quadruplets). Identical twins are formed from the *same* zygote – they are sometimes called **monozygotic twins**. When the zygote divides by mitosis, the two *genetically identical* cells formed do not 'stay together'. Instead, they separate and each cell behaves as though it were an individual zygote, dividing and developing into an embryo (Figure 17.8). Because they have developed from genetically identical cells (and, originally, from the same zygote), the embryos (and, later, the children and the adults they become) will be genetically identical.

Non-identical twins or **fraternal twins** develop from different zygotes and so are not genetically identical.

Seeds are part of the product of sexual reproduction in plants. Each seed contains an embryo which results from a pollen grain nucleus fusing with an egg cell nucleus. Embryos from the same plant will vary genetically because they are formed by different pollen grains fertilising different egg cells and so contain different combinations of genes.

Plant breeders have known about this variation for a long time. They realised that if a plant had some desirable feature, the best way to get more of that plant was not to collect its seeds, but to **clone** it in some way. Modern plant-breeding techniques allow the production of many thousands of identical plants from just a few cells of the original (see Chapter 20).

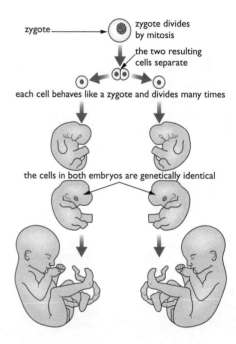

Figure 17.8 *How identical twins are formed.*

> Cloning is a process that produces a group of genetically identical offspring (a **clone**) from part of the parent organism. No sex cells are involved.

Asexual reproduction and cloning

When organisms reproduce asexually, there is no fusion of sex cells. A part of the organism grows and somehow breaks away from the parent organism. The cells it contains were formed by mitosis, so contain exactly the same genes as the parent. Asexual reproduction produces offspring that are genetically identical to the parent, and genetically identical to each other.

Asexual reproduction is common in plants (see Chapter 13). For example, flower bulbs grow and divide asexually each season to produce more bulbs. Asexual reproduction also occurs in some animals (see Chapter 9).

Genes and environment both produce variation

Pea plants are either tall or short because of the genes they inherit. There are no 'intermediate height' pea plants. However, all the tall pea plants are not *exactly* the same height and neither are all the short pea plants *exactly* the same height. Figure 17.9 illustrates the different types of variation in pea plants.

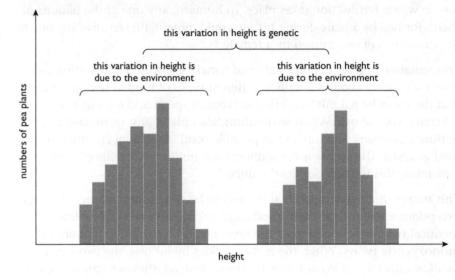

Figure 17.9 *Bar chart showing variation in height of pea plants.*

Several **environmental factors** can influence their height.

- They may not all receive the same amount of light and so some will not photosynthesise as well as others.

- They may not all receive the same amount of water and mineral ions from the soil: this could affect the manufacture of a range of substances in the plant.

- They may not all receive the same amount of carbon dioxide: again, some will not photosynthesise as well as others.

Similar principles apply in humans. Identical twins have the same genes, and often grow up to look very alike (although not quite identical). Also, they often develop similar talents. However, identical twins never look *exactly* the same. This is especially true if, for some reason, they grow up apart. The different environments affect their physical, social and intellectual development in different ways.

End of Chapter Checklist

You should now be able to:

● understand that division of a diploid cell at mitosis produces two cells, which contain identical sets of chromosomes

● understand that mitosis occurs during growth, repair, cloning and asexual reproduction

● understand that division of a cell by meiosis produces four cells, each with half the number of chromosomes, and that this results in the formation of genetically different haploid gametes

● understand that random fertilisation produces genetic variation of offspring

● understand that variation within a species can be genetic, environmental or a combination of both.

Questions

More questions on cell division can be found at the end of Section E on page 230.

1   Cells can divide by mitosis or by meiosis.

    a)   Give one similarity and two differences between the two processes.

    b)   Do cancer cells divide by mitosis or meiosis? Explain your answer.

    c)   Why is meiosis sometimes called reduction division?

2   Daffodils reproduce sexually by forming seeds and asexually by forming bulbs. Explain why:

    a)   the bulbs formed from a single daffodil plant produce plants very similar to each other and to the parent plant

    b)   the seeds formed by a single daffodil plant produce plants that vary considerably.

3   The diagram shows two cuttings. They were both taken from the same clover plant and planted in identical soil. After a few days, some nitrogen-fixing bacteria were added to the pot labelled 'inoculated'.

not inoculated   inoculated

    a)   Why were cuttings from the same plant used rather than seeds from the same plant?

    b)   What does this experiment suggest about the influence of genes and the environment on variation in the height of clover plants?

4   Some cells divide by mitosis, others divide by meiosis. For each of the following examples, say whether mitosis or meiosis is involved. In each case, give a reason for your answers.

    a)   Cells in the testes dividing to form sperm.

    b)   Cells in the lining of the small intestine dividing to replace cells that have been lost.

    c)   Cells in the bone marrow dividing to form red blood cells and white blood cells.

    d)   Cells in an anther of a flower dividing to form pollen grains.

    e)   A zygote dividing to form an embryo.

5   Variation in organisms can be caused by the environment as well as by the genes they inherit. For each of the following examples, state whether the variation described is likely to be genetic, environmental or both. In each case, give a reason for your answers.

    a)   Humans have brown, blue or green eyes.

    b)   Half the human population is male, half is female.

    c)   Cuttings of hydrangea plants grown in soils with different pH values develop flowers with slightly different colours.

    d)   Some pea plants are tall; others are dwarf. However, the tall plants are not exactly the same height and neither are all the dwarf plants the same height.

    e)   People in some families are more at risk of heart disease than people in other families. However, not every member of the 'high risk' families have a heart attack and some members of the 'low risk' families do.

6   In an investigation into mitosis, the distance between a chromosome and the pole (end) of a cell was measured. The graph shows the result of the investigation.

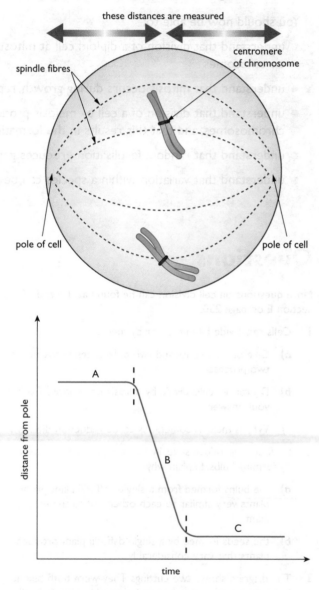

    a)   Describe two events that occur during stage A.

    b)   Explain what is happening during stage B.

    c)   Describe two events that occur during stage C.

Chapter 18: Genes and Inheritance

How and why do we inherit features from our parents? This chapter answers these questions by looking at the work of Gregor Mendel and how he has helped us to unravel the mysteries of inheritance.

Genes are sections of DNA that determine a particular feature (see Chapter 16) by instructing cells to produce particular proteins. As the DNA is part of a chromosome, we can also define a gene as 'part of a chromosome that determines a particular feature'. The ground-breaking research that uncovered the basic rules of how features are inherited was carried out by Gregor Mendel and published in 1865.

Gregor Mendel

Gregor Mendel (Figure 18.1) was a monk who lived in a monastery in Brno in what is now the Czech Republic. He became interested in inheritance and his first attempts at controlled breeding experiments were with mice. This was not well received in the monastery and he was advised to use pea plants instead. As a result of the experiments with pea plants, he was able to formulate the basic laws of inheritance.

Mendel established that, for each feature he studied:

- a 'heritable unit' (we now call it a **gene**) is passed from one generation to the next

- the heritable unit (gene) can have alternate forms (we now call these different forms **alleles**)

- each individual must have two alternate forms (alleles) per feature

- the sex cells only have one of the alternate forms (allele) per feature

- one allele can be dominant over the other.

Mendel was able to use his ideas to predict outcomes from breeding certain types of pea plant and then test his predictions by experiment. Mendel published his results and ideas in 1865 but very few people took any notice.

At that time, biologists had little knowledge of chromosomes and cell division, so Mendel's ideas had no physical basis. Also, biology then was very much a descriptive science and biologists of the day were not interested in the mathematical treatment of results. Mendel's work went against the ideas of the time that inheritance resulted from some kind of blending of features. The idea of a distinct 'heritable unit' just did not fit in.

It was not until 1900 that other biologists working on inheritance rediscovered Mendel's work and recognised its importance. In 1903, the connection between Mendel's suggested behaviour of genes and the behaviour of chromosomes in meiosis was noticed. The science of genetics was well and truly born.

Mendel's experiments on inheritance

Mendel noticed that many of the features of pea plants had just two alternate forms. For example, plants were either tall or dwarf, they either had purple or white flowers; they produced yellow seeds or green seeds. There were no intermediate forms, no pale purple flowers or green/yellow

Figure 18.1 *Gregor Mendel (1822–1884).*

201

seeds or intermediate height plants. Figure 18.2 shows some of the contrasting features of pea plants that Mendel used in his breeding experiments.

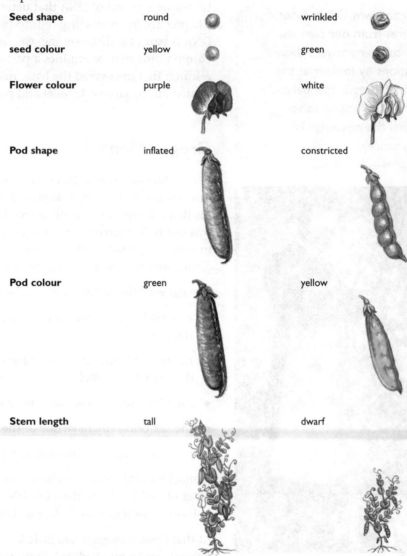

Seed shape	round		wrinkled	
Seed colour	yellow		green	
Flower colour	purple		white	
Pod shape	inflated		constricted	
Pod colour	green		yellow	
Stem length	tall		dwarf	

Figure 18.2 *Some features of pea plants used by Mendel in his breeding experiments.*

In his breeding experiments, Mendel initially used only plants that had 'bred true' for several generations. For example, any tall pea plants he used had come from generations of pea plants that had all been tall.

Mendel decided to investigate, systematically, the results of cross breeding plants that had contrasting features. These were the 'parent plants', referred to as '**P**' in genetic diagrams. He transferred pollen from one experimental plant to another. He also made sure that the plants could not be self-fertilised.

He collected all the seeds formed, grew them and noted the features that each plant developed. These plants were the first generation of offspring, or the 'F_1' generation. He did not cross-pollinate these plants, but allowed them to self-fertilise. Again, he collected the seeds, grew them and noted the features that each plant developed. These plants formed the second generation of offspring or the 'F_2' generation. When Mendel used pure-breeding tall and pure-breeding dwarf plants as his parents, he obtained the results shown in Figure 18.3.

P

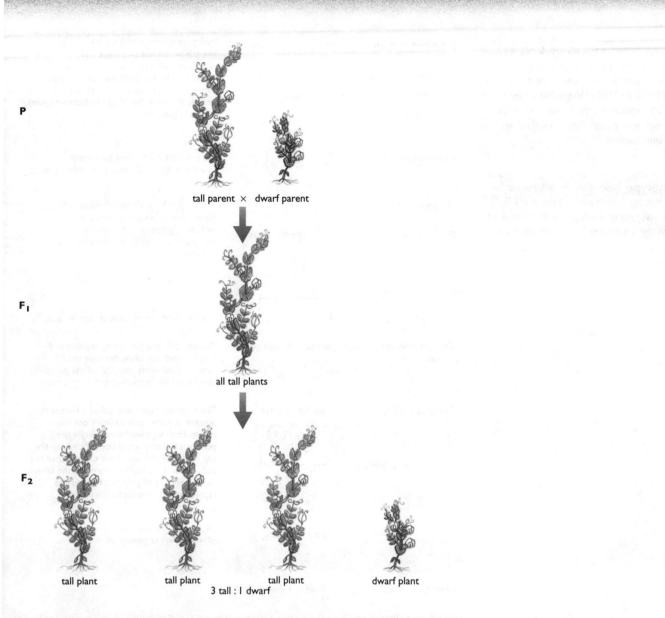

tall parent × dwarf parent

F₁

all tall plants

F₂

tall plant   tall plant   tall plant   dwarf plant

3 tall : 1 dwarf

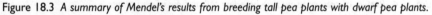

Figure 18.3 *A summary of Mendel's results from breeding tall pea plants with dwarf pea plants.*

Mendel obtained very similar results when he carried out breeding experiments using plants with different pairs of contrasting characters (Figure 18.4). He noticed the following two things in particular.

- All the plants of the F₁ generation were always of just one type. This type was not a blend of the two parental features, but one or the other. Every time he repeated the experiment with the same feature, it was always the same type that appeared in the F₁ generation. For example, when tall and dwarf parents were cross-bred, the F₁ plants were always all tall.

- There was always a 3:1 ratio of types in the F₂ generation. Three-quarters of the plants in the F₂ generation were of the type that appeared in the F₁ generation. One-quarter showed the other parental feature. For example, when tall and dwarf parents were cross-bred, three-quarters of the F₂ plants were always tall and one-quarter were dwarf.

Mendel was able to use these patterns in his results to work out how features were inherited, without any knowledge of genes and chromosomes.

Chapter 18: Genes and Inheritance

203

Whenever you have to work out a genetic cross, you should choose suitable symbols to represent the dominant and recessive alleles, give a key to explain which symbol is which and write out the cross exactly like the one shown.

Genotype describes the alleles each cell has for a certain feature, e.g. TT. **Phenotype** is the feature that results from the genotype (e.g. a tall plant).

Phenotype of parents: tall, dwarf

Genotype of parents: TT × tt

Both parents are pure breeding. The tall parent has two alleles for tallness in each cell. The dwarf parent has two alleles for dwarfness in each cell. Because each has two copies of just one allele, we say that they are **homozygous** for the height gene.

Gametes (sex cells): (T) (t)

The sex cells are formed by meiosis. As a result, they only have one allele each.

Genotype of F1: Tt

Phenotype of F1: all tall

The F1 plants have one tall allele and one dwarf allele. We say that they are **heterozygous** for the height gene. The plants are tall because the tall allele is dominant.

The F1 plants are allowed to self-fertilise.

Gametes from the F1 plants: male gametes (T) or (t); female gametes (T) or (t)

The sex cells are formed by meiosis and so only have one allele. Because the F1 plants are heterozygous, half of the gametes carry the T allele and half carry the t allele.

Genotypes of F2

male gametes \ female gametes	(T)	(t)
(T)	TT	Tt
(t)	Tt	tt

The diagram opposite is called a **Punnett square**. It allows you to work out the results from a genetic cross. Write the genotypes of one set of sex cells across the top of the square and those of the other sex cells down the side. Then combine the alleles in the two sets of gametes; the squares represent the possible fertilisations.

1 TT : 2 Tt : 1 tt

You can now work out the *ratio* of the different genotypes.

Phenotypes of F2: 3 tall : 1 dwarf

Figure 18.4 *Results of crosses using true-breeding tall and dwarf pea plants.*

The genotype of an organism is represented by two letters, each letter representing one allele of the gene that controls the feature. Normally, we use the initial letter of the dominant feature to represent the gene. Writing it as a capital letter indicates the dominant allele, the lower case letter represents the recessive allele. For the feature, height in pea plants, plants can be either tall or dwarf. Using the initial letter of the word 'tall', the alleles are shown as **T** and **t**. **TT** means that a plant has two alleles for tallness.
A plant with two alleles for dwarfness would be represented by **tt**. Although we use pea plants to illustrate Mendel's ideas, the same principles apply to other organisms also.

Explaining Mendel's results

We can now explain Mendel's results using the ideas of chromosomes, genes, mitosis and meiosis (Chapters 16 and 17).

- Each feature is controlled by a gene, which is found on a chromosome.
- There are two copies of each chromosome and each gene in all body cells, except the sex cells.
- The sex cells have only one copy of each chromosome and each gene
- There are two alleles (forms) of each gene.
- One allele is **dominant** over the other allele, which is **recessive**.
- When two different alleles (one dominant and one recessive) are in the same cell, only the dominant allele is expressed (is allowed to 'work').
- An individual can have two dominant alleles, two recessive alleles or a dominant allele and a recessive allele in each cell.

We can use the cross between tall and dwarf pea plants as an example (Figure 18.4). In pea plants, there are tall and dwarf alleles of the gene for height. We will use the symbol **T** for the tall allele and **t** for the dwarf allele. The term **genotype** describes the alleles each cell has for a certain feature (e.g. TT). The **phenotype** is the feature that results from the genotype (e.g. a tall plant).

Working out genotypes – the test cross

You cannot tell just by looking at it whether a tall pea plant is homozygous (TT) or heterozygous (Tt). Both these genotypes would appear equally tall because the tall allele is dominant. It would help if you knew the genotypes of its parents. You could then write out a genetic cross and perhaps work out the genotype of your tall plant. If you don't know the genotypes of the parents, the only way you can find out is by carrying out a breeding experiment called a **test cross**.

In a test cross, the factor under investigation is the unknown genotype of an organism showing the dominant feature. A tall pea plant could have the genotype TT or Tt. You must control every other possible variable *including the genotype of the plant you breed it with*. The only genotype you can be *certain* of is the genotype of plants showing the *recessive* feature (in this case dwarf plants). They *must* have the genotype tt.

> In a test cross, you breed an organism showing the dominant feature with one showing the recessive feature.

In this example, you must breed the 'unknown' tall pea plant (TT or Tt) with a dwarf pea plant (tt). You can write out a genetic cross for both possibilities (TT × tt and Tt × tt) and *predict* the outcome for each (Figure 18.5). You can then compare the results of the breeding experiment with the predicted outcomes to see which one matches most closely.

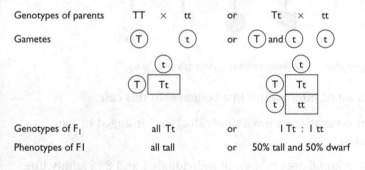

Genotypes of parents	TT × tt	or	Tt × tt

Gametes: T, t   or   T and t, t

Genotypes of F₁: all Tt   or   1 Tt : 1 tt
Phenotypes of F1: all tall   or   50% tall and 50% dwarf

Figure 18.5 *A test cross.*

From our crosses we would expect:

- *all* the offspring to be tall if the tall parent was homozygous (TT)

- *half* the offspring to be tall and *half* to be dwarf if the tall parent was heterozygous (Tt).

Ways of presenting genetic information

Writing out a genetic cross is a useful way of showing how genes are passed through one or two generations, starting with just two parents. To show a proper family history of a genetic condition requires more than this. We use a diagram called a **pedigree**. Polydactyly is an inherited condition in which a person develops an extra digit (finger or toe) on the hands and feet. It is determined by a dominant allele. The recessive allele causes the normal number of digits to develop.

If we use the symbol D for the polydactyly allele and d for the normal-number allele, the possible genotypes and phenotypes are:

- DD – person has polydactyly (has two dominant polydactyly alleles)

- Dd – person has polydactyly (has a dominant polydactyly allele and a recessive normal allele)

- dd – person has the normal number of digits (has two recessive, normal-number alleles).

We don't use P and p to represent the alleles as you would expect, because P and p look very similar and could easily be confused. The pedigree for polydactyly is shown in Figure 18.6.

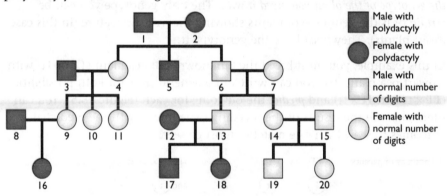

Figure 18.6 *A pedigree showing the inheritance of polydactyly in a family.*

We can extract a lot of information in a pedigree. In this case:

- there are four generations shown (individuals are arranged in four horizontal lines)

- individuals 4, 5 and 6 are children of individuals 1 and 2 (a family line connects each one directly to 1 and 2)

- individual 4 is the first-born child of 1 and 2 (the first-born child is shown to the left, then second born to the right of this, then third born and so on)

- individuals 3 and 7 are not children of 1 and 2 (no family line connects them directly to 1 and 2)

- 3 and 4 are father and mother of the same children – as are 1 and 2, 6 and 7, 8 and 9, 12 and 13, 14 and 15 (a horizontal line joins them).

It is usually possible to work out which allele is dominant from pedigrees. Look for a situation where two parents show the same feature and at least one child shows the contrasting feature. In this pedigree, 1 and 2 both have polydactyly, but children 4 and 6 do not. We can explain this in only one way:

- the normal alleles in 4 and 6 can only have come from their parents – 1 and 2, so 1 and 2 have normal alleles
- 1 and 2 show polydactyly, so they *must* have polydactyly alleles as well
- if they have both polydactyly alleles *and* normal alleles but show polydactyly, the polydactyly allele must be the dominant allele.

Now that we know which allele is dominant, we can work out most of the genotypes in the pedigree. All the people with the normal number of digits *must* have the genotype dd (if they had even one D allele, they would show polydactyly). All the people with polydactyly must have *at least one* polydactyly allele (they must be either DD or Dd).

From here, we can begin to work out the genotypes of the people with polydactyly. To do this we need to bear in mind that people with the normal number of digits must inherit one 'normal-number' allele from each parent, and also that people with the normal number of digits will pass on one 'normal-number' allele to each of their children.

From this we can say that any person with polydactyly who has children with the normal number of digits must be heterozygous (the child must have inherited one of their two 'normal-number' alleles from this parent), and also that any person with polydactyly who has one parent with the normal number of digits must also be heterozygous (the normal parent can only have passed on a 'normal-number' allele). Individuals 1, 2, 3, 16, 17 and 18 fall into one or both of these categories and must be heterozygous.

We can now add this genetic information to the pedigree. This is shown in Figure 18.7.

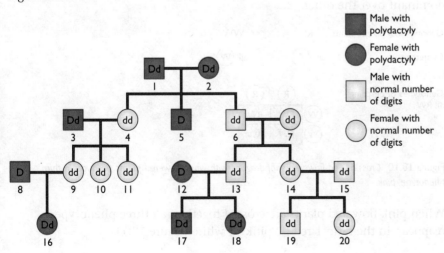

Figure 18.7 *A pedigree showing the inheritance of polydactyly in a family, with details of genotypes added.*

We are still left uncertain about individuals 5, 8 and 12. They could be homozygous or heterozygous. For example, individuals 1 and 2 are both heterozygous. Figure 18.8 shows the possible outcomes from a genetic cross between them. Individual 5 could be any of the outcomes indicated by the shading. It is impossible to distinguish between DD and Dd.

Genotypes of parents   Dd   ×   Dd

Gametes   (D) and (d)   (D) and (d)

female gametes

	D	d
D	DD	Dd
d	Dd	dd

Genotypes of children

male gametes

Figure 18.8 *Possible outcomes from a genetic cross between two parents, both heterozygous for polydactyly.*

Codominance

So far, all the examples of genetic crosses that we have seen involve **complete** dominance, where one **dominant** allele completely masks the effect of a second, or **recessive** allele. However, there are many genes with alleles that *both* contribute to the phenotype. If two alleles are expressed in the same phenotype, they are called **codominant**. For example, snapdragon plants have red, white or pink flowers (Figure 18.9).

If a plant with red flowers is crossed with one that has white flowers, all the plants resulting from the cross will have pink flowers. The appearance of a third phenotype shows that there is codominance. We can represent the alleles for flower colour with symbols:

R = allele for red flower

W = allele for white flower.

Figure 18.10 shows the cross between the parent plants. Note that the alleles for red and white flowers are given *different* letters, since one is not dominant over the other.

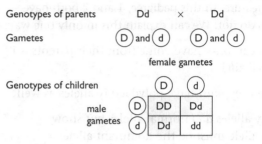

Figure 18.9 *Flower colours in snapdragons are caused by a gene showing codominance.*

Genotypes of parent plants   RR   ×   WW

Gametes   all (R)   all (W)

Genotypes of offspring all RW

	R	R
W	RW	RW
W	RW	RW

Figure 18.10 *Crossing red-flowered snapdragons with white-flowered plants produces a third phenotype, pink.*

When pink-flowered plants are crossed together, all three phenotypes reappear, in the ratio 1 red : 2 pink : 1 white (Figure 18.11).

Genotypes of parent plants   RW   ×   RW

Gametes   (R) all (W)   (R) all (W)

Genotypes of offspring 1RR : 2RW : 1WW

	R	W
R	RR	RW
W	RW	WW

Figure 18.11 *Crossing pink-flowered snapdragons.*

In fact, *most* genes do not show complete dominance. Genes can show a range of dominance, from complete dominance as in tall and dwarf pea plants through to equal dominance as in the snapdragon flowers, where the new phenotype is halfway between the other two.

Sex determination

Our sex – whether we are male or female – is not under the control of a single gene. It is determined by the X and Y chromosomes – the sex chromosomes. As well as the 44 non-sex chromosomes, there are two X chromosomes in all cells of females (except the egg cells) and one X and one Y chromosome in all cells of males (except the sperm). Our sex is effectively determined by the presence or absence of the Y chromosome. The full chromosome complement of male and female is shown in Figure 16.9 on page 189.

Because the Y chromosome, when present, causes a zygote to develop into a male, some people cannot resist describing it as 'dominant'. This is incorrect: dominant and recessive are terms that are only applied to individual alleles.

The inheritance of sex follows the pattern shown in Figure 18.12. In any one family, however, this ratio may well not be met. Predicted genetic ratios are usually only met when large numbers are involved. The overall ratio of male and female births in all countries is 1 : 1.

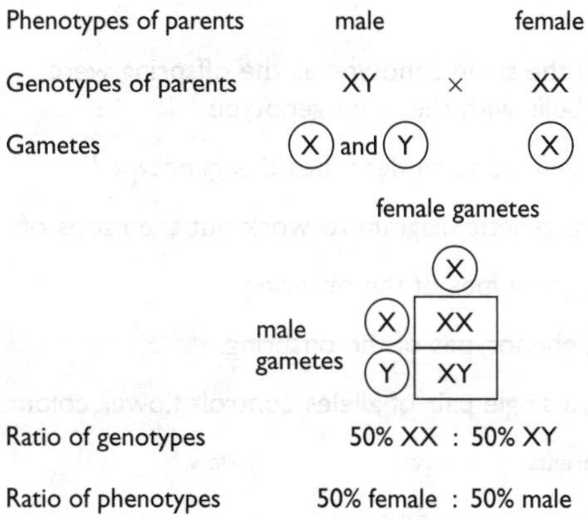

Phenotypes of parents	male	female
Genotypes of parents	XY ×	XX
Gametes	X and Y	X

female gametes

		X
male gametes	X	XX
	Y	XY

Ratio of genotypes	50% XX : 50% XY
Ratio of phenotypes	50% female : 50% male

Figure 18.12 *Determination of sex in humans.*

End of Chapter Checklist

You should now be able to:

- understand that genes exist in alternative forms called alleles which give rise to differences in inherited characteristics
- recall the meaning of the terms dominant, recessive, homozygous, heterozygous, phenotype, genotype and codominance
- describe the patterns of inheritance of a gene using a genetic diagram
- understand how to interpret family pedigrees
- predict probabilities of outcomes from genetic crosses involving a single gene
- recall how the sex of a person is controlled
- describe the determination of the sex of offspring at fertilisation, using a genetic diagram.

Questions

More questions on chromosomes, genes and inheritance can be found at the end of Section E on page 230.

1 Predict the *ratios* of offspring from the following crosses between tall/dwarf pea plants.

a) TT × TT, *b)* TT × Tt, *c)* TT × tt, *d)* Tt × Tt, *e)* Tt × tt, *f)* tt × tt.

2 In cattle, a pair of alleles controls coat colour. The allele for black coat colour is dominant over the allele for red coat colour. The genetic diagram represents a cross between a pure-breeding black bull and a pure-breeding red cow.
B = dominant allele for black coat colour; **b** = recessive allele for red coat colour.

Parents   black bull   red cow

BB   ×   bb

Gametes

Offspring

a) i) What term describes the genotypes of the pure-breeding parents?

ii) Explain the terms dominant and recessive.

b) i) What are the genotypes of the sex cells of each parent?

ii) What is the genotype of the offspring?

c) Cows with the same genotype as the offspring were bred with bulls with the same genotype.

i) What genetic term describes this genotype?

ii) Draw a genetic diagram to work out the ratios of:

- the genotypes of the offspring
- the phenotypes of the offspring.

3 In nasturtiums, a single pair of alleles controls flower colour.

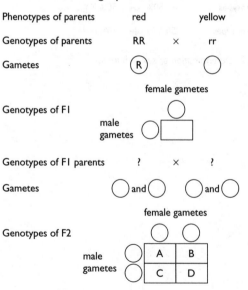

Phenotypes of parents	red	yellow
Genotypes of parents	RR ×	rr
Gametes	(R)	( )

female gametes

Genotypes of F1

male gametes

Genotypes of F1 parents   ? × ?

Gametes   ( ) and ( )   ( ) and ( )

female gametes

Genotypes of F2

male gametes

	A	B
	C	D

The allele for red flower colour is dominant over the allele for yellow flower colour. The diagram represents the results of a cross between a pure-breeding red-flowered nasturtium and a pure-breeding yellow-flowered nasturtium.

R = dominant allele for red flower colour; **r** = recessive allele for yellow flower colour.

a) Copy and complete the genetic diagram.

b) What are the colours of the flowers of A, B, C and D?

4   Cystic fibrosis is an inherited condition. The diagram shows the incidence of cystic fibrosis in a family over four generations.

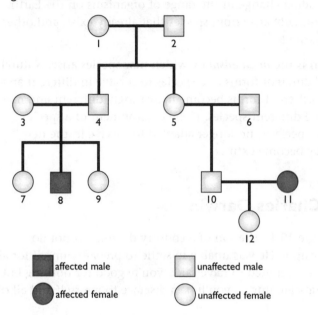

affected male   unaffected male

affected female   unaffected female

a) What evidence in the pedigree suggests that cystic fibrosis is determined by a recessive allele?

b) What are the genotypes of individuals 3, 4 and 11? Explain your answers.

c) Draw genetic diagrams to work out the probability that the next child born to individuals 10 and 11 will *i)* be male, *ii)* suffer from cystic fibrosis.

5   In guinea pigs, the allele for short hair is dominant to that for long hair.

a) Two short-haired guinea pigs were bred and their offspring included some long-haired guinea pigs. Explain these results.

b) How could you find out if a short-haired guinea pig was homozygous or heterozygous for hair length?

6   When two different alleles of a gene are expressed in the same phenotype, they are called codominant. Coat colour in shorthorn cattle is controlled by a codominant gene. 'Red' cattle crossed with 'white' cattle produce offspring which all have a pale brown coat, called roan.

a) Explain the terms gene, allele and phenotype.

b) Draw genetic diagrams to show the possible genotypes of offspring resulting from a cross between:

   i)   a red bull and a white cow

   ii) a red bull and a roan cow

   iii) a roan bull and a roan cow.

c) For each of the crosses in (b) state the ratio of the phenotypes you would expect from the cross.

Chapter 19: Natural Selection and Evolution

> Over millions of years, life on this planet has evolved from its simple beginnings into the vast range of organisms present today. This has happened by natural selection.

Humans have been asking the question 'Where did we come from?' for thousands of years. The theory of evolution, occurring by natural selection, is the most widely accepted scientific explanation of the answer to this question. The two terms are quite distinct.

- **Evolution** is a gradual change in the range of organisms on the Earth. New species continually arise from species that already exist, and other species become extinct.

- **Natural selection** is the *mechanism* by which new species arise. Natural selection 'allows' different forms of a species to survive in different areas. Over time, these different forms become increasingly different and may eventually become different species. If the environment of a species changes and that species is no longer adapted to survive in the new conditions, it may become extinct.

The work of Charles Darwin

Charles Darwin (Figure 19.1), the son of a country doctor, did not do particularly well at school. He was unable to settle to prepare himself for any profession. His father is reputed to have said: 'you're good for nothing but shooting guns and rat-catching … you'll be a disgrace to yourself and all of your family'.

At the age of 22, Charles Darwin became the ship's naturalist on HMS Beagle, which left England for a five-year voyage in 1831.

Figure 19.1 *Charles Darwin (1809–1882).*

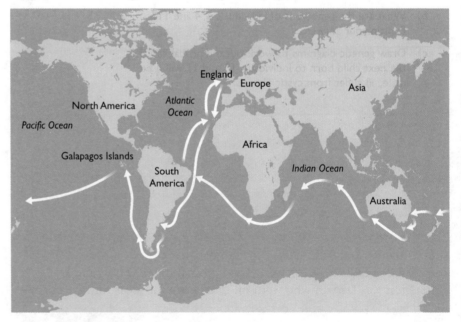

Figure 19.2 *The five-year journey of HMS Beagle.*

During the voyage, Darwin collected hundreds of specimens and made many observations about the variety of organisms and the ways in which they were adapted to their environments. He gained much information, in particular, from the variety of life forms in South America and the Galapagos Islands. Darwin was influenced by the work of Charles Lyell who was, at the time, laying the foundations of modern geology. Lyell was using the evidence of rock layers to suggest that the surface of the Earth was constantly changing. The layers of sediments in rocks represented different time periods. Darwin noticed that the fossils found in successive layers of rocks often changed slightly through the layers. He suggested that life forms were continually changing – evolving. This was in contrast to the religious ideas of special creation, a common belief that all life had been created at one time and had not changed since.

On his return to England, Darwin began to evaluate his data and wrote several essays, introducing the ideas of natural selection. He arrived at his theory of natural selection from observations made during his voyage on the Beagle and from deductions made from those observations. Darwin's observations were that:

- organisms tend to produce more offspring than are needed to replace them – a single female salmon can release 5 million eggs per year; a giant puffball fungus produces 40 million spores

- despite the over-reproduction, stable, established populations of organisms tend to remain the same size – the seas are not overflowing with salmon, and you are not surrounded by piles of giant puffball fungi!

- members of the same species are not identical – living things vary.

He made two important deductions from these observations.

- From the first two observations he deduced that there is a 'struggle for existence'. Many offspring are produced, yet the population stays the same size. There must be competition for resources and many must die.

- From the third observation he deduced that, if some offspring survive whilst others die, those organisms best equipped or best suited to their environment will survive to reproduce. Those less suited will die. This gave rise to the phrase 'survival of the fittest'.

Notice a key phrase in the second deduction – the best-suited organisms survive *to reproduce*. This means that those characteristics that give the organism a better chance of surviving will be passed on to the next generation. Those organisms that are less suited to the environment, survive to reproduce in smaller numbers. The next generation will have more of the type that is adapted and fewer of the less well adapted type. This will be repeated in each generation.

Another naturalist, Alfred Russell Wallace, had also studied life forms in South America and had reached the same conclusions as Darwin. Darwin and Wallace published a scientific paper on natural selection jointly, although it was Darwin who went on to develop the ideas further. In 1859, he published his now famous book 'The Origin of Species'.

This book changed forever the way in which biologists think about how species arise. Darwin went on to suggest that humans could have evolved from ape-like ancestors, for which he was ridiculed, largely by people who had misunderstood his ideas. He also carried out considerable research into plant tropisms (see Chapter 12).

Figure 19.3 *Darwin's ideas were unpopular and many newspapers of the time made fun of them.*

By using the phrase 'survival of the fittest', Darwin was not referring to physical fitness, but to biological fitness. This means how well suited, or well adapted, an organism is to its environment.

Darwin was not aware of genes and how they determine characteristics when he put forward his theory of natural selection. Gregor Mendel had yet to publish his work on inheritance.

Evidence for natural selection

The theory of natural selection proposes that some factor in the environment 'selects' which forms of a species will survive to reproduce under those conditions. Forms that are not well adapted will not survive. Any evidence for natural selection must show that:

- there is variation within the species

- changing conditions in the environment (a **selection pressure**) favours one particular form of the species (which has a **selective advantage**)

- the frequency of the favoured form increases (it is selected *for*) under these conditions (survival of the fittest)

- the frequency of the less well adapted form decreases under these conditions (it is selected *against*)

- the changes are not due to any other factor.

Natural selection in the peppered moth

The peppered moth has two forms, one is greyish-white with dark markings ('peppered') and one is much darker (Figure 19.4).

Figure 19.4 *These moths are different forms of the same species – Biston betularia, the peppered moth. Both forms are food for several species of birds. Both are found in areas with clean air and in smoke-polluted areas. Which form is best adapted to which area?*

Initially, nearly all the moths were of the peppered type. The first record of a dark moth in Manchester, England was in 1848. By 1895, 98% of the moths in Manchester were of the dark form. What had caused this change? The following pieces of information will give you some clues.

- Peppered moths are food for birds.

- Increasing industrialisation during the nineteenth century killed off many of the lichens growing on tree trunks and also covered the trunks with soot.

- The distribution of the two forms of peppered moth was linked to the degree of industrialisation (Figure 19.5).

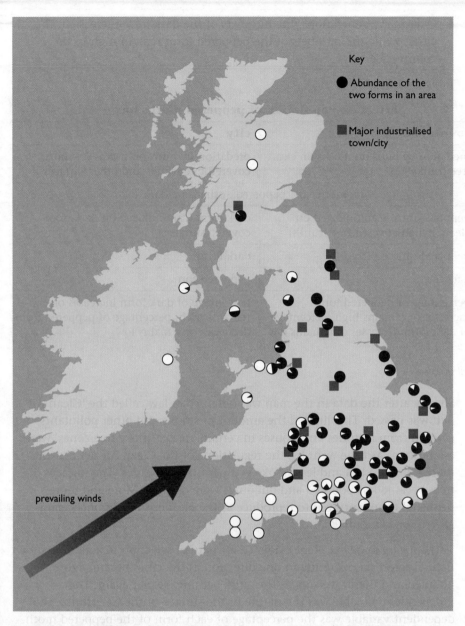

Figure 19.5 *The distribution of the two forms of the peppered moth in the British Isles in the 1950s.*

Natural selection explains the moth distribution in the following way.

- In any area there is an overproduction of offspring and so there is a struggle for existence. Because of this, the form most suited to its environment will survive.

- In the country, tree trunks are still relatively unpolluted; in the cities, the tree trunks and buildings are covered with soot.

- In the country, the peppered form is camouflaged; in the cities, the dark form is camouflaged.

- Camouflaged moths are less likely to be eaten by birds.

- In the country, more of the peppered form survive to reproduce; in the cities, more of the dark form survive to reproduce.

- Over many generations, the numbers of the dark form increase in the cities, while the numbers of the peppered form remain high in the countryside.

Table 19.1 illustrates this.

Feature of natural selection	Effect on population of peppered moths in:	
	countryside	city
selection pressure	predation by birds on moths on clean tree trunks	predation by birds on moths on soot-covered tree trunks and other surfaces
natural variation in the species	some moths are 'peppered', others are dark.	
type with selective advantage	peppered form (camouflaged on clean, lichen-covered tree trunks)	dark form (camouflaged on dark, soot-covered surfaces)
type selected for	peppered form	dark form
type selected against	dark form	peppered form
result of natural selection over many generations	percentage of peppered form increases or remains high, percentage of dark form decreases or remains low	percentage of dark form increases or remains high, percentage of peppered form decreases or remains low

Table 19.1: *Peppered moths as evidence for natural selection.*

Recently, some biologists have questioned the methods by which the peppered moth data was obtained. They do not, however, think that the conclusion about the way in which natural selection is thought to operate is necessarily wrong. They think that it presents a picture that is too clear cut and further data, obtained in a more rigorous manner, is needed to support the conclusion.

Shortly after the data in the map was obtained, a law called the 'Clean Air Act' was passed. This limited the amount of smoke and other pollutants emitted from factories and houses in certain areas. 'Smoke free zones' were established. As time went by, the regulations of the Clean Air Act became more rigid and less and less smoke was permitted in cities. The surfaces of trees became less polluted and buildings were cleaned. More and more peppered forms survived to reproduce as the cleaner surfaces once again gave them camouflage.

This appears to be excellent evidence for natural selection in action. It shows natural selection operating in one direction as the cities became more polluted and then reversing as the cities became cleaner again. The independent variable was the nature of the surface of the tree trunks, the dependent variable was the percentage of each form of the peppered moth. Industrialisation and the Clean Air Act changed the independent variable in the cities. Throughout it all, the countryside acted as a kind of unchanging control experiment. This showed that over the same period, when the independent variable was *not* changed, the percentage of each form of the peppered moth was unaltered. Other factors were not causing the change – it *must* have been the nature of the surfaces offering camouflage to different forms of the moth.

Natural selection in antibiotic-resistant bacteria

Alexander Fleming discovered penicillin, the first antibiotic, in 1929. Since then, other natural antibiotics have been discovered and many more have been synthesised in laboratories. The use of antibiotics has increased dramatically, particularly over the last 20 years. We now almost expect to be given an antibiotic for even the most trivial of ailments. This can be dangerous, as it leads to the development of bacterial resistance to an antibiotic (Figure 19.6).

Mutations happen all the time in all living organisms. In bacteria, a chance mutation could give a bacterium resistance to an antibiotic. In a situation where antibiotics are widely used, this new resistant bacterium has an advantage over non-resistant bacteria of the same type. The resistant bacterium will survive and multiply in greater numbers than the non-resistant types. The generation time of a bacterium can be as short as 20 minutes. This means that there could be 72 generations in a single day – the equivalent of about 1500 years of human generation time. The numbers of resistant types would increase with each generation. Very soon a population of bacteria could become almost entirely made up of resistant types. Table 19.2 shows how natural selection can introduce resistance to an antibiotic in a population of bacteria.

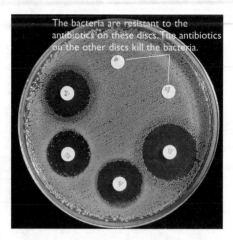

Figure 19.6 *Bacterial resistance to an antibiotic.*

Feature of natural selection	Effect on population of non-resistant bacteria
selection pressure	repeated use of antibiotics
natural variation in the species	some are resistant (due to a chance mutation), others are not
type with selective advantage	resistant type – will survive antibiotic treatment
type selected for	resistant type
type selected against	non-resistant type
result of natural selection over many generations	percentage of resistant types in the population increases

Table 19.2: *Bacteria and natural selection.*

Doctors are now more reluctant to prescribe antibiotics. They know that by using them less, the bacteria with resistance have less of an advantage and will not become as widespread.

Natural selection and sickle cell anaemia

Sickle cell anaemia is caused by a mutant allele. It affects the formation of haemoglobin in red blood cells. The abnormal haemoglobin causes the red blood cells to become distorted (sickle-shaped) when the oxygen concentration of the surroundings is low (Figure 19.7). The condition can be fatal in individuals homozygous for the allele.

Heterozygous 'carriers' of the allele usually show no symptoms of the disease at all, although 50% of the haemoglobin in their red blood cells is abnormal. They do have an important benefit, however. They are more resistant to malaria than people with 100% normal haemoglobin (homozygous for the normal allele).

Some people talk about bacteria becoming *immune* to antibiotics. This is a misunderstanding. *Individuals* become immune to *microorganisms* that infect them. This happens as a result of the immune response they make to those pathogens and usually takes a few days – a fraction of a lifetime. *Populations* of bacteria become resistant to antibiotics as a result of chance mutations and natural selection over many generations.

There is growing concern about so-called 'super-bugs' – bacteria that are resistant to several antibiotics. This multiple resistance is sometimes caused by 'jumping genes'. Bacteria can occasionally transfer genes between different species. A bacterium with a gene that gives resistance to penicillin could transfer this gene to a bacterium with a gene giving resistance to tetracycline (another antibiotic). This would produce a bacterium resistant to both antibiotics. Bacteria with multiple resistance to antibiotics will have a large selective advantage in any situation where those antibiotics are widely used.

Homozygous means having two alleles of a gene that are the same (e.g. two alleles for sickle cell or two normal alleles). Heterozygous means having two different alleles of a gene (e.g. one sickle cell allele and one normal allele). People heterozygous for sickle cell anaemia are called 'carriers'.

(a)
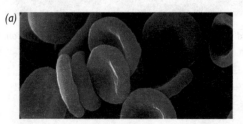

(b)

Figure 19.7 *(a) Normal red blood cells and (b) distorted red blood cells from a person suffering from sickle cell anaemia.*

The red blood cells of carriers look normal, but are slightly more fragile than normal red blood cells (because of the 50% abnormal haemoglobin). The malarial parasite is transmitted by the female *Anopheles* mosquito and spends part of its life cycle inside red blood cells. When these parasites enter the fragile red blood cells of carriers, the cells often burst before the parasite has time to develop and the parasite dies. The life cycle is broken. Table 19.3 shows how natural selection affects the incidence of sickle cell anaemia in an area where malaria is common.

Feature of natural selection	Effect on incidence of sickle cell anaemia
selection pressure	infection by the malarial parasite
natural variation in the species	carriers (people who are heterozygous for the sickle cell allele) and people homozygous for the normal allele; people homozygous for the sickle cell allele often die at an early age
type with selective advantage	carriers – malarial parasite cannot complete life cycle
type selected for	carriers
type selected against	people with 100% normal haemoglobin (homozygous for normal allele)
result of natural selection over many generations	numbers of heterozygotes in the population are higher than in areas where malaria is absent; numbers of people suffering from the disease are also higher than in other areas

Table 19.3: *Sickle cell anaemia and natural selection.*

The carriers have a selective advantage over those homozygous for the normal allele in areas where malaria is common. However, if two carriers marry, they can produce children who are homozygous for the sickle cell allele. As a result, sickle cell anaemia is more common in these areas also (Figure 19.8).

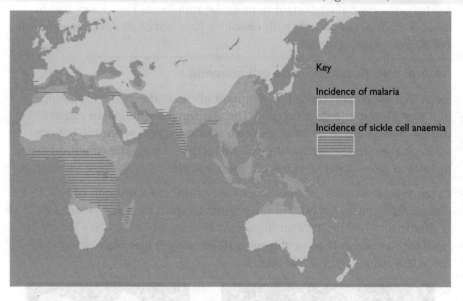

Figure 19.8 *A map showing areas of the world where sickle cell anaemia and malaria are common.*

Natural selection and the formation of new species

Natural selection favours the survival of individuals with an advantage over others in the population. Consequently, over time, the least well-adapted members of a population do not survive to reproduce, and the population becomes increasingly adapted to its environment. Suppose that there were two populations of the same species in different environments. Different forms would have an advantage in the *different* environments (Figure 19.9).

> Biologists define a species as a group of individuals that share common genes and can interbreed to produce fertile offspring (offspring that can also breed and produce offspring).

1 A population of plants lives in a fairly normal type of soil, with normal rainfall.

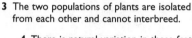

2 Some of these plants colonise a different area, where water is found much deeper in the soil and the rainfall is considerably less. In this new environment, natural selection favours those plants with longer roots (able to reach the soil water) and smaller leaves with fewer stomata (to minimise water loss).

3 The two populations of plants are isolated from each other and cannot interbreed.

4 There is natural variation in these features in both populations as a result of sexual reproduction and gene mutation.

5 In the original population, longer roots and smaller leaves give no advantage and natural selection maintains the original form for as long as the environment remains stable.

6 In the new population, longer roots and smaller leaves give an advantage, as plants with these features gain more water and lose less than those without them. In each generation, more plants with these features survive than those without them.

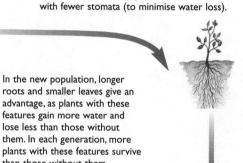

7 The new plants become more and more different from the original population. Long-rooted and small-leaved forms survive best and the population eventually consists almost entirely of this type.

8 Eventually the two populations are so different that they cannot interbreed. At this point we consider them to be separate species.

Figure 19.9 *How natural selection can lead to the formation of a new species.*

The course of evolution

Many biologists now believe that there is sufficient evidence to suggest that evolution has followed the general course outlined below.

- Life began in water as a result of reactions between chemicals in the early Earth's atmosphere and oceans.

- The first life forms were unicells (single cells), similar to bacterial cells.

- These unicells became more complex as the cells acquired more and more organelles (such as mitochondria and chloroplasts).

- Simple multicellular organisms evolved from the unicells – possibly by unicells undergoing cell division but the two cells formed failing to separate.

- The multicellular organisms became more and more complex, giving rise to plants, animals, fungi and other types of organisms.

- Some of these organisms colonised the land and the evolution of land animals, plants and fungi began (Figure 19.10).

> You could carry out an Internet search on the 'endosymbiont' theory as to how early cells acquired their organelles.

A niche is a description of the habitat of an organism and the role of the organism in that habitat. For example, the niche of a lion could be described as 'predator of wildebeest on the Serengeti plains in Africa'. The niche of a camel is that of herbivore in hot deserts.

From time to time catastrophic events caused mass extinctions. Niches that had been filled by one species became 'vacant'. Other species filled these niches. As they occupied the new niches, they evolved into different species as a result of natural selection. For example, when the dinosaurs became extinct, the small mammals that existed at the time were able to fill many of the niches left vacant by the dinosaurs and then evolve into the mammals of today (see Figure 19.10).

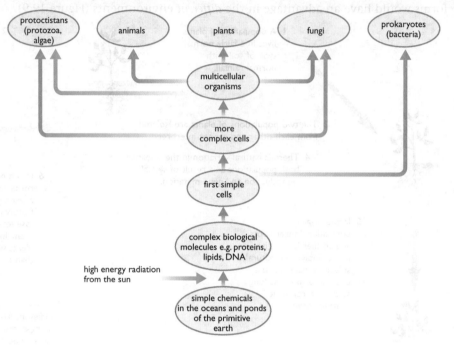

Figure 19.10 *The main stages in evolution.*

End of Chapter Checklist

You should now be able to:

● understand that many mutations are harmful but some are neutral and a few are beneficial

● understand that mutant organisms can increase in a population by natural selection.

Questions

More questions on natural selection and evolution can be found at the end of Section E on page 230.

1 a) What does the term 'survival of the fittest' mean?

b) Which two biologists arrived at the same idea concerning the 'survival of the fittest' at the same time?

c) Why were the ideas of natural selection controversial when they first appeared in the nineteenth century?

2 The changes in the distribution of the peppered moth as areas became industrialised is often used as evidence of natural selection. There are two forms of the peppered moth, the peppered form and the dark form.

a) Explain why the dark form of the moth became much more common in industrialised cities.

b) Explain why the dark form of the moth remained extremely rare in the countryside during the same period.

c) Suggest why the two types of the peppered moth have not become separate species.

3 Warfarin is a pesticide that was developed to kill rats. When it was first used in 1950, it was very effective. Some rats, however, had a mutant allele that made them resistant to warfarin. Nowadays the pesticide is much less effective.

a) Use the ideas of natural selection to explain why warfarin is much less effective than it used to be.

b) Suggest what might happen to the number of rats carrying the allele for warfarin resistance, if warfarin were no longer used. Explain your answer.

4 In the Galapagos Islands, Charles Darwin identified a number of species of finch. He found evidence to suggest that they had all evolved from one ancestral type, which had colonised the islands from South America. The main differences between the finches was in their beaks. The diagram shows some of the beak types and that of the likely ancestral finch.

a) Explain how the seed-eating finches are adapted to their environment.

b) Explain how the finches that eat insects and live in woodland are adapted to their environment.

c) Use the information in the diagram to help you explain how the common ancestor could have evolved into the different type of finches.

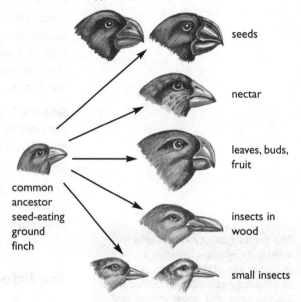

common ancestor seed-eating ground finch

seeds

nectar

leaves, buds, fruit

insects in wood

small insects

5 Write an essay outlining how a biologist who accepts evolution as a fact, might try to convince a sceptical person (one who does not necessarily accept evolution as a fact). In your essay, you should refer to possible doubts or objections by the sceptical person and evidence that could possibly answer these objections.

Chapter 20: Selective Breeding

> Humans have been selectively breeding animals and plants ever since they first became farmers. This chapter looks at how the process has changed over the years and highlights some moral and ethical issues linked with current practices.

About 12 000 years ago, the human way of life changed significantly. Humans began to grow plants and keep animals for milk and meat. They became farmers rather than hunters. This change first took place in the Middle East. Similar changes took place a little later in the Americas (where potatoes and maize were being grown) and in the Far East (where rice was first cultivated).

In the Middle East, humans first grew the cereal plants wheat and barley, and domesticated sheep and goats. Later, they domesticated cattle and pigs. Cultivating crops and keeping stock animals made it possible for permanent settlements to appear – human village life began. Because of the more certain food supply, there was spare time, for the first time ever, for some people to do things other than hunt for food.

Ever since the cultivation of the first wheat and barley and the domestication of the first stock animals, humans have tried to obtain bigger yields from them. They cross-bred different maize plants (and barley plants) to obtain strains that produced more grain. They bred sheep and goats to give more milk and meat – selective breeding had begun. Today, animals and plants are bred for much more than food. They are bred to produce a range of medicines, and for research into spare-part surgery and the action of drugs.

Selective breeding is best described as the breeding of only those individuals with desirable features. It is sometimes called '**artificial selection**', as human choice, rather than environmental factors, is providing the **selection pressure** (see Chapter 19).

The methods used today for selective breeding are vastly different from those used only 50 years ago. Modern gene technology makes it possible to create a new strain of plant within weeks, rather than years.

Traditional selective breeding

Plants

Traditionally, farmers have bred crop plants of all kinds to obtain increased yields. Probably the earliest example of selective breeding was the cross-breeding of strains of wild wheat. The aim was to produce wheat with a much increased yield of grain and with shorter, stronger stems (Figure 20.1). This wheat was used to make bread.

> The production of modern bread wheats by selective breeding is probably one of the earliest examples of producing genetically modified food. Each original wild wheat species had 14 chromosomes per cell. The wild emmer hybrid had 28 chromosomes per cell. Modern bread wheat has 42 chromosomes per cell. Selective breeding has modified the genetic make-up of wheat.

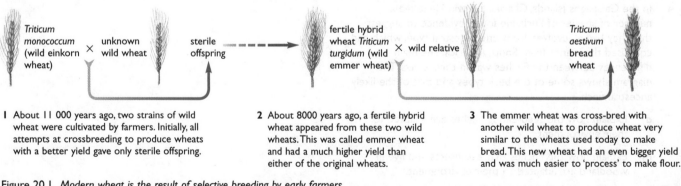

Triticum monococcum (wild einkorn wheat) × unknown wild wheat → sterile offspring → fertile hybrid wheat Triticum turgidum (wild emmer wheat) × wild relative → Triticum aestivum bread wheat

1 About 11 000 years ago, two strains of wild wheat were cultivated by farmers. Initially, all attempts at crossbreeding to produce wheats with a better yield gave only sterile offspring.

2 About 8000 years ago, a fertile hybrid wheat appeared from these two wild wheats. This was called emmer wheat and had a much higher yield than either of the original wheats.

3 The emmer wheat was cross-bred with another wild wheat to produce wheat very similar to the wheats used today to make bread. This new wheat had an even bigger yield and was much easier to 'process' to make flour.

Figure 20.1 *Modern wheat is the result of selective breeding by early farmers.*

Other plants have been selectively bred for certain characteristics. *Brassica* is a genus of cabbage-like plants. One species of wild brassica (*Brassica olera*) was selectively bred to give several strains, each with specific features (see Figure 20.2). Some of the strains had large leaves, others had large flower heads, and others produced large buds.

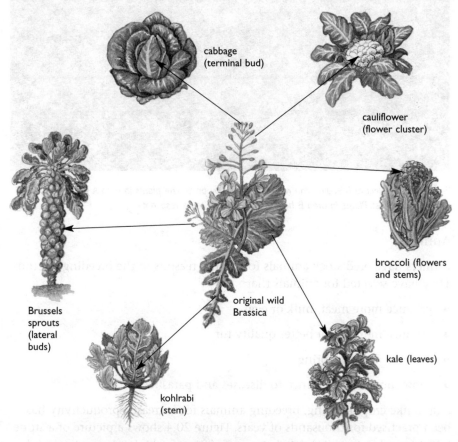

Figure 20.2 *Selectively breeding the original wild brassica plants to enhance certain features has produced several familiar vegetables.*

Selective breeding has produced many familiar vegetables. Besides the ones produced from *Brassica*, selective breeding of wild *Solanum* plants has produced the many strains of potatoes that are eaten today. Carrots and parsnips are also the result of selective breeding programmes.

Crop plants are bred to produce strains that:

• give higher yields

• are resistant to certain diseases (the diseases would reduce the yields)

• are resistant to certain insect pest damage (the damage would reduce the yield)

• are hardier (so that they survive in harsher climates or are productive for longer periods of the year)

• have a better balance of nutrients in the crop (for example, plants that contain more of the types of amino acids needed by humans).

Figure 20.3 shows a field of potato plants. Some have been bred to be resistant to insect pests, while others were not selectively bred in this way.

Plant breeders have not just bred plants for food. Nearly all garden flowers are the result of selective breeding. Breeders have selected flowers of a particular size, shape, colour and fragrance. Roses and orchids are among the most selectively bred of our garden plants.

Figure 20.3 *Selective breeding can reduce damage by pests. The plants in area A are bred to be resistant to a pest. Plants in area B have not been bred to be resistant.*

Animals

Farmers have bred stock animals for similar reasons to the breeding of crops. They have selected for animals that:

- produce more meat, milk or eggs
- produce more fur or better quality fur
- produce more offspring
- show increased resistance to diseases and parasites.

Again, like crop breeding, breeding animals for increased productivity has been practised for thousands of years. Figure 20.4 shows a picture of a stone tablet found in Iran and dated at over 5000 years old. It appears to record the results of breeding domesticated donkeys.

Figure 20.4 *The tablet of stone with these markings is over 5000 years old. Does it show a breeding programme for domestic donkeys?*

For many thousands of years, the only way to improve livestock was to mate a male and a female with the features that were desired in the offspring. In cattle, milk yield is an important factor and so high yielding cows would be bred with bulls from other high yielding cows.

Since about 1950, the technique of **artificial insemination** (AI) has become widely available. Bulls with many desirable features are kept and semen is obtained from them. The semen is diluted, frozen and stored. Farmers can buy quantities of this semen to inseminate their cows. AI makes it possible for the semen from one prize bull to be used to fertilise many thousands of cows.

Modern sheep are domesticated wild sheep, and pigs have been derived from wild boars. Just think of all the varieties of dogs that now exist. All these have been derived from one ancestral type. This original 'dog' was a domesticated wolf (Figure 20.5). In domesticating the wolf, humans gained an animal that was capable of herding stock animals. The sheepdog has all the same instincts as the wolf except the instinct to kill. This has been selectively 'bred out'.

Modern selective breeding

Cloning plants

The term cloning describes any procedure that produces genetically identical offspring. Taking cuttings of plants and growing them is a traditional cloning technique (Figure 20.6).

All the cuttings contain identical genes as they are all parts of the same parent plant. As they grow, they form new cells by mitosis, copying the genes in the existing cells exactly. The cuttings develop into a group of genetically identical plants – a **clone**. Any differences will be due to the environment. Many garden flowers have traditionally been propagated this way.

Figure 20.5 *The many different breeds of dog all originate from a common ancestor – the wolf.*

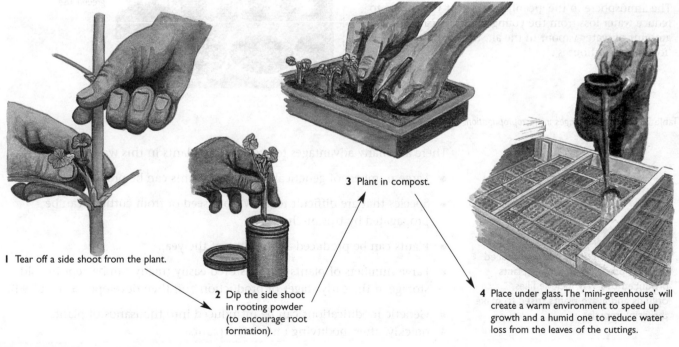

I Tear off a side shoot from the plant.

2 Dip the side shoot in rooting powder (to encourage root formation).

3 Plant in compost.

4 Place under glass. The 'mini-greenhouse' will create a warm environment to speed up growth and a humid one to reduce water loss from the leaves of the cuttings.

Figure 20.6 *Taking stem cuttings.*

Some modern cloning techniques are essentially the same as taking cuttings – removing pieces of a plant and growing them into new individuals. The technology, however, is much more sophisticated. By using the technique of **micropropagation**, thousands of plants can quickly be produced from one original (Table 20.1).

Stages	Illustrations
The tips of the stems and side shoots are removed from the plant to be cloned. These parts are called **explants**. The explants are trimmed to a size of about 0.5–1 mm. They are then placed in an agar medium that contains nutrients and plant hormones to encourage growth. More explants can be taken from the new shoots that form on the original ones. This can be repeated until there are enough to supply the demand.	Figure 20.7 *Explants growing in a culture medium.*
The explants with shoots are transferred to another culture medium containing a different balance of plant hormones to induce root formation.	Figure 20.8 *Explants forming roots.*
When the explants have grown roots, they are transferred to greenhouses and transplanted into compost. They are then gradually acclimatised to normal growing conditions. The atmosphere in the greenhouse is kept very moist to reduce water loss from the young plants. Because of the amount of water vapour in the air, they are often called 'fogging greenhouses'.	Figure 20.9 *Young plants being grown in compost in a greenhouse.*

Table 20.1: *The main stages in micropropagation.*

There are many advantages to propagating plants in this way.

- Large numbers of genetically identical plants can be produced rapidly.
- Species that are difficult to grow from seed or from cuttings can be propagated by this method.
- Plants can be produced at any time of the year.
- Large numbers of plants can be stored easily (many can be kept in cold storage at the early stages of production and then developed as required).
- Genetic modifications can be introduced into thousands of plants quickly, after modifying only a few plants.

Many strains of bananas are infertile. They are now commonly reproduced by micropropagation. Other plants produced this way include lilies, orchids and agave plants (used to make the drink tequila).

Cloning animals

We have been able to clone plants by taking cuttings for thousands of years. It is now possible to make genetically identical copies of animals. The first, and best-known, example of this is the famous cloned sheep, Dolly.

Dolly was produced by persuading one of her mother's ova (egg cells) to develop into a new individual without being fertilised by a sperm. The nucleus of the ovum was removed and 'replaced' with a cell taken from the udder of another sheep. The cell that was formed had the same genetic information as all the cells in the donor and so developed into an exact genetic copy. The stages in the procedure are shown in Figure 20.10. Figure 20.11 shows how an udder cell is inserted into an egg cell that has had its nucleus removed.

The nucleus of an ovum is haploid (see Chapter 18). It cannot develop into a new individual because it only has half the chromosomes of normal body cells. An ordinary diploid body cell, even though it has all the chromosomes, is too specialised. Transferring a diploid nucleus into an egg cell that has had its nucleus removed creates a cell that is capable of developing into a new individual. In practice, it is easier to transfer a small whole cell rather than attempt to transfer just the nucleus, as the nucleus alone could too easily be damaged.

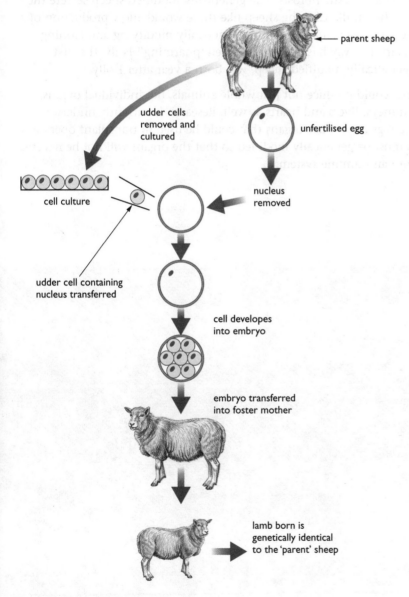

parent sheep

udder cells removed and cultured

unfertilised egg

cell culture

nucleus removed

udder cell containing nucleus transferred

cell developes into embryo

embryo transferred into foster mother

lamb born is genetically identical to the 'parent' sheep

Figure 20.10 *How 'Dolly' was produced.*

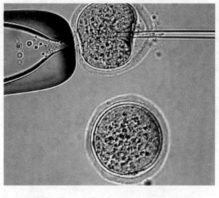

Figure 20.11 *Inserting an udder cell into an egg cell that has had its nucleus removed.*

Dolly was only produced after many unsuccessful attempts. Since then, the procedure has been repeated using other sheep as well as rats, mice and pigs. Some of the animals produced are born deformed. Some do not survive to birth. Biologists believe that these problems occur because the genes that are transferred to the egg are 'old genes'. These genes came from an animal that had already lived for several years and from cells specialised to do things other than produce sex cells. It will take much more research to make the technique reliable.

Down on the 'pharm'

Cloning animals has special value if the animal produces some important product. Sheep have been genetically modified (see Chapter 22) to produce several human proteins. One of these is used to treat conditions such as emphysema and cystic fibrosis. The genetically modified sheep secrete the protein in their milk. Cloning sheep like these would allow production of much more of this valuable protein. Genetically modifying and cloning mammals in this way has been nicknamed 'pharming'! Polly, the first cloned, genetically modified sheep, was born a year after Dolly.

'Pharming' could produce not just whole animals, but individual organs, such as kidneys, livers and hearts as well. Research is currently underway into pharming pigs to produce organs that could be used in transplant operations. The pigs must be genetically modified so that the organs will not be rejected by the human immune system.

Animals that have had genes transferred from other species are called **transgenic animals**.

End of Chapter Checklist

You should now be able to:

● understand that plants with desired characteristics can be developed by selective breeding, for example, wheat with increased yield and reduced stem length

● understand that animals with desired characteristics can be developed by selective breeding, for example, cattle with increased meat or milk yield

● describe the process of micropropagation

● understand how micropropagation can be used to produce commercial numbers of cloned plants with desirable characteristics

● describe the stages in cloning mammals, illustrated by Dolly the sheep

● evaluate the potential for using cloned transgenic animals to produce human antibodies or organs for transplant (see also Chapter 22).

Questions

More questions on selective breeding can be found at the end of Section E on page 230.

I   Selective breeding is sometimes called 'artificial selection'.

    a)   How is selective breeding similar to natural selection?

    b)   How is selective breeding different from natural selection?

2   Selective breeding of crop plants often aims to increase the yield of the crop.

    a)   Describe, and explain the reasons for, three other aims of selective breeding programmes in crop plants.

    b)   Describe two advantages of micropropagation over the more traditional technique of taking cuttings.

    c)   Explain why plants produced by micropropagation will be genetically identical to each other and to the parent plant.

3   The diagram shows some of the features of a cow that might be used as a basis for a breeding programme.

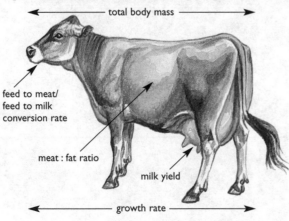

a)   Which features would you consider important in a breeding programme for dairy cattle?

b)   Assume that you had all the techniques of modern selective breeding available to you. Describe how you would set about producing a herd of high-yielding beef cattle.

4   The diagram shows the results of a breeding programme to improve the yield of maize (sweetcorn).

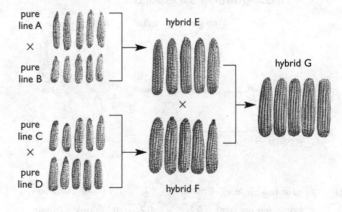

a)   Describe the breeding procedure used to produce hybrid G.

b)   Describe three differences between the corn cobs of hybrid G and those of C.

c)   How could you show that the differences between hybrid G and hybrid C are genetic?

5   Write an essay about the benefits and concerns of selective breeding of animals. You should produce about one side of A4 typed-up work. Use books and the Internet to find out more information.

Chapter 20: Checklist

229

End of Section Questions

1 For natural selection to operate, some factor has to exert a 'selection pressure'. In each of the following situations, identify both the selection pressure and the likely result of this selection pressure.

a) Near old copper mines, the soil becomes polluted with copper ions that are toxic to most plants.
(*2 marks*)

b) In the Serengeti of Africa, wildebeest are hunted by lions.
(*2 marks*)

c) A farmer uses a pesticide to try to eliminate pests of a potato crop.
(*2 marks*)

Total 6 marks

2 Micropropagation produces thousands of genetically identical plants. Small 'explants' from the parent plant are grown in culture media.

a) Outline the main stages in micropropagation.
(*4 marks*)

b) Explain why the plants formed by micropropagation are genetically identical.
(*2 marks*)

c) In some cases, the explants used contain only a few cells with neither roots nor shoots. Plant hormones are added to the culture media to encourage root and shoot formation. Two of these hormones are called kinetin and auxin. The diagram shows the effects of using different concentrations of the two hormones on root and shoot growth of the explants.

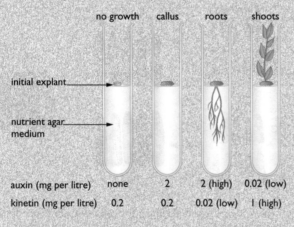

	no growth	callus	roots	shoots
auxin (mg per litre)	none	2	2 (high)	0.02 (low)
kinetin (mg per litre)	0.2	0.2	0.02 (low)	1 (high)

i) What is the effect of adding kinetin or auxin without any other hormone?
(*2 marks*)

ii) Describe how you would treat these explants to produce first shoots and then roots.
(*3 marks*)

d) Explain one advantage and one disadvantage of micropropagation.
(*2 marks*)

Total 13 marks

3 The diagram shows the inheritance of PTC tasting in a family. Although PTC has a very bitter taste, some people cannot taste it.

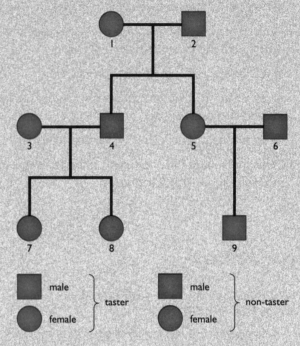

a) What evidence in the diagram suggests that the allele for PTC tasting is dominant?
(*2 marks*)

b) Using **T** to represent the tasting allele and **t** to represent the non-tasting allele, give the genotypes of individuals 3 and 7. Explain how you arrived at your answers.
(*4 marks*)

c) Why can we not be sure of the genotype of individual 5?
(*2 marks*)

d) If individuals 3 and 4 had another child, what is the chance that the child would be able to taste PTC? Construct a genetic diagram to show how you arrived at your answer.
(*4 marks*)

Total 12 marks

4 The diagrams A to F show an animal cell during cell division.

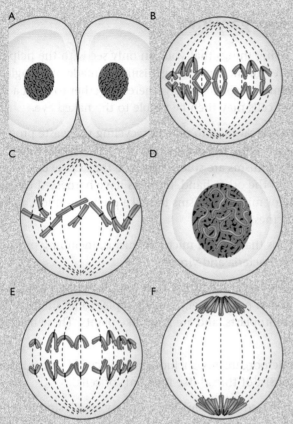

a) Put the pictures in the correct order. *(3 marks)*

b) Is the cell going through mitosis or meiosis? Explain your answer. *(2 marks)*

c) This cell has eight chromosomes which is its diploid number. How many chromosomes would a diploid human cell have? *(1 mark)*

d) Describe two differences between mitosis and meiosis. *(2 marks)*

Total 8 marks

5 The following flowchart shows how Dolly the sheep was cloned.

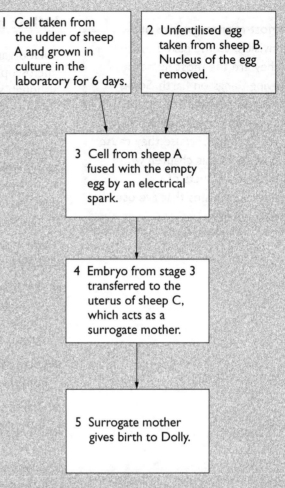

a) Where did scientists get the DNA to put into the unfertilised egg from sheep B? *(1 mark)*

b) How does the nucleus removed from an egg differ from the nucleus of an embryo? *(1 mark)*

c) Dolly is genetically identical to another sheep in the diagram. Which one? *(1 mark)*

d) Give two ways in which this method is different from the normal method of reproduction in sheep. *(2 marks)*

e) Suggest two advantages of producing animal clones. *(2 marks)*

Total 7 marks

Chapter 21: Using Microorganisms

What are microorganisms?

Microorganisms are living things that you can only see with the help of a microscope. The 'bodies' of most microorganisms are made of a single cell, although sometimes millions of cells are gathered together to form a **colony**. The colony of cells may then be visible to the naked eye.

Microorganisms have critical roles to play in recycling the waste products of organisms, as well as recycling the organisms themselves when they die. Many types of microorganisms are studied because they cause disease in animals and plants. On the other hand, humans have harnessed the great reproductive capacity of microorganisms to make useful products, such as food, drink and medicines.

There are several groups that we call microorganisms, including protozoa and algae, some fungi, bacteria and viruses.

- **Protozoa** are made of single cells that have features like an animal cell. *Amoeba*, which lives in pond water, is an example. Some single-celled organisms have chloroplasts, and are more like plants. These belong to a group called **algae**.

- Many **fungi** are microorganisms, including single-celled **yeasts**, as well as **moulds**, which consist of thread-like filaments of cells.

- **Bacteria** are single-celled organisms made of very small, simple cells.

- **Viruses** are much smaller than bacteria, and are not cells at all. In fact they can be thought of as half-way between a living organism and a chemical.

Figure 21.1 shows just a few examples of the many types of microorganisms.

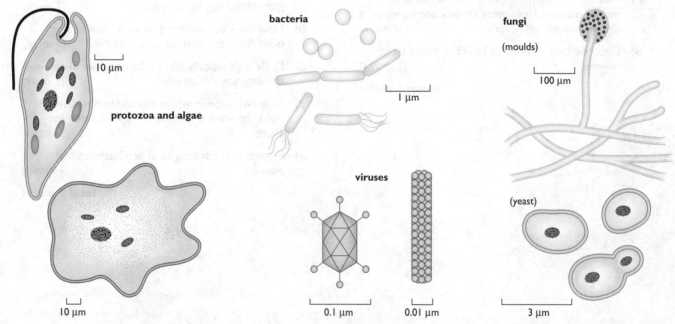

Figure 21.1 *Some examples of microorganisms. They are not drawn to the same scale. Notice the range of size, as shown by the scale bar alongside each organism. One micrometre (1 μm) is a millionth of a metre, or a thousandth of a millimetre.*

Fermentation and biotechnology

Many microorganisms obtain their energy by anaerobic respiration, which does not need oxygen (see Chapter 1). The original meaning of the word **fermentation** was simply anaerobic respiration. For example, anaerobic respiration of sugars by yeast makes ethanol. This is called 'alcoholic fermentation'. Louis Pasteur, who studied this subject a great deal, described fermentation as 'life without air'. Nowadays, however, many other processes carried out by microorganisms are called fermentation, and many of them are aerobic (use oxygen).

The word 'biotechnology' may be new, but humans have used some biotechnology processes for thousands of years. Since ancient times, fermentation by yeast has been used to make wine and beer, and to produce bread. Other fermented products do not use yeast. Yoghurt is made by the action of bacteria on milk, and other bacteria and moulds are used in cheese manufacture. Another bacterium is used to convert the ethanol in wine into vinegar.

Our ancestors used biotechnology to make products like wine, beer and cheese, but they did not understand *how* they were made, and had no idea of the existence of microorganisms. Nowadays we understand what is happening when fermentation takes place, and can use biotechnology to produce not just foods but a vast range of products, from medicines like penicillin to chemicals such as enzymes and fuels.

Many products are made by altering the genes of microorganisms, so that they code for new products. This is called **genetic engineering** and makes **genetically modified organisms**, or **GMOs**. It is a topic that you will read about in Chapter 22.

Industrial fermenters

A fermenter is any vessel that is used to grow microorganisms used for fermentation. A glass jar used to make wine at home is a fermenter, and even a baking tray containing a ball of dough could be called a fermenter.

Industrial fermenters are large tanks that can hold up to $200\,000\,dm^3$ of a liquid culture (Figure 21.2). They enable the environmental conditions such as temperature, oxygen and carbon dioxide concentrations, pH and nutrient supply to be carefully controlled so that the microorganisms will yield their product most efficiently. A simplified diagram of the inside of a fermenter is shown in Figure 21.3.

Many microorganisms use an external food source from their growth medium to obtain energy. In doing this, they change substances in the medium. This is the modern meaning of fermentation. It is used by humans to make many important products. The use of microorganisms to make products useful to humans is called **biotechnology**.

Figure 21.2 *An industrial fermenter holds hundreds of thousands of dm³ of a liquid culture.*

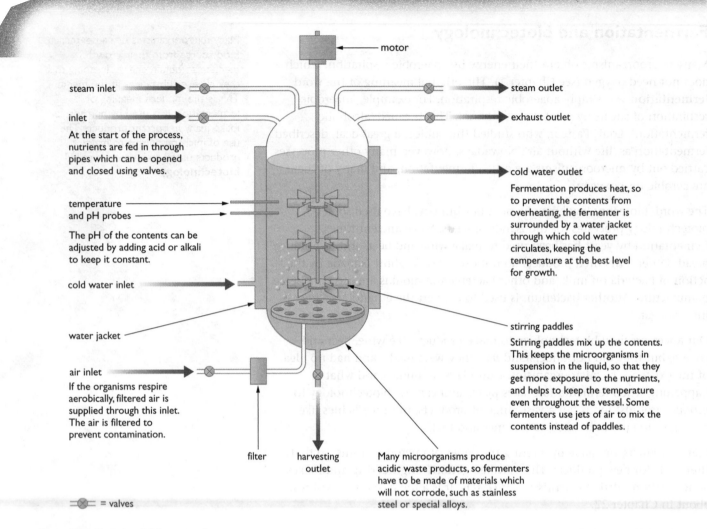

motor

steam inlet

inlet

At the start of the process, nutrients are fed in through pipes which can be opened and closed using valves.

temperature and pH probes

The pH of the contents can be adjusted by adding acid or alkali to keep it constant.

cold water inlet

water jacket

air inlet

If the organisms respire aerobically, filtered air is supplied through this inlet. The air is filtered to prevent contamination.

steam outlet

exhaust outlet

cold water outlet

Fermentation produces heat, so to prevent the contents from overheating, the fermenter is surrounded by a water jacket through which cold water circulates, keeping the temperature at the best level for growth.

stirring paddles

Stirring paddles mix up the contents. This keeps the microorganisms in suspension in the liquid, so that they get more exposure to the nutrients, and helps to keep the temperature even throughout the vessel. Some fermenters use jets of air to mix the contents instead of paddles.

filter

harvesting outlet

Many microorganisms produce acidic waste products, so fermenters have to be made of materials which will not corrode, such as stainless steel or special alloys.

= valves

Figure 21.3 *An industrial fermenter. Fermenters like this are used to make many products, such as the antibiotic penicillin.*

It is important to realise that the running of the fermenter is highly automated. Its contents are monitored by special probes which record temperature, pH, oxygen and carbon dioxide levels and so on to provide the best environment for growth of the microorganisms. The data from these probes is fed to a computer which controls the internal environment of the fermenter. For example, if the temperature starts to rise, cold water is passed more quickly through the water jacket.

When fermentation is finished, the products are collected through an outlet pipe. Before the fermenter is filled with new nutrients and culture, the inside of the tank and all the pipes must be cleaned and sterilised. This is usually done with very hot steam under high pressure. If the inside of the fermenter and the new nutrients are not sterile, two problems are likely to develop. Firstly, any bacteria or fungi that managed to get in would compete with the organism in the culture, reducing the yield of product. Secondly, the product would become contaminated with waste products or cells of the 'foreign' organism.

An example of the use of an industrial fermenter: the production of penicillin

The first step in the manufacture of the antibiotic penicillin is to make a broth of spores of the mould *Penicillium*. This 'starter culture' is used in a fermenter of the type described on page 233. The culture solution contains sugar and other nutrients, and oxygen is supplied to allow the mould to respire. Most culture media for *Penicillium* contain a waste product of the starch industry, called 'corn steep liquor'. It contains sugars such as lactose (milk sugar) which the mould uses as an energy source, as well as other nutrients needed for growth.

The contents of the fermenter are kept at a steady 24 °C. The spores develop into filaments of cells which multiply rapidly, doubling their mass every six hours. After about 40 hours, as they start to use up the nutrients in the broth, the cells begin to produce penicillin, and continue to produce it for several more days. The penicillin is secreted out of the cells, so that at the end of fermentation the fermenter contains a dense broth of cells, unused nutrients and penicillin solution.

The broth is filtered to remove the cells, and the penicillin is then extracted from the watery solution by using organic solvents. It is re-dissolved back into water and made to crystallise out as pure penicillin. The crystals are collected and chemically treated to produce a range of penicillins for treating different kinds of bacterial infection.

'Traditional' biotechnology

The production of beer, wine and bread all involve the respiration of yeast. When yeast cells are deprived of oxygen, they respire anaerobically, breaking sugar down into ethanol and carbon dioxide:

glucose → ethanol + carbon dioxide

This ethanol is the alcohol in alcoholic drinks like wine or beer. In bread making, carbon dioxide from the yeast produces gas bubbles which expand when the dough is baked, making the bread 'light'.

Making beer

Beer is made from **barley**. Unlike grapes, barley contains starch not sugars. The starch first has to be broken down into sugar so that the yeast cells can ferment it to ethanol. When barley seeds germinate, they produce the enzyme **amylase**, which breaks down starch into maltose, or malt sugar. This can be used by the yeast as an energy source in fermentation, so the first step in beer production is to get the barley seeds to germinate. This is

Figure 21.4 *Froth forming on the surface of the beer as yeast ferments the sugars to alcohol and carbon dioxide.*

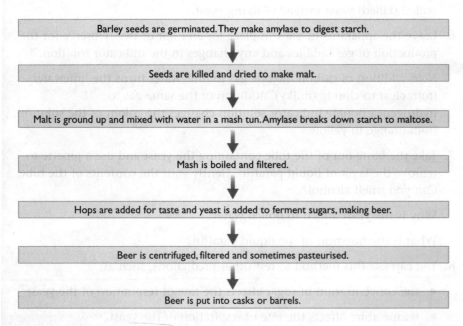

Barley seeds are germinated. They make amylase to digest starch.

↓

Seeds are killed and dried to make malt.

↓

Malt is ground up and mixed with water in a mash tun. Amylase breaks down starch to maltose.

↓

Mash is boiled and filtered.

↓

Hops are added for taste and yeast is added to ferment sugars, making beer.

↓

Beer is centrifuged, filtered and sometimes pasteurised.

↓

Beer is put into casks or barrels.

Figure 21.5 *Flow chart showing the stages in beer production.*

Remember – you often hear people say that beer is 'made from hops'. Hops are only used to *flavour* beer. The source of sugar for beer production is the starch in barley seeds (Figure 21.6).

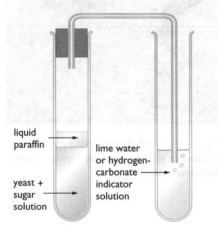

Figure 21.6 *Malting barley seeds (top) are the source of sugar for fermentation. Hop flowers (bottom) add a bitter flavour to the beer.*

done by soaking them in water and laying them out on a flat surface in a **malthouse**. When the seeds have started to germinate, they are killed by heating, without destroying the enzymes. This produces a dried product called **malt**, which can be stored.

To turn malt into beer, the malt is ground up and mixed with hot water in a large vessel called a **mash tun**. The enzymes in the mash now act on the starch, breaking it down into maltose, producing a sweet liquid. This liquid is boiled to stop the enzymes working, and filtered. At this point **hops** are added. Hops give the beer a bitter flavour and stop bacteria growing. Yeast is then added. After a while, the yeast uses up the oxygen in the mixture, and starts to respire the sugars anaerobically. Fermentation carries on for several days (Figure 21.4). To make different types of beer, different species of yeast are used. Brewer's yeast (*Saccharomyces cerevisiae*) is used to make ales, and *Saccharomyces carlsbergensis* for lagers. When fermentation is finished, the beer is centrifuged, filtered and sometimes pasteurised. It is finally put into modern aluminium casks or traditional wooden barrels. The process is summarised in Figure 21.5.

Experiment to show the products of anaerobic respiration in yeast

You can show the production of carbon dioxide by yeast with a simple experiment.

Carry out the following:

1. Carefully boil a small amount of water in a boiling tube to drive off any air that is dissolved in the water.

2. Dissolve a small amount of sugar in the boiled water and allow it to cool.

3. Add a little yeast and stir.

4. Set up the apparatus as shown in Figure 21.7. Carefully add a thin layer of liquid paraffin to the surface of the yeast/sugar mixture, using a pipette.

5. Set up a control apparatus exactly as shown in Figure 21.7, but using boiled (killed) yeast instead of living yeast.

6. Leave the apparatus in a warm place for an hour or two. Observe for the production of gas bubbles and any changes in the indicator solution.

   Note: addition of carbon dioxide gas to lime water turns the limewater from clear to cloudy (milky). Addition of the same gas to hydrogencarbonate indicator solution changes the colour of the solution from orange to yellow.

7. Take the bung out of the tube containing the yeast and use a pipette to remove the layer of liquid paraffin. Gently sniff the contents of the tube. Can you smell alcohol?

   Why is the yeast added to boiled water?

   What is the function of the liquid paraffin?

8. You can use this method to test other predictions, such as:

   • the concentration of sugar affects the rate of respiration of the yeast

   • temperature affects the rate of respiration of the yeast.

You might plan experiments to test these hypotheses.

liquid paraffin

lime water or hydrogen-carbonate indicator solution

yeast + sugar solution

Figure 21.7 *Apparatus to show the products of anaerobic respiration in yeast.*

Making yoghurt

Whereas the production of beer depends on fermentation by yeast, the production of yoghurt uses a quite different organism. Yoghurt is milk that has been fermented by certain species of bacteria, called **lactic acid bacteria**. (These bacteria are also used in cheese manufacture.) The effect of the fermentation is to turn the liquid milk into a semi-solid food with a sour taste.

To make yoghurt, milk is first pasteurised at 85–95 °C for 15–30 minutes, to kill any natural bacteria that it contains, then **homogenised** to disperse the fat globules. It is then cooled to 40–45 °C and inoculated with a starter culture of two species of bacteria. These bacteria produce lactic acid, as well as starting to digest the milk proteins. The culture is kept at this temperature for several hours, while the pH falls to about 4.4 (these are the optimum conditions for the bacteria). The mixture thickens as the drop in pH causes the milk proteins to coagulate.

When fermentation is finished, the yoghurt is stirred and cooled to 5 °C. Flavourings, colourants and fruit may then be added, before it is packaged for sale.

The drop in pH as the yoghurt forms gradually reduces the reproduction of the lactic acid bacteria (although it doesn't kill them). It also helps to prevent the growth of other microorganisms, and so preserves the nutrients of the milk. The steps in yoghurt production are summarised in the flow chart (Figure 21.8).

Two types of bacteria commonly used in both yoghurt and cheese production are different species of *Lactobacillus* and *Streptococcus*. Both ferment lactose in milk to lactic acid. Lactic acid causes physical and chemical changes in milk, such as coagulating the milk protein and turning the mixture acidic.

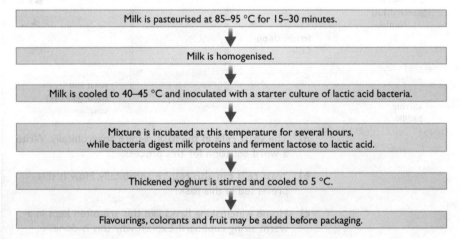

Figure 21.8 *Flow chart showing the stages in yoghurt production.*

End of Chapter Checklist

You should now be able to:

● interpret and label a diagram of an industrial fermenter and explain the need to provide suitable conditions in the fermenter for the growth of microorganisms

● understand the role of yeast in the production of beer

● describe a simple experiment to investigate carbon dioxide production by yeast, in different conditions

● understand the role of bacteria in the production of yoghurt.

Questions

More questions on growing useful organisms can be found at the end of Section F on page 249.

1   The diagram shows an industrial fermenter which is used to make the antibiotic penicillin.

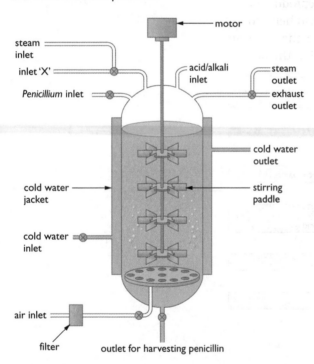

a)   Explain how the fermenter is sterilised before use.

b)   Why does air need to be pumped through the fermenter? Why is the air filtered?

c)   Explain how a steady temperature is maintained in the fermenter.

d)   What is supplied through the inlet marked 'X'?

e)   Explain what would happen to the growth of *Penicillium* in the fermenter if the paddles stopped working.

2   The diagram shows a fermentation flask used to make wine at home.

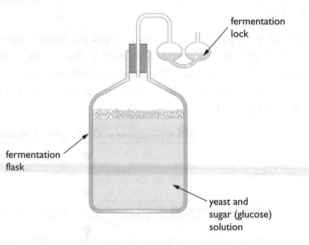

a)   The yeast cells in the flask respire anaerobically. Write a word equation for this process.

b)   Yeast cells can also respire aerobically. How is this prevented in this flask?

c)   Home winemaking flasks like this are often kept in a warm airing cupboard. Explain why this is done.

d)   Wine usually contains no more than about 14% ethanol (alcohol). Explain why.

3   Answer these questions about making yoghurt. Try at first to answer them without looking back to the section on page 237!

a)   Why is the milk pasteurised at the start of the process?

b)   Why is the mixture of milk and bacteria incubated at 45 °C?

c)   What causes the milk to thicken?

d)   Why does fermentation eventually stop?

e)   Explain how making yoghurt is a way of preserving the nutrients from milk.

Chapter 22: Genetic Modification

In this chapter, we will look at ways in which it is now possible to manipulate genes and produce **genetically modified organisms** or **transgenic organisms**. This is the science of 'genetic engineering'. But first, we must remind ourselves what genes are made of and how they work.

Ever since Gregor Mendel first identified his 'heritable factors', biologists have tried to find out more and more about genes. We now know what genes are made of and we have a good idea of how they actually work. We have just produced the first ever gene map of all the human genes in the Human Genome Project.

DNA – the stuff of genes

A gene is a section of one strand of a DNA molecule that codes for the production of a protein. Each sequence of three bases (a triplet) in the DNA strand codes for one amino acid. Different genes produce different proteins because each has a unique sequence of bases that codes for a unique sequence of amino acids – that results in a unique protein (Figure 22.1).

the order of the bases on one strand of the DNA forms a genetic 'code' for …

… the order of amino acids in a protein

Figure 22.1 *The role of DNA in protein synthesis.*

The protein that is produced could be:

- an enzyme that controls a particular reaction inside a cell or in the digestive system

- a structural protein like the keratin in hair, collagen in skin or one of the many proteins found in the membranes of cells

- a hormone

- a protein with a specific function such as haemoglobin or an antibody.

Recombinant DNA

A transgenic organism is one that contains a gene or several genes from another species. For example, some bacteria have had human genes transferred to them that allow them to make human insulin. Some sheep secrete AAT in their milk because they have the human gene that directs the manufacture of this substance. Because they contain 'foreign' genes, they are no longer quite the same organisms. They are transgenic.

Producing recombinant DNA is the basis of gene technology or genetic engineering. A section of DNA – a gene – is snipped out of the DNA of one species and inserted into the DNA of another. This new DNA is called **recombinant** DNA, as the DNA from two different organisms has been 'recombined'. The organism that receives the new gene from a different species is a **transgenic** organism.

The organism receiving the new gene now has an added capability. It will manufacture the protein its new gene codes for. For example, a bacterium receiving the gene from a human that codes for insulin production will make human insulin. If these transgenic bacteria are cultured by the billion in a fermenter, they become a human insulin factory.

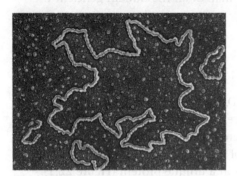

Figure 22.2 *Bacterial DNA.*

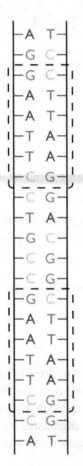

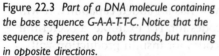

Figure 22.3 *Part of a DNA molecule containing the base sequence G-A-A-T-T-C. Notice that the sequence is present on both strands, but running in opposite directions.*

Producing genetically modified (transgenic) bacteria

The breakthrough in being able to transfer DNA from cell to cell came when it was found that bacteria have two sorts of DNA – the DNA found in their bacterial 'chromosome' and much smaller circular pieces of DNA called **plasmids** (Figure 22.2).

Bacteria naturally 'swap' plasmids, and biologists found ways of transferring plasmids from one bacterium to another. The next stage was to find molecular 'scissors' and molecular 'glue' that could snip out genes from one molecule of DNA and then stick them back into another. Further research found the following enzymes that were able to do this.

- **Restriction endonucleases** are enzymes that cut DNA molecules at specific points. Different restriction enzymes cut DNA at different places. They can be used to cut out specific genes from a molecule of DNA.

- **DNA ligases** are enzymes that join cut ends of DNA molecules.

Each restriction endonuclease recognises a certain base sequence in a DNA strand. Wherever it encounters that sequence, it will cut the DNA molecule. Suppose a restriction enzyme recognises the base sequence G-A-A-T-T-C. It will only cut the DNA molecule if it can 'see' the base sequence on both strands. Figure 22.3 illustrates this.

Some restriction enzymes make a straight cut and the fragments of DNA they produce are said to have 'blunt ends'. Other restriction enzymes make a staggered cut. These produce fragments of DNA with overlapping ends with complementary bases. These overlapping ends are often called 'sticky ends' because fragments of DNA with exposed bases are more easily joined together by ligase enzymes. This is shown in Figure 22.4.

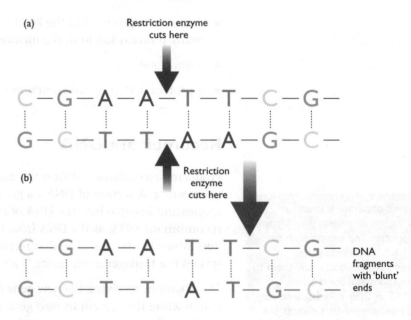

Figure 22.4 *How restriction enzymes cut DNA.*

Biologists now had a method of transferring a gene from any cell into a bacterium. They could insert the gene into a plasmid and then transfer the plasmid into a bacterium. The plasmid is called a **vector** because it is the means of transferring the gene. The main processes involved in producing a transgenic bacterium are shown in Figure 22.5.

There is a lot more to producing recombinant DNA and transgenic bacteria than is shown here. You could carry out an Internet search or search appropriate CD-encyclopaedias to find out more.

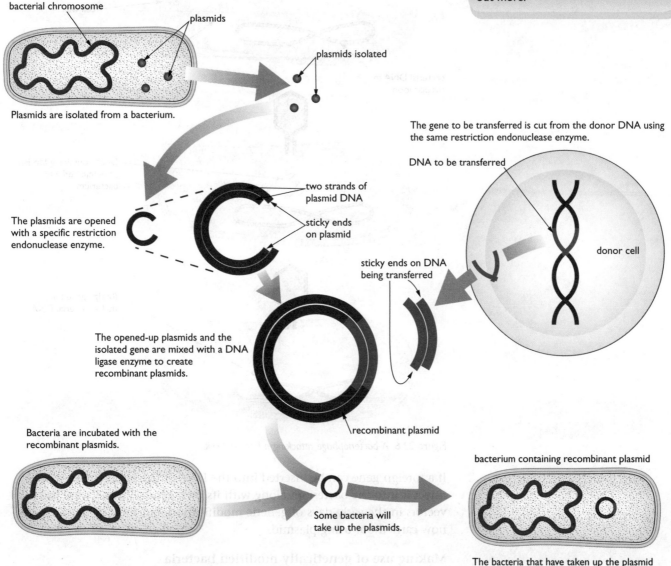

bacterial chromosome

plasmids

Plasmids are isolated from a bacterium.

plasmids isolated

The gene to be transferred is cut from the donor DNA using the same restriction endonuclease enzyme.

DNA to be transferred

two strands of plasmid DNA

sticky ends on plasmid

The plasmids are opened with a specific restriction endonuclease enzyme.

donor cell

sticky ends on DNA being transferred

The opened-up plasmids and the isolated gene are mixed with a DNA ligase enzyme to create recombinant plasmids.

recombinant plasmid

Bacteria are incubated with the recombinant plasmids.

bacterium containing recombinant plasmid

Some bacteria will take up the plasmids.

The bacteria that have taken up the plasmid now contain the gene from the donor cell. This could be a gene controlling the production of human insulin.

Figure 22.5 *Stages in producing a transgenic bacterium.*

Another vector that has been used to introduce foreign DNA into bacterial cells is the bacteriophage. A bacteriophage, or 'phage', is a virus that attacks a bacterium. It does this by attaching to the cell wall of the bacterium and injecting its own DNA into the bacterial cell (Figure 22.6). This DNA becomes incorporated into the DNA of the host cell, and eventually causes the production of many virus particles.

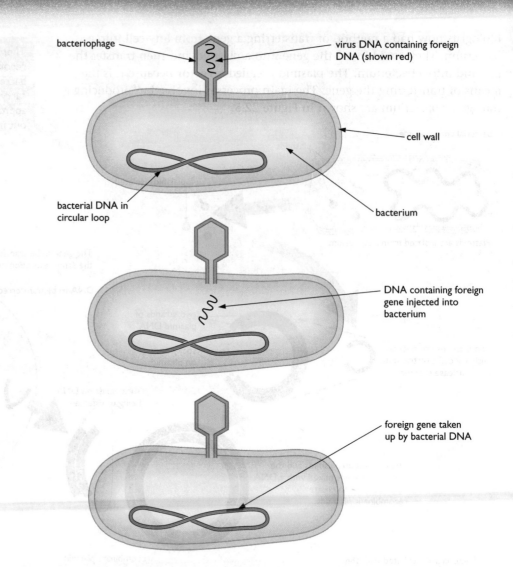

bacteriophage

virus DNA containing foreign
DNA (shown red)

cell wall

bacterial DNA in
circular loop

bacterium

DNA containing foreign
gene injected into
bacterium

foreign gene taken
up by bacterial DNA

Figure 22.6 *A bacteriophage attacking a bacterial cell.*

If a foreign gene can be inserted into the DNA of the virus, the virus will inject it into the bacterium along with its own genes. Viruses were used as vectors in the early days of genetic modification, but most gene transfer is now carried out using plasmids.

Making use of genetically modified bacteria

Different bacteria have been genetically modified to manufacture a range of products. Once they have been genetically modified, they are cultured in fermenters to produce large amounts of the product (see Chapter 21). Some examples are described here.

More insulin is required every year because the number of diabetics increases worldwide each year and diabetics now have longer life spans.

- **Human insulin** People suffering from diabetes need a reliable source of insulin. Before the advent of genetic engineering, the only insulin available came from other animals. This is not quite the same as human insulin and does not give quite the same control of blood glucose levels.

- **Enzymes for washing powders** Many stains on clothing are biological. Blood stains are largely proteins, grease marks are largely lipids. Enzymes can digest these large, insoluble molecules into smaller, soluble ones. These then dissolve in the water. Amylases digest starch, proteases digest proteins and lipases digest lipids. Bacteria have been genetically engineered to produce enzymes that work at higher temperatures, allowing even faster and more effective action.

- **Enzymes in the food industry** One bacterial enzyme used in the food industry is **glucose isomerase**. This enzyme turns glucose into a similar sugar called fructose. Fructose is much sweeter than glucose and so less is needed to sweeten foods. This has two advantages – it saves money (less is used) and it means that the food contains less sugar and is healthier.

- **Human growth hormone** The pituitary gland of some children does not produce sufficient quantities of this hormone and their growth is retarded. Injections of growth hormone from genetically modified bacteria restore normal growth patterns.

- **Bovine somatotrophin (BST)** (a growth hormone in cattle) This hormone increases the milk yield of cows and increases the muscle (meat) production of bulls. Giving injections of BST to dairy cattle can increase the milk yield by up to 10 kg per day. To do this they need more food, but this increased cost is more than offset by the increased income from the increased milk yield (Table 22.1).

	Feed (kg/day)	Milk output (kg/day)	Milk to feed ratio
without BST	34.1	27.9	0.82
with BST	37.8	37.3	0.99

Table 22.1: *Effects of BST on milk yield.*

- **Human vaccines** Bacteria have been genetically modified to produce the antigens of the Hepatitis B virus. This is used in the vaccine against Hepatitis B. The body makes antibodies against the antigens but there is no risk of contracting the actual disease from the vaccination.

Since the basic technique of transferring genes was worked out, many unicellular organisms have been genetically modified to produce useful products. Also, other techniques for transferring genes into larger organisms have been developed.

Producing genetically modified plants

The gene technology described so far can transfer DNA from one cell to another cell. In the case of bacteria, this is fine – a bacterium only has one cell. But plants have billions of cells and to genetically modify a plant, each cell must receive the new gene. So, any procedure for genetically modifying plants has two main stages:

- introducing the new gene or genes into plant cells
- producing whole plants from just a few cells.

Biologists initially had problems in inserting genes into plant cells. They then discovered a bacterium called *Agrobacterium*, which regularly inserts plasmids into plant cells. Now that a vector had been found, the rest became

Before human growth hormone from genetically modified bacteria was available, the only source of the hormone was from human corpses. This was a rather gruesome procedure and had health risks. A number of children treated in this way developed Creutzfeld–Jacob disease (the human form of 'mad cow' disease). When this became apparent, the treatment was withdrawn.

possible. Figure 22.7 outlines one procedure that uses *Agrobacterium* as a vector.

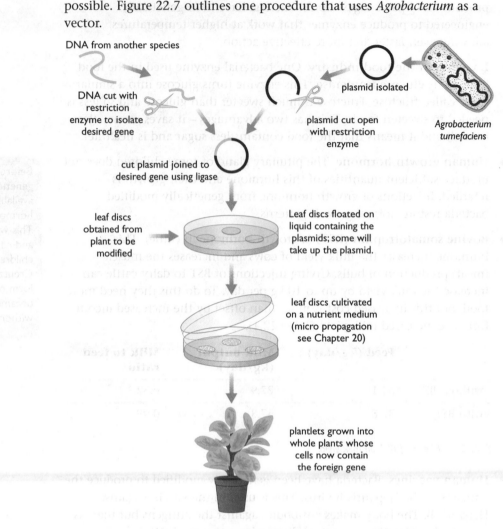

DNA from another species

DNA cut with restriction enzyme to isolate desired gene

plasmid isolated

plasmid cut open with restriction enzyme

Agrobacterium tumefaciens

cut plasmid joined to desired gene using ligase

leaf discs obtained from plant to be modified

Leaf discs floated on liquid containing the plasmids; some will take up the plasmid.

leaf discs cultivated on a nutrient medium (micro propagation see Chapter 20)

plantlets grown into whole plants whose cells now contain the foreign gene

Figure 22.7 *Genetically modifying plants using* Agrobacterium.

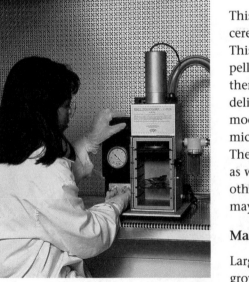

Figure 22.8 *The gene gun.*

This technique cannot be used on all plants. *Agrobacterium* will not infect cereals and so another technique was needed for these. Enter the gene gun! This is, quite literally, a gun that fires a golden bullet (Figure 22.8). Tiny pellets of gold are coated with DNA that contains the desired gene. These are then 'fired' directly into plant tissue. Research has shown that if young, delicate tissue is used, there is a good uptake of the DNA. The genetically modified tissue can then be grown into new plants using the same micropropagation techniques as those used in the *Agrobacterium* procedure. The gene gun has made it possible to genetically modify many cereal plants as well as tobacco, carrot, soybean, apple, oilseed rape, cotton and many others. There is, however, much debate about GM crops in the media. You may like to investigate further on the Internet and in the press.

Making use of genetically modified plants

Large numbers of genetically modified plants are already available to plant growers and farmers. There have been examples of fruit and vegetables with extended shelf lives.

Some plants have been modified to be resistant to herbicides (weedkillers). This allows farmers to spray herbicides at times when they will have maximum effect on the weeds, without affecting the crop plant. There are concerns that this will encourage farmers to be less careful in their use of herbicides. In another example, genes from Arctic fish that code for an 'anti-freeze' in their blood have been transferred to some plants to make them frost resistant.

The gene gun has allowed biologists to produce genetically modified rice called 'golden rice' (Figure 22.9). This rice has had three genes added to its normal DNA content. Two of these come from daffodils and one from a bacterium. Together, these genes allow the rice to make beta-carotene – the chemical that gives carrots their colour. It also colours the rice, hence the name 'golden rice'. More importantly, the beta-carotene is converted to vitamin A when eaten. This could save the eyesight of millions of children in less economically developed countries who go blind because they have no source of vitamin A in their diet.

Figure 22.9 *Golden rice.*

Genetically modified plants are also helping humans to resist infection. Biologists have succeeded in modifying tobacco plants and soybeans to produce antibodies against a range of infectious diseases. If these can be produced on a large scale, they could be given to people who are failing to produce their own antibodies. Other modified tobacco plants produce the hepatitis B antigens that could be used as the basis for a vaccine. There is always a risk with a vaccine containing viruses that they may somehow become infectious again. This could not happen with a vaccine containing only plant-produced antigens.

Antibodies and antigens produced in this way are sometimes called 'plantibodies' and 'plantigens'!

Besides the specific examples given, research into the genetic modification of plants hopes to provide (or provides already) plants with:

- increased resistance to a range of pests and pathogens
- increased heat and drought tolerance
- increased salt tolerance
- a better balance of proteins, carbohydrates, lipids, vitamins and minerals – more nutritious crop plants.

In addition, some genetically modified oilseed rape plants will be used in large-scale production of biodegradable plastics and anti-coagulants.

One of the biggest achievements would be to modify crop plants like cereals and potatoes to allow nodules of nitrogen fixing bacteria to form on their roots. At the moment only legumes (peas, beans and other plants with seeds in 'pods') can do this (see Figure 14.15 on page 162). Biologists know that the ability is genetically controlled. However, they cannot transfer these genes to other plants yet. If they could, vast areas of infertile soil would be able to yield good crops of cereals without the need to use large quantities of fertilisers.

The bacteria in the root nodules would obtain nitrogen from the air in the soil and 'fix' it in a more usable form (usually ammonia). By doing this, they would make a supply of usable nitrogen available to the plants. The plants

What if you could receive a 'vaccination' every time you ate a banana? Scientists are researching the possibility of transferring the genes that produce the antigens for several diseases to bananas. If they succeed, then when you eat the banana, the antigens will stimulate an immune response. There will be no risk of you catching the disease – and no need to have needles stuck in you!

would convert this into plant protein and use the protein for growth. The cost of producing these crops would decrease dramatically.

Producing genetically modified animals

Producing genetically modified animals poses some of the same problems as those connected with modifying plants. Animals, like plants, are multicellular. It is not enough simply to transfer a gene to a cell. That cell must then grow into a whole organism. The plasmid technology used to create genetically modified plants depends on the modified cells being grown into whole plants using micropropagation. No such micropropagation techniques exist for animals.

Scientists researching the production of genetically modified animals had to find other techniques. The most successful involves injecting DNA directly into a newly fertilised egg cell. This develops into an embryo, then an adult (Figure 22.10).

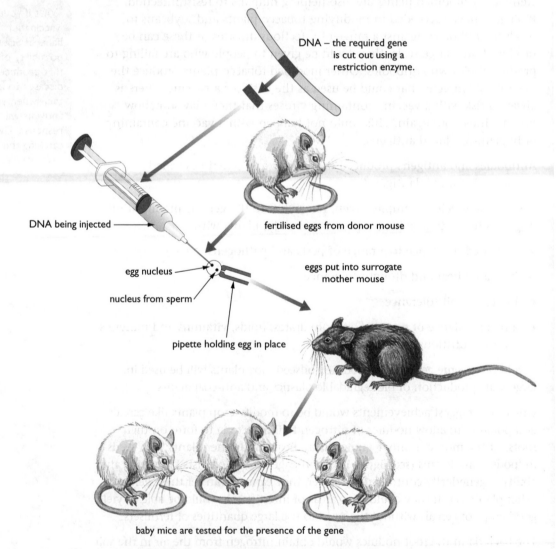

DNA – the required gene is cut out using a restriction enzyme.

DNA being injected

fertilised eggs from donor mouse

egg nucleus

nucleus from sperm

eggs put into surrogate mother mouse

pipette holding egg in place

baby mice are tested for the presence of the gene

Figure 22.10 The procedures used in producing genetically modified animals.

Research of this kind can produce beneficial results similar to those achieved by genetically modifying plants:

- increased production of a particular product, e.g. higher milk yield

- increased resistance to disease and other parasites

- manufacture of human antibodies

- manufacture of specific medicinal products

- production of low cholesterol milk

- production of organs for transplantation (xenotransplantation).

In addition, there is the potential to **clone** the genetically modified animals (see Chapter 20). This might make it possible to produce large numbers of animals, all genetically identical, which could be used for production of human antibodies, or to provide organs for human recipients. The most advanced research in xenotransplantation involves the genetic modification of pigs to produce hearts for transplants. However, there are a number of risks associated with xenotransplants.

- There may be a much greater immune rejection of xenotransplants than normal human transplants.

- The transplanted organ may carry pathogens such as viruses. These may be harmless to the donor animal but harmful to humans.

- Some viruses may be 'hidden' in the DNA of the transplanted organ, so that we are unaware that it is being passed to the recipient.

- Treatment of the recipient with immuno-suppressant drugs (drugs that lower the patient's immune response, to stop the organ being rejected) could allow pathogens to reproduce in their body.

Apart from these medical problems, many people believe that it is morally and ethically wrong to use animals like pigs in this way, and argue that we should not even be carrying out research into xenotransplants. What do you think?

> **Xenotransplantation** means transplanting organs from other animals into humans. Transgenic pigs have been produced with genes that code for the main human 'marker antigens'. The cells of the pig's organs therefore have these human antigens on their surface and the organs would be less likely to be rejected by a recipient. If this became possible on a large scale, it could help to overcome the shortage of donor organs for transplantation.

End of Chapter Checklist

You should now be able to:

- recall the meaning of 'transgenic'
- describe the use of restriction enzymes and ligase enzymes
- describe how plasmids and viruses can act as vectors
- understand that large amounts of human insulin can be manufactured from genetically modified bacteria that are grown in a fermenter
- evaluate the potential for using genetically modified plants to improve food production
- evaluate the potential for using cloned transgenic animals, e.g. for production of human antibodies and organs for transplantation.

Questions

More questions on gene technology can be found at the end of Section F on page 249.

1 The diagram shows the main stages in transferring the human insulin gene to a bacterium.

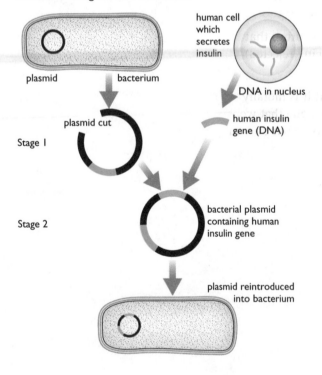

plasmid

bacterium

plasmid cut

Stage 1

Stage 2

human cell which secretes insulin

DNA in nucleus

human insulin gene (DNA)

bacterial plasmid containing human insulin gene

plasmid reintroduced into bacterium

a) Name the enzymes used at stages 1 and 2.

b) What is the role of the plasmid in this procedure?

c) How would the insulin-producing bacteria be used to produce significant amounts of insulin?

d) Why is the insulin produced this way preferred to insulin extracted from other animals?

2 Carry out an Internet search to find out more about the use of transgenic animals for organ transplantation. What are the arguments for and against its use? What are the ethical objections?

3 Producing genetically modified plants and animals is more complex than producing genetically modified bacteria.

a) Describe two ways in which genes can be introduced into plant cells.

b) How are these genetically modified cells used to produce whole organisms?

c) What sort of animal cell is genetically modified and then used to produce the whole organism?

4 Write an essay about the importance of genetic engineering. In your essay you should make reference to:

a) important potential benefits resulting from genetic engineering in animals and plants

b) concerns about the risks resulting from genetic engineering in animals and plants.

1 Rust fungi infect the leaves of many crop plants.

a) Explain two ways in which an infection by rust fungi can reduce crop yield. *(2 marks)*

b) Explain how genetic engineering could help to reduce the damage caused to crop plants by rust fungi. *(1 mark)*

c) Infections of rust fungi can be controlled by spraying the affected crops with a solution of copper sulphate. In an investigation into the effectiveness of this method of control, a field of potatoes was divided into two plots. As soon as the first signs of infection appeared, one plot was sprayed with copper sulphate solution. The other plot was left unsprayed. The relative amount of infection in the two plots was monitored over 50 days. The table shows the results of the investigation.

Day	Relative amount of infection	
	Control (unsprayed)	Sprayed plants
0	0	3
10	17	8
20	32	10
30	48	15
40	62	17
50	65	18

i) Plot a graph of this data. *(4 marks)*

ii) What was the relative infection of sprayed and unsprayed plants on day 24? *(2 marks)*

iii) Why was it necessary to have a control group? *(1 mark)*

iv) The investigation was repeated a year later. On day 30, the relative amounts of infection were 45 (unsprayed) and 36 (sprayed). Suggest an explanation for these results. *(2 marks)*

Total 12 marks

2 Some genes are transferred from one plant species to another. These genes are called 'jumping genes'. Environmentalists are concerned that genetically modified plants may transfer some of their genes to wild species. Explain their concern about genetically modified plants that:

a) have genes that make them resistant to herbicides (weedkillers) *(2 marks)*

b) have genes that make them resistant to pests *(2 marks)*

c) have genes that increase the yield of the crop they can produce. *(2 marks)*

Total 6 marks

3 The diagram shows a fermenter of the type used to grow microorganisms used to produce human insulin. Insulin is used to treat people with diabetes.

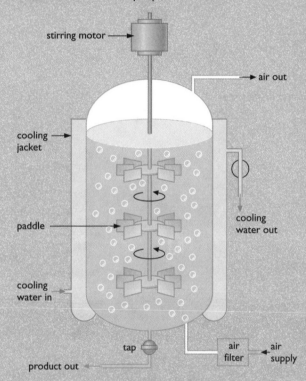

a) Explain why air is pumped through the fermenter. *(2 marks)*

b) Why is it necessary to keep the temperature in the fermenter constant? *(2 marks)*

c) Suggest one other condition that must be kept constant inside the fermenter. *(1 mark)*

d) The fermenter is sterilised by steam. Suggest why this is better than using disinfectants. *(2 marks)*

e) Insulin can also be obtained from animal pancreases. Suggest two advantages of using microorganisms to produce the insulin needed by diabetics. *(2 marks)*

Total 9 marks

4 a) Explain the meaning of the following terms:

    i)   a transgenic organism

    ii)   a plasmid

    iii) a bacteriophage.   *(6 marks)*

b) Explain the importance of the following enzymes in genetic engineering:

    i)   restriction endonuclease enzymes

    ii) ligase enzymes.   *(6 marks)*

Total 12 marks

5 Three organisms are used in the production of beer: barley, hops and *Saccharomyces cerevisiae*.

a) What type of organism is *Saccharomyces cerevisiae*?   *(1 mark)*

b) 'The respiration of *Saccharomyces cerevisiae* is essential to the production of beer.' Explain this statement. Include a chemical word equation in your answer.   *(3 marks)*

c) Explain the role of barley in beer production.   *(2 marks)*

d) Write down two reasons that hops are added during the production of beer.   *(2 marks)*

Total 8 marks

Practical Investigations

Experimental work is an integral part of the study of biology, and assessment of experimental skills makes up 20% of the final mark for the IGCSE. These skills may be assessed in two alternative ways. In some schools, you will take a written alternative to coursework examination. Other schools will submit coursework, which is assessed by your teacher. This appendix deals with the second option.

It isn't difficult to achieve full marks, or nearly full marks, for your coursework, but it does take time and patience. If you are prepared to spend that time, it can make a great difference to your final grade.

The next few pages show you how to gain a high score on an investigation. It is important to listen to your teacher's advice on exactly what you need to do in order to get *full* marks. After all, he or she will be marking your piece of work, and will have up-to-date knowledge of what your examiners want.

The investigation we will use as an example is:

Investigate the effect of temperature on the rate of a reaction catalysed by the enzyme trypsin.

You must realise that the version in this book is **incomplete**. You will find it in full on the website at www.longman.co.uk/gcsebiology.

How to start

Start by reading about enzymes in Chapter 1 of this book. The section on how enzymes work, and how they are affected by factors such as pH and temperature, is particularly relevant. It describes the role of the active site of the enzyme, and why enzymes have an optimum temperature at which they work best.

You can then look up trypsin in Chapter 4. Page 49 tells you that it is a protease, in other words an enzyme that digests proteins into short chains of amino acids. It is made by the pancreas in humans and other mammals.

You now need a substrate for the enzyme to digest. Powdered milk contains a white protein. When you mix the milk powder with water, it forms an opaque suspension. This means that it is cloudy and you cannot see through it because the protein is not very soluble (Figure 1a). You can use this as a substrate for the trypsin. If you add a solution of trypsin to the milk suspension in a test tube, it will gradually turn clearer. It never turns completely clear, but eventually you can see through it. We say it is *translucent* (Figure 1b).

(a)    (b)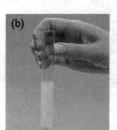

Figure 1 *Here you can see the effect of trypsin on the powdered milk protein* (a) *before treatment with the enzyme* and (b) *after treatment.*

You should now try some preliminary experiments with the milk and trypsin to find out the colour of the digested milk (called the 'end-point colour') and roughly how long it takes for the enzyme to break the protein down. It's no use if this takes hours to happen! You can make a solution that has the same appearance as the end-point by adding an equal volume of 0.1 M hydrochloric acid to a sample of milk. This will break the protein down immediately, without using any enzyme. It is called an 'end-point colour standard'.

Planning

Your teacher will be marking the planning part of your work by matching it to this checklist. The important terms are explained in the following pages.

If you can	Mark awarded
outline a simple procedure	2
plan to collect valid evidence plan the use of suitable equipment or sources of evidence	4
use scientific knowledge and understanding to plan and communicate a procedure; to identify key factors to vary, control or take into account; and to make a prediction where appropriate decide a suitable extent and range of evidence to be collected	6
use detailed scientific knowledge and understanding to plan and communicate an appropriate strategy, taking into account the need to produce precise and reliable evidence, and to justify a prediction when one has been made use relevant information from preliminary work, where appropriate, to inform the plan	8

To score 8 marks, your work must match both the statements in that box, as well as all the other statements for 6, 4 and 2 marks. In other words, for full marks, you need to do everything in the table. It is important to aim for the highest possible mark. Even if you miss it, you can still score well.

You can score odd-numbered marks if your work falls just short of a level. For example, you might score 7 marks if you satisfied the first statement needed for 8 marks, but didn't do any preliminary experiments when some would have been helpful.

You can use the following main headings to help you to get everything in a logical order.

What I am going to do

This investigation aims to find out the effect of temperature on the activity (rate of reaction) of trypsin. This can be done by heating trypsin and its substrate (the powdered milk) to a certain temperature in a water bath, then mixing them and finding out how long the enzyme takes to turn the milk translucent. The procedure is then repeated at other temperatures. The rate of a reaction can be calculated from the time it took to finish.

To measure the rate of any reaction, you can either measure how quickly a reactant is used up, or how quickly a product is formed. In this reaction, you can measure how quickly the reactant (the milk protein) is used up.

What I already know

To score 8 marks for planning, not only must everything be based on 'detailed scientific knowledge and understanding', but you have to make it clear how you are going to *use* that knowledge and understanding. List all the relevant things you have found out from books or other sources, and say why you think they might be useful to you. For example:

> I know that enzymes work best at an optimum temperature. For human enzymes this is normally close to body temperature (37 °C). Below this temperature, the molecules of enzyme and substrate have less kinetic energy, are moving more slowly and therefore are less likely to collide. Because of this, the rate of reaction is less at low temperatures. At high temperatures (usually above 50 °C), enzymes are destroyed or denatured by heat, so the rate again decreases. I will therefore carry out the reaction at a range of temperatures, from room temperature (about 20 °C) to a temperature that should cause denaturing (80 °C).

> It is important to get each solution to the correct temperature before you mix them, otherwise they will start reacting at the wrong temperature. This is called **equilibrating** the solutions to the right temperature. After you have mixed them, you must keep them at this temperature while they react, by leaving them in the water bath.

The key factors to vary, control or take into account

Don't just list the key factors. Explain why you are choosing to control some things and vary others, and why some things don't matter (if that happens to be the case). Your explanations should again 'use detailed scientific knowledge and understanding'. For example:

> I am going to use the same concentration of trypsin in all my experiments. If the concentration of the enzyme were increased, this would mean that the chance of an enzyme molecule colliding with a substrate molecule would be higher, which would affect the rate of reaction. The volumes of trypsin and milk suspension must also be constant (5 cm^3 of each). I will take care to measure these volumes as accurately as possible. If either varies, this will upset the final concentration of enzyme and substrate in the mixture.

> Remember that none of the examples given are complete. There are other factors that you will need to control.

Preliminary work

Preliminary work involves doing experiments to find out the best conditions for carrying out your investigation. It is essential if you are going to score 8 marks for planning. Describe your preliminary work carefully, and say exactly how it helped you to decide your final plan. Again, wherever possible, explain your choices in terms of 'detailed scientific knowledge and understanding'. For example:

> From my preliminary experiments, I found that 5 cm^3 of trypsin solution took less than 10 minutes to digest 5 cm^3 of the milk suspension to the same appearance as the end-point colour standard. This is a reasonable length of time that can be measured by a stopwatch. It will also allow me to carry out a number of readings at each temperature in the time available, so that I could get reliable evidence to test my predictions.

Producing precise and reliable evidence

'Precise' means that you are measuring things as accurately as possible. Particularly where the quantity you are measuring is small, you should try to measure it using the most accurate equipment you have available. 'Reliable' means that if you repeat your readings, you will get the same results. For example:

> The end-point of the reaction is difficult to judge with accuracy, so I will not attempt to measure the time to less than the nearest second. I will measure the volume of trypsin solution using a graduated pipette. This is accurate to $\pm 0.1\,cm^3$, which is a 2% margin of error. I will repeat the experiment three times at each temperature to check whether my findings are reliable. If my measurements of the reaction time at any temperature don't agree, I will go on repeating the experiment to find out whether I can reject any odd results.

Safety

List all the safety aspects of your plan in detail, explaining why you need to take each precaution. For example:

> Some people are allergic to enzymes, so I will be careful to mop up any spillages and will wash my hands after the practical work.

Doing the experiment

Describe what you are going to do in detail, listing all the apparatus you need. Draw diagrams if they will help your description.

When you have finished describing your method, read it through carefully and ask yourself whether someone else could carry it out successfully if they did it exactly what you have written. You can assume that they know how to use standard apparatus like pipettes and thermometers, but you should stress any unusual points. For example:

> It is important that the enzyme and milk have time to equilibrate to each temperature. To ensure this, I will measure the temperature inside the boiling tubes and keep the solutions at the chosen temperature for three minutes before I mix them together. Afterwards I will put the tube containing the mixture back into the water bath, so that the contents don't cool down while the reaction is taking place.

My prediction

Again, your predictions must be based on 'detailed scientific knowledge and understanding'. For example:

> I predict that temperature will affect the activity of the enzyme trypsin. The trypsin used in this experiment is obtained from bovine (cow) pancreas. Since cows are mammals like humans, the enzyme is likely to have an optimum temperature similar to human trypsin, approximately 40 °C. At temperatures below the optimum, the lower kinetic energy of the enzyme and substrate molecules will result in fewer collisions, and a lower rate of reaction. At temperatures above the optimum, the heat will cause the enzyme molecules to denature, so there are fewer of them to catalyse the reaction.

Ask your teacher how many repeat (replicate) experiments he or she expects you to carry out in order to gain full marks. You also need to know how many readings you need to take. In this investigation how many different temperatures will be needed? Ten-degree intervals between 20 °C and 80 °C should be OK. However, you may need to do more to find the optimum temperature more precisely.

Obtaining evidence

Your teacher will be using this checklist.

If you can	Mark awarded
collect some evidence using a simple and safe procedure	2
collect appropriate evidence that is adequate for the activity record the evidence	4
collect sufficient systematic and accurate evidence and repeat or check when appropriate record clearly and accurately the evidence collected	6
use a procedure with precision and skill to obtain and record an appropriate range of reliable evidence	8

This is a relatively easy section to gain full marks for. You should record your readings or measurements in neatly constructed table(s) that clearly present your findings in a logical order. Tables need a title and the *correct units* must be given. Any observations should also be recorded.

Drawing up a table of results

For example, the 'raw data' of measurements of the time of the reaction at different temperatures, measured in minutes and seconds, might look like this.

Temperature (°C)	Time to completion of reaction (minutes and seconds)		
	(1)	(2)	(3)
20	8 17	7 54	8 31
30	2 28	3 38	3 14
35	2 16	2 12	2 00
40	1 40	1 50	1 30
45	1 26	1 30	1 26
50	1 19	1 20	1 26
55	1 25	1 32	1 25
60	1 42	1 50	1 54
65	2 50	3 20	(7 12) 3 22*
70	7 35	10 12	9 36
80	>30**	>30	>30

* First measurement was anomalous and was repeated to check reliability. It was not used in later calculations of rate.

** Reaction had not taken place by 30 minutes

Table 1: *Time taken for the enzyme trypsin to digest milk protein at different temperatures. Columns show three replicates at each temperature.*

Notice that the times are given as mixed units (minutes and seconds) and will need to be converted to decimal fractions of a minute before they can be used to calculate rates. Calculations like these, from the raw data, are assessed in the next checklist.

Analysing your evidence and drawing conclusions

Your teacher will be using this checklist.

If you can	Mark awarded
state simply what is shown by the evidence	2
use simple diagrams, charts or graphs as a basis for explaining the evidence	4
identify patterns and trends in the evidence	
construct and use suitable diagrams, charts, graphs (with lines of best fit where appropriate), or use numerical methods to process evidence for a conclusion	6
draw a conclusion consistent with the evidence and explain it using scientific knowledge and understanding	
use detailed scientific knowledge and understanding to explain a valid conclusion drawn from processed evidence	8
explain the extent to which the conclusion supports the prediction, if one has been made	

Notice that to gain 6 or 8 marks you don't necessarily have to draw graphs. You can use 'numerical methods' instead. This means doing some reasonably complicated calculations. Although working out a simple average is a 'numerical method', it isn't complicated enough to earn you 6 (or 8) marks.

Calculations

Converting the times in minutes and seconds into time in minutes, then finding a mean time at each temperature, and finally calculating the rate of the reaction, is complicated enough to gain the first point in the 6 marks box.

For example, a time of 2 minutes and 45 seconds is equal to $2\frac{45}{60}$ minutes, or 2.75 minutes. The rate of the reaction is found from this time as shown below.

> You need to show how you arrived at this formula, not just use it.

If the trypsin digested $5\,cm^3$ of milk protein in 2.75 minutes, the rate of reaction in cm^3 per minute is:

volume of milk ÷ time = 5 ÷ 2.75 = 1.82 cm^3/min (or 1.82 $cm^3\,min^{-1}$)

256

Now you can calculate the mean (average) rates at each temperature. It would be best to construct another table for this.

Temperature (°C)	Time (min)			Mean time (min)	Mean rate (cm^3 min^{-1})
	(1)	(2)	(3)		
20	8.28	7.90	8.52	8.23	0.61
30	2.47	3.63	3.23	3.11	1.61
35	2.27	2.20	2.00	2.16	2.31
40	1.67	1.83	1.50	1.67	2.99
45	1.43	1.50	1.43	1.45	3.45
50	1.32	1.33	1.43	1.36	3.68
55	1.42	1.53	1.42	1.46	3.42
60	1.70	1.83	1.90	1.81	2.76
65	2.83	3.33	3.37	3.18	1.57
70	7.58	10.20	9.60	9.13	0.55
80	>30	>30	>30	>30	<0.17

Table 2: *Time taken for the enzyme trypsin to digest milk protein at different temperatures. Columns show three replicates at each temperature, mean time and mean rate of reaction.*

Now you should plot a graph of the mean reaction rate against temperature (Figure 2).

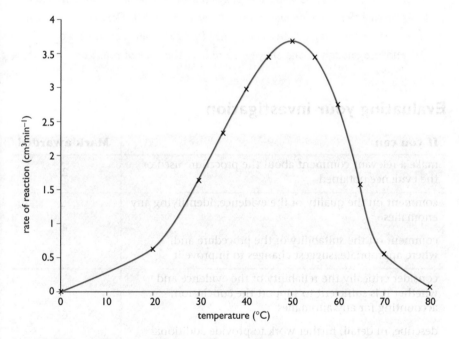

Figure 2 *The rate of reaction of trypsin at different temperatures.*

If you draw a line graph like this, you must connect the points with a 'line of best fit' to fulfil the first point in the 6 marks box. A 'best fit' line is not necessarily straight. In Figure 2 it is a smooth curve passing through the data points. It may also be a smooth curve that lies between each of the points, with some falling on the line, and an equal number either side of it.

Drawing your conclusions

You have to decide whether your results fit your original prediction. Remind the person marking your work exactly what your prediction was. Don't just refer back to your original scientific explanation. Give it again, together with any modifications that your results show to be necessary. For example:

> I predicted that the rate of reaction would increase with temperature, as the kinetic energy of the molecules increased, until the optimum temperature for the enzyme was reached. Above the optimum, the rate of reaction would decrease as the enzyme molecules were denatured. As shown in Figure 2, the results I have obtained fit the general pattern of my prediction. The rate increases from 0.61 cm^3 min^{-1} at 20 °C, to a maximum of 3.68 cm^3 min^{-1} at 50 °C. It then decreases to 0.55 cm^3 min^{-1} at 70 °C. At 80 °C, the rate was very slow, and no change in the appearance of the milk protein could be detected after 30 minutes. It is probable that the enzyme had been fully denatured at this temperature, so that the rate of reaction was zero. However, I predicted that the optimum temperature would be about 40 °C, and Table 2 and Figure 2 show that it was higher than this, at about 50 °C.

It doesn't matter if your prediction doesn't match your results, but you must be able to use your knowledge and understanding to come up with a convincing explanation. For example:

> It is possible that the optimum temperature for trypsin is closer to 50 °C. Alternatively, it may be that the enzyme and milk were not held at each temperature for long enough before they were mixed. Denaturation is a time-dependent process, and it may need longer than 3 minutes at 50 °C to denature enough of the enzyme to reduce the rate of reaction.

Evaluating your investigation

If you can	Mark awarded
make a relevant comment about the procedure used or the evidence obtained	2
comment on the quality of the evidence, identifying any anomalies comment on the suitability of the procedure and, where appropriate, suggest changes to improve it	4
consider critically the reliability of the evidence and whether it is sufficient to support the conclusion, accounting for any anomalies describe, in detail, further work to provide additional relevant evidence	6

Students often achieve low marks for this last stage. It is worth almost as much as the other three sections, and your answer must be detailed and specific.

Evaluating the experiment

You need to point out any results that appear to be wrong or out of place (anomalous), and try to account for them. For example:

> Although the experiment produced repeatable results (Table 1) some replicate measurements were anomalous, for example the third measurement of the reaction time at 65 °C. This was checked by repeating the experiment at this temperature, which led me to reject the first value. I also noticed that the measurements of the rate of reaction became more variable at higher temperatures (Table 2). This could be due to the difficulty in maintaining the water bath at a constant temperature. This is particularly true at high temperatures, when the beaker will cool more quickly. I noticed that however carefully I tried to keep the temperature constant by applying the Bunsen flame or removing it, it still varied by as much as ±2 °C.

Improving the experiment

Make sure that the improvements you suggest are detailed and specific to your investigation. You won't get much credit for general comments like 'use more accurate equipment' or 'take more care with measurements'. Some better examples of improvements are as follows.

> The temperature could have been kept more constant by using an electric, thermostatically controlled water bath. These can maintain a temperature to within ±0.5 °C.

> The end-point of the reaction was difficult to judge with accuracy, even when comparing it with the end-point colour standard. There are machines called 'colorimeters' that can be used to measure the cloudiness of a suspension. If I had a colorimeter available, I could have compared the cloudiness of the experimental tubes with the cloudiness of the end-point standard.

> In my experimental method I did not control the pH of the reaction mixture. pH affects enzymes, and the pH of the mixture may have changed at different temperatures. I could have controlled the pH by adding a set volume of a buffer solution to the enzyme. Buffer solutions are used to keep the pH constant. I know from my background reading that trypsin works well at neutral to slightly alkaline pH, so a buffer with a pH between 7 and 8 would be suitable.

Extending your experiment

To gain the full 6 marks, you must describe *in detail* how you might extend this investigation to provide additional *relevant* evidence. It's no use, for example, saying that you could repeat this sort of experiment with another enzyme, or find the effect of concentration on the rate of reaction. In this investigation, one problem is that denaturing takes time. It would be a good idea to find out how quickly the trypsin is denatured at high temperatures.

> I could extend this investigation by finding out how quickly trypsin is denatured at high temperatures. From Figure 2, I can see that the rate of reaction is greatly decreased at 65 °C, so I would select that temperature to investigate.

I would set up two water baths, one at 65 °C and one at a lower temperature where the enzyme works well, such as 40 °C. I would place a test tube containing 5 cm^3 of trypsin in the 65 °C bath for exactly one minute. I would then remove the tube and place it in the 40 °C water bath, along with another tube containing 5 cm^3 of milk. When these tubes were both at 40 °C, I would mix their contents, and return the tube containing the mixture to the water bath. I would then measure how long the mixture took to go translucent, as before.

I would repeat this procedure, exposing the trypsin to different periods of time at 65 °C, such as ...

You should go on to describe exactly what you would do, what periods of exposure to the high temperature you would choose, and what you predict would happen.

Exam tips

Very few people enjoy revising for examinations. Being very well organised with your revision will mean you revise for as little time as possible. Revising for hours on end without a break is not productive – your concentration will not last and you will not retain the facts.

Where to revise
Somewhere quiet away from distractions. You need good lighting and you should be comfortable.

When to revise
As soon as possible after school finishes each day, before you get too tired to work effectively.

How to revise
Have a plan and stick to it. Think about how many topics you need to cover. Make a list of all the topics and mark those that you find difficult. Revise a mixture of easy and more challenging topics each day. This will give you the satisfaction of making progress every day. When you have revised something, tick it on your list. This will show clearly how much still needs to be done.

Divide your time
Working for a whole evening without a break will achieve less than dividing your time into segments. Split your evening into revision time and leisure breaks. Take at least 10 minutes off for each hour worked. When you start again, take 5 minutes to review the previous topic, then move on.

Group revision
Some students find that revision is less boring and more effective in a group. Ask each other questions, choose topics in turn, share good ideas.

Organising the information
Think of ways to organise the information you need to revise. You can use summaries, checklists, file cards, sticky-notes, flow-schemes and key words.

Past paper questions
Read examination papers from previous years. This will show you the styles of questions and indicate which topics are more likely to be repeated. Look carefully at the marks printed on the paper and the spaces left for answers. Fill the space provided and make points according to marks available. For example, make two points if there are two marks available.

Mathematical requirements
You will be awarded marks for every part of the answer that is correct, even if the final answer is wrong. Always have a go and show your working. Don't forget to state the units you are working in.

Index

absorption, ileum 50–1
accommodation, eyes 72
acid rain 175, 176–7
active transport 10, 134
ADH *see* anti-diuretic hormone
adrenaline 80–2
aerobic respiration 7
afterbirth 102
agriculture
    environmental factors 167–73
    genetically modified plants 244–6
    pollution 177–9
    selective breeding 222–31
Agrobacterium 243–4
AI *see* artificial insemination
air pollution 174–7
airways *see* breathing
algae 133–4, 177–8, 232
alleles 189–90, 201, 204, 206–9
alveoli 29–30, 31
amino acids 40, 85–6
amnion 101–2
amylase 5–6, 48–9
anaemia 41, 217–18
anaerobic respiration 7–8, 236
animals 16–17
    breathing 26–36
    cell structure 2
    circulatory systems 54–6
    clones 227–8
    digestion 37–53
    feeding relationships 157–60
    gas exchange 26–36
    genetically modified 246–7
    natural selection 214–16
    osmosis 126
    overgrazing problems 172
    physiology 26–109
    seed dispersal 148
    selective breeding 224–5
    see also human body
antibiotic-resistant bacteria 216–17
antibodies 62–3
anti-diuretic hormone (ADH) 90–1
arteries 56, 58, 59–60
arterioles 59, 88
artificial insemination (AI) 225
artificial selection
    see selective breeding
asexual reproduction 97–100,
    145, 197
assimilation, digestion 51
atrio-ventricular valves 57
auxins 140–2
axons 68

baby deliveries 102
bacteria 19–20

genetically modified 240–3
    natural selection 216–17
    nitrogen cycle 162
    yoghurt production 237
bacteriophages 241–2
balanced diet 37–42
bananas 226
barley 235–6
basement membrane 88
base-pairing rule 186
beer production 235–6
Benedict's solution 43
beri-beri 42
bias in sampling 155
bile 50
bioaccumulation, pesticides 179–80
biological pest control 170–1
biomagnification, DDT 180
biomass 158–9
biomes 154
biotechnology 233–5
birds 91–2
bladder 86, 87
blind spots 71
blood 54–65
    alveoli function 29–30
    chromosomes 189
    clots 63
    composition 61–3
    glucose control 81–2
    kidney functions 86, 87–90
    sickle cell anaemia 217–18
    temperature control 94
    vessels 29–30, 56, 58–60, 88
bone marrow 195
bovine somatotrophin (BST) 243
Bowman's capsule 88
brain 67, 75–6
brassica plants 223
breathing 26–36
bronchi 27, 31
bronchitis 31
BST *see* bovine somatotrophin
bulbs 145

cacti 129
calculations for investigations 256–7
calorimeters 44
camouflage 215–16
cancer 31–3, 195
capillaries 29–30, 56, 59–60
carbohydrases 47, 49
carbohydrates 37–8, 85–6, 118
carbon cycle 161–2
carbon dioxide 7–9, 115–16, 174–5
carbon monoxide 33, 175
carcinogens in cigarettes 32
cardiac cycle 57

cardiac muscle 57, 58
carnivores 157
cartilage 27
catalysts, definition 3
cattle, selective breeding 224–5
cells
    bacteria 19–20
    blood cells 61–3
    chromosomes 189
    colonies 232
    differentiation 11–12
    division 11–12, 194–200
    energy sources 6–9
    enzyme functions 3–6
    leaves 114–15
    meiosis 98
    membranes 3
    movement of materials 9–11
    organs 12–13
    osmosis 124–7
    plants 124–7, 131–2, 146
    respiration 6–11
    sickle cell anaemia 217–18
    structure 1–3
    surface membranes 3
    tissues 12–13
    yeasts 7, 17
cellulose 3, 38, 118
central nervous system (CNS) 67–9,
    73–5
cerebellum 76
cerebrum 75–6
cervix dilation 102
chemical coordination
    animals 79–83
    plants 137–44
chemical digestion 46–7
chitin 17
chlorophyll 3, 112, 113, 118
chloroplasts 3
cholesterol 39
choroid of eyes 69
chromosomes 185–93
    cell structure 2
    human body 194
    meiosis 196
    mutations 190–1
    sex determination 209
    sexual reproduction 98–9
    structure 188–91
cigarettes *see* smoking
cilia 27, 31
circular muscles 47
circulation 54–65
classification of living organisms 16
clinostats 142–3
clones 97, 197, 225–8, 247
clots in blood 63

CNS *see* central nervous system
codominance 208–9
coleoptiles 138–42
colon 51
colonies of cells 232
combustion 161
communities in ecosystems 154
competition 156
complementary bases, DNA 186
concentration gradient 9–10
conclusions to investigations 256–8
consumers in ecosystems 154, 157
coordination
    animal physiology 66–78
    chemicals in animals 79–83
    chemicals in plants 137–44
cornea 69, 70
coronary heart disease 58
corpus luteum 104–5
cortex of kidneys 87
cotyledons 149
cows, selective breeding 224–5
Crick, Francis 185
crop plants
    genetically modified 244–6
    rotation 171
    selective breeding 222–4
    yield improvements 167–8
cross breeding 202–9
cross-pollination 146
cuticles, leaves 114
cuttings, plants 225–6
cycling nutrients 161–3, 169
cytoplasm 2

Darwin, Charles 138–9, 212–13
DDT pollution 179–80
decomposers
    bacteria 20
    ecosystems 154
    nitrogen cycle 162
deforestation 174–5
deletion, gene mutations 187
denaturing enzymes 5
dendrons 68
denitrification 162
deoxyribonucleic acid *see* DNA
dermis 93
desertification 172
diabetes 82, 242
diaphragm, gas exchange 26
dicots 149
diet 37–42
differentiation in cells 11–12
diffusion
    cell respiration 9–11
    definition 123
    mineral uptake 133–4
digestion 37–53
    definition 46
    enzymes 4–6, 46–50

process 46–50
    temperature effects 5–6
diploid cells 189, 194
dispersal of fruits/seeds 148
diuresis 90
division of cells 11–12, 194–200
DNA 185–93
    code 186
    gene makeup 239
    ligases 240
    recombinant DNA 239–43
    replication 187–8
    structure 185–6
dogs 225
'Dolly' the sheep 227–8
dominant alleles 190, 204, 206–9
dormancy of seeds 149
dorsal root 73
double circulatory systems 55–6
Down's syndrome 190–1
duodenum 47, 49
duplication, gene mutations 187

ecological pyramids 158–9
ecology 154–84
ecosystems 154–65
egestion 51
ejaculation 99
embryos 11, 100
emphysema 31
endocrine system 79–80
endotherms 91
energy
    cells 6–9
    flow 160
    food 44–6
environmental factors 154–84
    human influences 166–84
    natural selection 214, 219
    variation 198
enzymes 3–6
    digestion 46–50
    DNA 186
    restriction endonucleases 240
    saprotrophic nutrition 19
    transgenic bacteria 242–3
epidermis 93, 126–7
equilibration 253
eutrophication 169, 177–8
evaluating investigations 258–60
evidence for investigations 253–4, 255–8
evolution 212–21
exam tips 261
excretion 51, 84–96
exercise effects 30, 58
exhalation 27–8
exocrine glands 79, 80
experiment methods 251–60
external fertilisation 99
extinctions 220

extracellular enzymes 4, 19
eyes 69–72

faeces 47, 51
farms *see* agriculture
fats 38–9
fatty acids 39
feeding
    carbon cycle 161
    ecosystems 156
    nitrogen cycle 162
    relationships 157–60
fermentation 233–5
fertilisation 97–100, 146–7
fertilisers 169, 177–9
fetus 101–2
fibre in diet 38
fibrin 63
'fight or flight' hormones 80–1
fish
    circulatory systems 55
    farming 173
    overfishing 172–3
flaccid cells 125
flagella 20
flowers 224
follicles, menstruation 104
follicle stimulating hormone (FSH) 102, 104–5
food 37–53
    agricultural production 167–73
    chains 157, 160, 180
    energy 44–6
    enzymes 243
    industry 243
    plants 110–22
    tests 42–3
    webs 157–8, 167
fossilisation 161
Franklin, Rosalind 185
freshwater pollution 177–9
fructose 38, 118
fruits 147–8
FSH *see* follicle stimulating hormone
fungi 17–19, 232

gametes 97–8
gas exchange 26–36
    alveoli 29–30
    leaves 115, 116–17
    system 26–7
gene gun 244, 245
genes 185–93
    alleles 189–90
    antibiotic-resistant bacteria 217
    asexual reproduction 97
    cell structure 2
    codominance 208–9
    DNA makeup 239
    genetically modified plants 243–4
    inheritance 201–11

mutations 187–8
  presenting information 206–9
  sexual reproduction 98
  variation 198
genetically modified organisms (GMOs)
    233, 239–50
    animals 228, 246–7
    bacteria 240–3
    plants 243–6
genetic engineering 232–50
genotypes 204, 205, 207–8
geotropisms 137–8, 140–1, 142–3
germination 149
giving up smoking 34
glands 79–80
global warming 174–5
glomeruli 88
glucagon 82
glucose
    balanced diet 37–8
    cell respiration 7
    control in blood 81–2
    plants 112–13, 118–19
    test 43
glucose isomerase 243
glycerol 39
glycogen 38, 51, 81–2
GMOs see genetically modified
    organisms
'golden rice' 245
gravity, plants 137–8
greenhouse effect 174–5
greenhouses 167–8
'grey matter' 74, 75
growth hormones 243
growth responses see tropisms
guard cells 114, 131–2

habitats
    ecosystems 154
    natural selection 220
    sampling 155–6
haemoglobin 33, 62
hair erector muscles 94
haploid cells 146, 189, 194
heart 56
    disease 58
    rate 58–9
    structure and function 57–9
heat
    cell respiration 8–9
    see also temperature
hepatic portal vein 51
herbivores 157
histones 188
homeostasis 84–96
homeotherms 91
homogenisation 237
hops 236
hormones 76, 79–80
    'fight or flight' 80–1

growth hormones 243
menstrual cycle 103–5
plants 138–43
reproduction 102–5
water control 90–1
human body
    brain 75–6
    chromosomes 185, 194
    circulatory systems 54–6
    digestive system 48
    eyes 69–72
    gas exchange system 26–7
    heart structure and function 57–9
    organ systems 12–13
    reproduction 97–109
    see also individual parts/functions
      of body
human environmental impact 166–84
human growth hormone 243
humidity, transpiration rates 133
Hydra reproduction 97
hydrochloric acid 49
hydroponics 120, 168
hydrotropisms 138
hyphae 17–19
hypodermis 93
hypothalamus
    hormones 76, 80
    temperature control 92–3
    water content control 90
hypotheses, definition 8

ileum 47, 50–1
immune system 21
indicator species, pollution 176, 178
industrial fermenters 233–5
industrialisation effects 214–16
ingestion 46
inhalation 27–8
inheritance 201–11
insect-pollination 146
insects 17, 214–16
insulin 82, 242
interactions in ecosystems 156–60
intercostal muscles 26, 27–8
internal environment 84
internal fertilisation 99–100
intestines 47, 49–51
inversions, gene mutations 187
invertebrates 16
investigation methods 251–60
iodine, starch test 110–11
ions 119–20, 133–4
iris 69, 70–1, 73
Islets of Langerhans 82
isotopes 113

jelly experiment 10–11

kidneys 84, 86, 87–90
kilojoules 44

Knop's solution 119
kwashiorkor 40

lacteals 51
lactic acid 8, 237
lactose 38
lanolin 141–2
large intestine 51
leaves
    gas exchange 115, 116–17
    starch test 110–12
    structure 113–15
    transpiration 129–33
LH see luteinising hormone
lichens 176
life processes 1–25
ligases, DNA 240
light
    photosynthesis 115, 116–18
    stimuli for plants 137–43
    transpiration rates 133
limiting factors, photosynthesis 117
lipases 48–50
lipids 38–9, 43, 118
liver 51
living organism variety 16–25
longitudinal muscles 47
loop of Henlé 89–90
lung cancer 31–3
lungs
    gas exchange system 26–7
    smoking effects 30–4
    ventilation 27–8
luteinising hormone (LH) 102, 104–5
lymphatic system 51
lymphocytes 61, 62–3

magnesium 119–20
malaria 217–18
mammals
    circulatory systems 54–5
    temperature control 91–2
    see also animals; human body
mechanical digestion 46–7
medulla 58–9, 76, 87
meiosis 98, 100, 194, 196
memory cells, blood 62–3
Mendel, Gregor 201–5
menstrual cycle 103–5
mesophyll 114
methane pollution 177
microorganisms 232–50
micropropagation 226
microvilli, ileum 50–1
minerals 40–1, 119–20, 133–4
mitochondria 3
mitosis 11–12, 98, 100, 145, 194–6
modification, genetic 233, 239–50
monocots 149
monoculture 171
moths 214–16

motor neurones 68–9, 73
moulds 17–19, 232
Mucor 18–19
mucus 27, 31
multicellular organisms 1, 16
muscles
    breathing 26, 27–8
    cell respiration 7–8
    digestion 47, 49
    eyes 70–1, 72
    heart 57
    skin 94
    urinary system 86
mutagens 188
mutations
    bacteria 217
    chromosomes 190–1
    genes 187–8
mutualism, nitrogen cycle 162
mycelium 17
myelination of neurones 68–9

natural selection 188, 212–21
negative feedback principle 91
nephrons 87–90
nervous system 67–9, 79–80
neurones 67–9, 73
neurotransmitters 74–5
new species 219
niches 220
nicotine 32, 34
night blindness 41–2
nitrates 119–20, 177–9
nitrogen
    cycle 162–3, 169
    genetically modified plants
        245–6
nitrogenous waste 85
nitrogen oxides 176
nucleotides 186–7
nucleus of cells 2
nutrients cycling 161–3, 169

oestrogen 103
oils 38–9
onions 126–7
optimum temperature
    crop plants 168
    enzymes 4–5
organelles 2
organisms 1–25
organ systems 12–13
osmosis 10, 123–8
ova 97–9, 100, 103–4, 146–7
ovaries 80, 98
overfishing 172–3
overgrazing 172
ovulation 103–4
oxygen debt 8
oxygen in plants 112–13
oxyhaemoglobin 62

palisade layer, leaves 114
pancreas 47, 49–50, 80, 82
partially permeable membranes 123–4
pathogens 20
pea plants 201–5
pedigrees 206–7
penicillin 234–5
peppered moths 214–16
pepsin 49
percentages, interpretation 29
periods 104
peristalsis 47
permeability
    cells 3, 10
    transport in plants 123, 134
pesticides 170, 179–80
pests
    agriculture 170–1
    genetically modified plants 245
    selective breeding 223–4
phages *see* bacteriophages
phagocytes 61, 62
'pharming' 228
phenotypes 204–5
pH factors, enzymes 5
phloem 115, 130–1
phosphate 119–20
photosynthesis 112–18
    carbon cycle 161
    energy flow 160
    rates 117–18
    transport in plants 123
phototropisms 137–40
physiology
    animals 26–109
    definition 91
    plants 110–53
pituitary gland 76, 79–80
placenta 100–1, 102, 105
planning investigations 252–4
plants 16
    agriculture 167–8
    cell structure 2–3
    chemical coordination 137–44
    ecosystems 156–7
    excretion 86
    food 110–22
    gene codominance 208–9
    genetically modified 243–6
    inheritance 201–5
    nitrogen cycle 162
    physiology 110–53
    reproduction 145–53
    selective breeding 222–4
    starch production 110–13, 115
    transport 123–36
    viruses 21
plasma 61
plasmids 20, 240–2
plasmolysis 125
platelets 61, 63

pleural layers 27
pollen grains 146–7
pollination 146–7
pollution 174–80, 216
polydactyly 206–8
polysaccharides 112
pondweed 112, 117–18
populations
    ecosystems 154
    growth 167
potassium 119–20
potatoes 127–8, 145
potometers 132–3
practical investigation methods 251–60
precipitation 163
predictions in investigations 254
pregnancy 45, 100–2
preliminary work 253
producers, ecosystems 154, 157
progesterone 104–5
proteases 48–9
proteins 39–40
    cell structure 2–3
    DNA 186, 239
    enzymes 4
    homeostasis 85–6
    test 43
protozoa 232
puberty 102–3
pulmonary circulation 56
pyramids, feeding relationships 158–60

quadrats 155–6

rain *see* acid rain; precipitation
random sampling 155–6
receptors 66–7, 79
recessive alleles 190, 204, 206, 208–9
recombinant DNA 239–43
red blood cells 61–2, 189, 217–18
reflex actions 59, 71, 73–5
refraction, eyes 70
renal... *see* kidneys
replication, DNA 187–8
reproduction
    hormones 102–5
    humans 97–109
    natural selection 213
    plants 145–53
respiration
    breathing comparison 26
    carbon cycle 161
    cells 6–11
    energy flow 160
    mitochondria 3
    plants 113, 115–16
    yeast 236
response *see* stimulus and response
restriction endonucleases 240
retina 70–1
revision tips 261

rice 245
rickets 41
root nodules 162
roots 128–9, 138, 141–3
roughage 38

safety in investigations 254
saliva 48–9
salts 85
sampling habitats 155–6
saprotrophic nutrition 19
saturated fats 39
scurvy 41–2
seeds
    dispersal 148
    dormancy 149
    formation 147–8
selection 185–231
selective breeding 222–31
selectively permeable membranes 134
self-pollination 146
semen 100
sensory neurones 67–9
septum, heart 58
sex chromosomes 189–90, 196
sex determination 209
sexual reproduction
    humans 97–109
    plants 145–8
    variation 197
sheep, cloning 227–8
shoots 137–8, 141
sickle cell anaemia 217–18
single cell organisms 1, 54
single circulatory systems 55–6
skin 93–4, 195
small intestine 47, 49–51
smoking
    effects on lungs 30–4
    giving up 34
    statistics 33–4
soda lime, starch test 112
species, definition 219
sperm 97–9, 100, 102
sphincter muscles 49, 86
spinal cord 67, 73–4
stamens 146
starch 16
    balanced diet 38
    plants' producing 110–13, 115
    test 43
stems, structure 130–1
stimulus and response 66–7
stomach 49–50
stomata 114, 129, 131–2
substitution, gene mutations 187
substrate of enzymes 4
sucrose 16, 38, 118
sugars 37–8, 118–19
    see also glucose

sulphur dioxide 175–6
super-bugs 217
surface area to volume ratios 54–5
suspensory ligaments, eyes 72
sweat glands 93–4
synapses 68, 74–5
systemic circulation 56

tables of results 255–6
tar in cigarettes 32
teeth 38
temperature
    control in body 91–4
    crop plants 168
    enzymes 4–6
    transpiration rates 133
test cross 205
testes 80, 98
testosterone 102
tests
    food 42–3
    starch 110–12
thermal pollution 179
thermoregulatory centre 92
thorax 26–7
time management, revision 261
tips for the exam 261
tissue fluid 84–5
tissues 12–13, 30–4
trachea 27, 31
transduction 66
transgenic animals 228
    see also genetically modified
        organisms
transpiration 129–33
    rates 132–3
    stream 115, 130
transplants, genetic modification 247
trophic levels, food chains 157, 160
tropisms 137–43
tubers 127–8, 145
tumours, lung cancer 32
turgid cells 125
twins 197–8

ultrafiltration, kidneys 88
unicellular organisms see single cell
        organisms
unsaturated fats 39
urea 85–6
urethra 86
urinary system 86–91
urine 85–6

vaccines 243, 245
vacuole of cells 3
valves
    heart 57–8
    veins 60
variation 185–231

environment 198
genes 198
meiosis 196
sexual reproduction 197
vascular bundles, stems 130–1
vasoconstriction 94
vasodilation 94
vectors, plasmids 241
veins 56, 58, 59–60
ventilation 26, 27–8
ventral root 73
vertebrates 16
villi, ileum 50–1
viruses 19, 20–1, 232, 241–2
Visking tubing 123
vitamins 41–2
volume potometers 132–3
voluntary actions 74, 76

washing powder enzymes 242–3
waste elimination 51
water
    body content 90–1
    culture experiments 119
    cycle 163
    loss through leaves 129–33
    plants 128–33, 138
    pollution 177–9
    potential 124, 126
    uptake by roots 128–9
Watson, James 185
weeds 170
wheat 222
white blood cells 61, 62–3
wind-pollination 146

xenotransplantation 247
xylem 115, 130–1

yeasts 7, 17, 232, 235–6
yields, crop plants 167–8
yoghurt production 237

zygotes 11, 97–9, 189, 197